100 MATHS LESSONS

YEAR R

Published by Scholastic Ltd,
Villiers House,
Clarendon Avenue,
Leamington Spa,
Warwickshire CV32 5PR

© 2000 Scholastic Ltd
Text © Anne Farr 2000
2 3 4 5 6 7 8 9   0 1 2 3 4 5 6 7 8 9

SERIES CONSULTANT
Ann Montague-Smith

AUTHOR
Anne Farr

EDITOR
Kate Pearce

ASSISTANT EDITOR
David Sandford

SERIES DESIGNER
Joy White

DESIGNER
Rachael Hammond

COVER PHOTOGRAPH
Kim Oliver

ILLUSTRATIONS
Lynda Murray

British Library Cataloguing-in-Publication Data
A catalogue record for this book is available from the British Library.

ISBN 0-439-01692-4

ACKNOWLEDGEMENTS

The publishers wish to thank:
The National Numeracy Strategy: Framework for Teaching Mathematics © Crown Copyright.
Reproduced under the terms of HMSO Guidance Note 8.
Galt Educational and NES Arnold Educational Supplies for kindly loaning the equipment used
on the front cover.

CONTENTS

INTRODUCTION

ABOUT THE SERIES

100 Maths Lessons is a series of year-specific teachers' resource books, for Reception to Year 6, that provide a core of support material for the teaching of mathematics within the National Numeracy Strategy *Framework for Teaching Mathematics* (March 1999) and within the structure of the 'dedicated mathematics lesson'. Each book offers three terms of medium-term planning grids, learning outcomes and lesson plans. The majority of the maths lessons are given in detail, with comprehensive outlines for all the others needed to provide support for teachers for a whole year of maths teaching. Photocopiable activity pages and resources are included to support the learning. Regular assessment is built into the structure of the book, with assessment activity pages which can be kept as evidence of attainment.

The content of these activities is appropriate for and adaptable to the requirements of Primary 1 in Scottish schools. In schools which decide not to adopt the National Numeracy Strategy, choose activities to match your planning.

The activities in this book are designed to encourage pupils to develop their understanding and skills of counting, and of comparing and ordering numbers. They will help you to introduce addition and subtraction and begin to show children how to use mental strategies in these areas. During Reception, the children will also start to explore measures, shapes and space, money and 'real-life' problems. All these concepts and skills are introduced through practical activities, direct teaching and discussion. Children will start to record their work appropriately, and be encouraged to use and apply their new learning in mathematics in a range of tasks. There is a strong emphasis during this time on the use of familiar contexts such as stories, number rhymes and counting games. Play is used to support the development of mathematical understanding and is seen as an essential element at this early age. The role-play area can be set up to support many different aspects of the numeracy strategy, for example a post office will allow the children to investigate mass and use money. During the plenary sessions, encourage the children to explain what they have been doing in their group activities and say what they have found out. Mathematics should be *fun* giving children enjoyment and an enthusiasm to learn.

USING THIS BOOK

THE MATERIALS

This book contains over 150 lessons, provided in a variety of formats. The National Numeracy Strategy has not specified the number of lessons that each topic might require as it is envisaged that this will be determined by you, in consultation with the mathematics co-ordinator, depending on the time allocated for settling children into the Reception class. Therefore, this book offers a set of five (or occasionally eight) flexible lessons, some in full and others in grid format, for each topic unit during the three terms.

For each lesson, there are ideas for developing the children's oral and mental maths, a detailed explanation of the **Whole-class teaching activity**, ideas for **Group activities** and a related **Play activity**, suggestions for **Differentiation**, and guidance for the **Plenary** session. The book follows the Reception 'Planning grid' given in the National Numeracy Strategy *Framework for Teaching Mathematics*. These materials should be regarded as a core for developing your own personalised folder for the year. More detail on planning and managing all aspects of the National Numeracy Strategy can be found in the *Framework*.

ADAPTING AND PERSONALISING THE MATERIALS

The materials are based upon the 'Teaching programme and planning grid' for Reception from the National Numeracy Strategy *Framework for Teaching Mathematics*. What follows is a suggested method of using this book to its full potential, however, you may need to make adjustments to these materials in order to meet the learning needs of your pupils:
● Separate the pages of the book and place them in an A4 ring binder.
● Check that the activities are of a suitable level for your pupils and agree with colleagues who teach the higher years that the entry level is a good match.

● Add your own favourite materials in the relevant places.

● If your school uses a published scheme, insert suitable teacher and pupil resources into your file to supplement these materials.

PREPARING A SCHEME OF WORK

All schools are required to write detailed schemes of work, and this series has been designed to facilitate this process. The termly 'Planning grids' given in these books (see page 20 for example) are provided at the beginning of the work for each term and list all the learning outcomes.

	LEARNING OUTCOMES	ORAL AND MENTAL STARTER	WHOLE-CLASS TEACHING ACTIVITY	PLENARY
LESSON 1	● Count reliably up to 10 everyday objects (first to 5, then 10, then beyond).	WASH DAY: Recognising numbers from 0–20.	ALL TENS: Counting objects in different ranges	NUMBERS: Identifying mistakes in counting

ORGANISATION

The **Organisation chart** outlines the key activities for each part of each maths lesson and can be used as a weekly plan.

LESSON PLANS

After the **Organisation chart** comes a short section detailing which lessons are shown as full lesson plans and which are extensions of what has already been taught in a previous lesson. Some of these will be shown in grid form.

DETAILED LESSON PLANS

Each detailed lesson plan is written to the following headings:

Resources

Provides a list of what you need for that lesson.

Preparation

Outlines any advance preparation needed before the lesson begins.

Learning outcomes

Lists separately the Learning outcomes for the **Oral and mental starter** and the **Whole-class teaching activities**. For many of the activities, several objectives could be linked to one activity, so the outcomes listed are the main focus intended for that lesson. They are based upon the objectives in the 'Teaching programme: Reception' from the *Framework for Teaching Mathematics*. All the objectives are covered at least once in this book. The key objectives are highlighted in bold in the Learning outcomes, as they are in the *Framework*. If a lesson does not cover an objective in its entirety, then only the portion which is intended to be covered is listed in the 'Learning outcomes' (or any of the grids provided).

Vocabulary

The National Numeracy Strategy *Mathematical Vocabulary* booklet has been used to provide the vocabulary lists. New or specific vocabulary to be used during the lesson is listed. Use this vocabulary with the whole class so that all the children have a chance to hear it and begin to understand it. Encourage pupils to use the vocabulary when asking or answering questions, so that they develop an understanding of its mathematical meaning. Where flashcards are suggested, these can be made by printing out onto card the appropriate sections from the CD-ROM which should have accompanied your school's copy of the *Framework for Teaching Mathematics*.

Oral and mental starter

This is designed to occupy the first 5–10 minutes of the lesson, but the duration is not critical. It contains activity suggestions to develop oral and mental work to be used with the whole class and is based on what has already been taught. Some suggestions for differentiated questioning are included to show how all the children can benefit.

WHOLE-CLASS TEACHING ACTIVITY AND GROUP ACTIVITIES

These sections set out what to do in the main teaching session. This should last for about 15–20 minutes. During this time you will be involved in whole-class, interactive teaching. After this, the class can be organised to work on the Group activities which follow up the concepts, understanding and skills introduced or developed in the whole-class activity.

A play activity has been suggested to support the work carried out in each lesson, indicated by the symbol 🐭 . These ideas can be used over different periods of time, but it is suggested that a particular focus be given to support the specific unit. You may decide to integrate your own ideas for the play activity.

Differentiation

This section offers guidance on work for the more able and less able children within the class, suggesting reinforcement or extension. Many of the ideas will provide challenges to encourage pupils to use and apply their mathematics.

Plenary

The plenary is an important part of the lesson and good planning and time management should ensure that this always takes place. It is a chance to bring the children together again for a 10-minute whole-class session. This might involve reinforcing concepts, skills and understanding from the whole-class teaching activity, reciting a number rhyme, singing a song with role-play or playing a game. Many of the plenary sessions involve children in giving feedback from the group activities. This offers opportunities for the children to share with others what they have been doing, encourages speaking and listening skills, and gives you opportunities to assess their progress by asking specific questions to individuals or groups to reinforce essential mathematical vocabulary and/or correct mistakes and misconceptions while observing and listening to the children. In the plenary, you should also summarise key facts learned, make links to other topics and plan for the next topic.

EXTENSION LESSON PLANS

These give guidance on extending to subsequent lessons those already described in detail.

RESOURCES	Nursery rhyme: 'Mary, Mary, c garden). **Group activites:** cop cubes, beads, buttons; biscu
LEARNING OUTCOMES	**ORAL AND MENTAL STARTE** ● **Say and use the number r** stories, counting games and
ORAL AND MENTAL STARTER	SHOW ME: Count in ones t **teaching activity** from Less
WHOLE-CLASS TEACHING ACTIVITY	MARY'S GARDEN: Recite th copy of 'Mary's garden'. Ho
GROUP ACTIVITIES	**1.** Give each child a copy of objects in the garden.
DIFFERENTIATION	Less able: provide opportun More able: count to 10, the
PLENARY	Feedback from activities.

OUTLINE LESSON PLANS

These contain brief descriptions, as grids (see left), of further lessons. These extend the scope of the book to give sufficient material for a year's work. Since they develop work already introduced, there are no vocabulary suggestions as the same range of words will be needed as in the previous, related lesson(s).

USING THE LESSON PLANS

The plans are designed so that you can work through them in order, if you wish. However, you may prefer to choose the lessons that are appropriate for your pupils, and combine these with your favourite activities from other sources. By placing the pages of this book into a ring binder you can easily incorporate your own supplementary materials.

WEEKLY PLANNING

If you wish to use the ready-prepared plans, follow the Organisation chart which appears at the beginning of each Unit. However, if you prefer to plan your week using some of the lesson plans in the book, and some activities you have chosen yourself, then make some photocopies of the blank 'Weekly planning chart' on page 10 of this book. These can then be completed on a weekly basis with details of all the activities which you intend to use, those chosen from this book and those which you have taken from other sources. You may prefer to enlarge the chart to A3.

MIXED-AGE CLASSES

If you have a mixed-age class, you will probably need to use the materials from more than one book in this series. The blank 'Weekly planning chart' on page 10 is a useful planning tool, as you can combine planning from two (or more) books onto this chart.

CLASSROOM ORGANISATION
WHOLE-CLASS TEACHING
During a whole-class session it is important that all the children can see you, the board or flip chart and their table top. In many classrooms space is at a premium, so it is worth spending time considering how the furniture can best be arranged. If you have a carpeted area for whole-class work, think about whether the lesson you are planning to teach would work well with the children seated on the carpet, or whether they would be better placed at their tables, especially if you want them to manipulate apparatus such as interlocking cubes, or if they need to spread out numeral cards in front of them.

GROUP WORK
The organisation and management of Reception classes is often very different from the rest of the primary school. You will need to consider the most effective way of organising and managing the mathematics lessons. If an integrated approach is used, some children may be working on mathematical activities with others doing other 'subjects'. In this case it will be essential to plan thoroughly so that all the children in the class are addressing the key and other Learning outcomes. Regular assessment of the children's progress should be carried out with the keeping of accurate and informative records of individual strengths and needs. These should be used to support children and plan further learning.

Again, it is important that the pupils sit so that they can see you, and the board or flip chart if necessary. While they are working in groups, you may wish to ask whole-class questions, or remind pupils of how much time is left to complete their task, so eye contact will help to ensure that everyone is listening. Allow opportunities to observe, question and join in with children 'working' on the play activities. These present ideal moments to support and assess children's mathematical learning in context.

WORKING WITH OTHER ADULTS
If you have classroom helpers, brief them before the lesson starts on which group you would like them to work with, the purpose of the task, the vocabulary they should be helping to develop, and give some examples of the type of questions they should be asking. Check that all the resources needed are available or, if not, that the helper knows where to find them. You may want to ask a classroom helper to work with just one or two pupils; perhaps they are finding the work difficult, or have been absent and this is an opportunity to catch up on missed work. Whatever the reason, always ensure that the helper is well briefed before the lesson starts, and allow a few minutes after the lesson has finished to discuss any specific observations which the helper would like to make.

CHILDREN WITH SPECIAL EDUCATIONAL NEEDS
Include children with special educational needs in the whole-class work. If you have a classroom helper ask him or her to sit beside the pupils with special needs to provide support. This could include repeating the questions quietly, or encouraging them to use individual resources (such as counting apparatus, a number line or number cards) to find the answer. During differentiated questioning, ensure that some questions are specifically focused for these pupils and encourage them to answer appropriately.

To assist all pupils in reading new vocabulary, and particularly to help those with reading difficulties, make flashcards for the specific mathematics vocabulary which will be used in a series of lessons and encourage the children to read these.

Pupils who are partially sighted or deaf will need to sit near you, so consider carefully the layout of the classroom. Those with emotional or behavioural difficulties will benefit from the structure and routines of the daily maths lesson and, where possible, from the support of a helper who can encourage on-task working. For children who are learning English as an additional language, speak more slowly, repeat instructions, and provide visual clues on worksheets or puzzle cards. For pupils who have an Individual Education Plan (IEP) which includes mathematics as an area of learning difficulty, you may need to supplement these activities with others at an appropriate level which can be linked to the work of the rest of the class or modify the presentation of these activities to encourage inclusion.

HOME-SCHOOL LINKS
The partnership between home and school is an important feature in the Early Years. The promotion of positive attitudes to mathematics can be encouraged by involving parents and carers in the mathematical activities children meet in the classroom. Some of the

activities in this book could be shared with a parent or carer. Offer a range of different types of tasks and encourage pupils to share number rhymes and songs, familiar stories and counting games at home. Suggest games which will help the children to learn some number facts, or rhymes that encourage the development of counting skills, for example 'One, two, three, four, five'. Encourage children to bring in items from home that can be used for mathematical displays, for example 'Pattern' and 'Shapes'.

RESOURCES

PHOTOCOPIABLE SHEETS

These support the work and can be resource pages or activity sheets. They are marked with the photocopiable symbol . Some sheets have many applications and are used throughout the book: these appear at the end of this Introduction on pages 12–18. Others can be found at the end of the relevant Units.

RESOURCE SHEETS

These include numeral and pictorial cards and individual number tracks, and can be found on pages 12–18. Make sufficient of these at the start of the year for each pupil to have at least one (set). You may wish to ask for help from parents and friends of the school to make these resources. Copy the pages onto card, then cut out and laminate as required.

For the numeral cards, consider whether to use different-coloured card so that the children can put them away more easily, using the colour of their set as an aid. These cards can be stored in small polythene bags or tins so that the pupils can keep their resources in their own desks or trays. Alternatively, store these with a rubber band around each set and give them out at the beginning of the lesson. Store class sets of items such as number tracks and dotty cards (a rubber band around each set) in marked boxes.

ACTIVITY SHEETS

These are located at the end of the relevant Units and relate to specific activities. Some activities suggest an extra A3 enlargement for group or whole-class use.

CLASSROOM EQUIPMENT

All the equipment used in this book will normally be found within any primary school. The following list shows what will be needed on a regular basis. Alternatives are suggested where they would be equally appropriate instead. It is important that you create a mathematically-stimulating environment for the children, where they regularly encounter numbers. It is therefore assumed that all classrooms will have a long class number line with large numerals and a large 100 square. Ideally the children should be able to read all the numbers easily from their seats. A chalk board and chalk, or flip chart and marker pens, are essential for interactive whole-class sessions. You will also need:

● A 'washing line' strung across the room, with numbers 1 to 9, then 0 and 10 to 20 and beyond pegged on, plus numbered cut-outs of clothes for 'wash-day' counting.

● Counting apparatus, such as counters, sorting toys, wooden cubes, beads and laces.
● Measuring apparatus, including 'junk' materials.
● Shape apparatus: for example, shape tiles, 2-D and 3-D shapes, and feely bag.

● Construction kits, Plasticine etc.
● Coins, preferably real.
● Dice: both 1–6 and blank.
● Roamer, PIXIE or PIP.
● Dominoes.
● Lots of interlocking cubes, such as Multilink.
● Straws.

USING INFORMATION COMMUNICATIONS TECHNOLOGY

Make use of your favourite mathematical software as a paired or small group activity. Programmable toys can be used to support counting, number recognition, addition, problem solving, shape and space, position and measure. There are a range of Early Years programs to develop logical thinking, problem solving, counting and number skills. Current examples at the time of going to press include: *Millie's Math House* (IONA), *EasyShapes* (Porters), *Pond* (Resource), *Noisy Numbers 0–5* (SEMERC), *Freddy Teddy* (Topologika), *Sequencer* (SEMERC), *Tizzy's Toybox* (Sherston), *123-CD* (Sherston), *Percy Teaches Maths* (Neptune), *Playground (Topologika), Numbers Words and Pictures* (BlackCat). Use a range of ICT including tape recorders, cameras, calculators, scales, as well as computers.

PUBLICATIONS

Use your favourite mathematical stories, poems and rhymes as well as the published material available in school. The following Scholastic publications contain useful ideas: *Developing Mental Maths with 5–7 year olds*; *Maths Focus Kit 1*; *Early Years Essentials: Learning to Count* and *Learning about Shape*; *Skills for Early Years* maths series; *Learning in the Early Years/Learning in the Early Years Photocopiables: Mathematics*.

ASSESSMENT

During the week at the end of each half term, an assessment period is built into the planning. This gives you the opportunity to make medium-term assessments of the key objectives for Reception, listed in the National Numeracy Strategy *Framework for Teaching Mathematics*. The aim of these assessments is to:
● Find out what progress each pupil has made, what he or she knows, understands and can do, whether he or she can apply and use their mathematics in context, and whether he or she has any weaknesses.
● Give you information on which to base feedback to pupils and their parents or carers. It will also help you to plan work for the next few weeks.

ASSESSMENT ADVICE

This is placed just before the assessment activities. Here you will find information on the aspects of mathematics which are to be assessed, some assessment activities for oral and mental starters which can be used with the whole class, and others which can be used with groups, pairs and individuals; and advice on using the photocopiable assessment tasks provided with the Term 2 and 3 activities.

ASSESSMENT ACTIVITIES

These activities have been designed so that you can observe pupils at work, and ask questions. Explain the purpose of the activity to them before they begin, as this will help them to demonstrate to you the things that you want to observe, such as clear recording, discussion of which strategy they used, why they used it, and so on. Target small groups for a specific activity and period of time, and work with them, observing how individuals respond to the activity. You may find it useful to have a notebook handy to make informal notes on observations and discussions.

If you have a classroom helper, he or she can also be involved in the assessment process. Explain the purpose of the assessment, what to do, and what to look for. After the lesson has finished, make time to discuss observations and keep notes on individual pupils' achievements and weaknesses.

ASSESSMENT PHOTOCOPIABLE SHEETS

There are two photocopiable sheets for each half term assessment period for Terms 2 and 3. Each sheet has specific assessment criteria written at the bottom. Photocopy the pages for individual pupils to complete while you observe others undertaking the assessment activities. Mark the completed sheets, then give pupils feedback on their strengths, and set targets for improvement in their areas of weakness. The sheets can be kept in a portfolio as part of the evidence of the children's achievement.

CLASS ASSESSMENT RECORDING SHEET

This will be found on page 11. It lists the key objectives for Reception from the *Framework*. Photocopy the sheet, enlarge it to A3, and record individuals' progress on it. By the end of the year, after six assessment sessions, you will have a wealth of assessment evidence to pass on to the children's next teacher. Each assessment offers opportunities to assess all the relevant key objectives that have been taught in that half term. Some key outcomes reoccur in later assessments. It is not necessary to assess every child each time. Use your assessment records to decide whether to reassess a child or whether it is appropriate to leave a specific assessment objective which has already been learned.

Weekly planning chart

(Photo-enlarge to A3.)

Week beginning:

Learning objectives
for oral and mental
skills:

	Oral and mental starter	Whole class-teaching activity	Differentiation	Plenary	Resources
Monday					
Tuesday					
Wednesday					
Thursday					
Friday					

Reception: class assessment record sheet

Name	Key objectives: Reception	Say and use the number names in order in familiar contexts.	Count reliably up to 10 everyday objects.	Recognise numerals 1 to 9.	Use language such as more or less, greater or smaller, heavier or lighter, to compare two numbers or quantities.	In practical activities and discussion, begin to use the language involved in adding and subtracting.	Find one more or one less than a number from 1 to 10.	Begin to relate addition to combining two groups of objects, and subtraction to 'taking away'.	Talk about, recognise and recreate simple patterns.	Use language such as circle or bigger to describe the shape and size of solids and flat shapes.	Use everyday words to describe position.	Use developing mathematical ideas and methods to solve practical problems.	Other:

Numeral cards

0 | 1 | 2

3 | 4 | 5

6 | 7 | 8

9 | 10

Number tracks

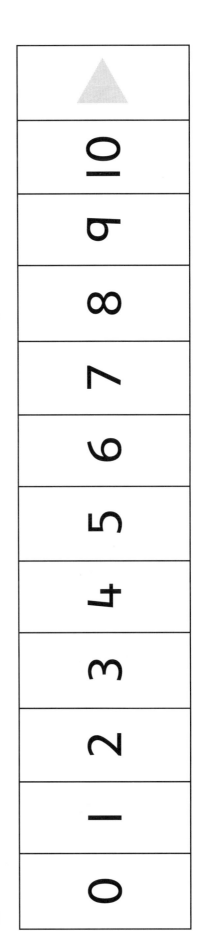

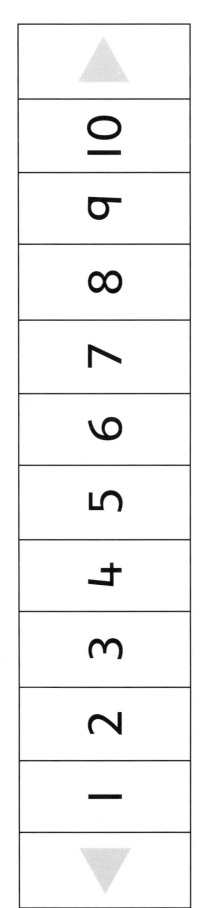

▲
10
9
8
7
6
5
4
3
2
1
0

▲
10
9
8
7
6
5
4
3
2
1
▼

20
19
18
17
16
15
14
13
12
11
▼

Frogs and lilly pads

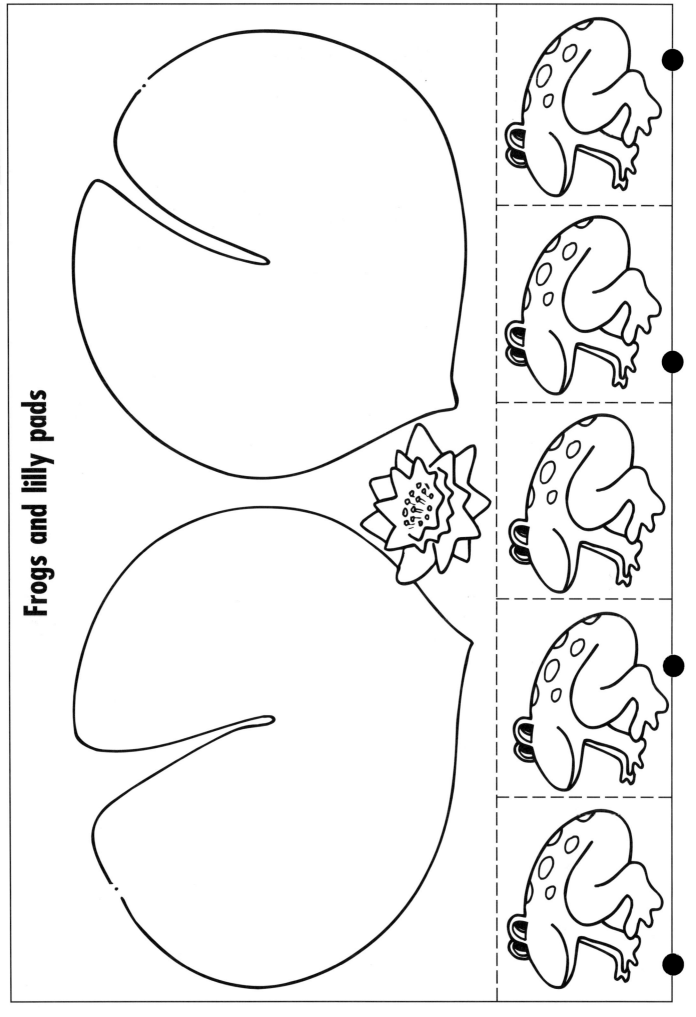

Ladybird template

Money pets

Elephants and spider's web

Dotty cards

TERM 1

The emphasis in the autumn term is on counting, recognising, comparing and ordering numbers to 5, 10, then beyond. The use of number rhymes, songs, stories, counting games and practical activities play a vital role in children's developing understanding of numbers. The introduction and use of appropriate mathematical vocabulary is an essential and integral part of each lesson.

In 'Money' children sort coins, including £1 and £2 coins. Opportunities for role-play activities allow for 'real life' sorting, paying and giving change.

In 'Shape and space' children describe the size and shape of solids and flat shapes. They begin to recognise, make and explore simple repeating and symmetrical patterns and observe familiar 2-D and 3-D shapes and patterns in their environment. Activities involving position, direction and movement are also introduced.

In 'Measures' children begin to compare and order quantities. They start to develop language such as lighter or heavier, empty or full, more or less to compare two then three quantities. Time is introduced through familiar events and children learn and order the days of the week.

ENLARGE THIS SHEET TO A3 AND USE IT AS YOUR LONG TERM PLANNING GRID.

ORAL AND MENTAL SKILLS: Say and use the number names in order in familiar contexts such as number rhymes, songs, stories, counting games and activities (first to five, then ten, then 20 and beyond). **Count reliably up to 10 everyday objects** (first to 5, then 10). Recite the number names in order, continuing the count forwards or backwards from a given number. Count reliably in other contexts, such as clapping sounds. **Begin to use the vocabulary involved in adding. Find one more or less than a number from 1 to 10.**

Unit	Topic	Objectives: children will be taught to...
1	Counting	● Recite the number names in order, continuing the count forwards or backwards from a given number. ● **Count reliably up to 10 everyday objects** (first to 5, then 10, then beyond). ● **Say and use the number names in order in familiar contexts** such as number rhymes, songs, stories, counting games and activities (first to five, then ten).
2	Counting	● **Say and use the number names in order in familiar contexts** such as number rhymes, songs, stories, counting games and activities (first to five, then ten). ● Recite the number names in order, continuing the count forwards and backwards from a given number. ● **Count reliably up to 10 everyday objects** (first to 5, then 10, then beyond).
3	Shape and space	● **Use language such as circle or bigger to describe the shape and size of solids and flat shapes.** ● Begin to name solids such as a cube, cone, sphere... and flat shapes such as a circle, triangle, square, rectangle. ● Use a variety of shapes to make models, pictures and patterns, and describe them.
4	Counting Measures	● **Say and use the number names in order in familiar contexts** such as number rhymes, songs, stories, counting games and activities (first to five, then ten, then twenty and beyond). ● **Use mathematical language such as more or less, taller or shorter, wider or narrower.** ● **Compare quantities** by making direct comparisons of two, then three lengths. ● **Use language such as longer or shorter to compare two quantities**, then more than two, by making direct comparisons of lengths. ● **Use language such as more or less to compare two quantities** by filling and emptying containers.
5	Counting Adding	● Begin to recognise 'none' and 'zero' when counting. ● Recite the number names in order, continuing the count forwards and backwards from a given number. ● **Recognise numerals 1 to 4, then 0 and 10.** ● **In practical activities and discussion, begin to use the language involved in adding.** ● Find one more than a number.
6	Assess and review	

ORAL AND MENTAL SKILLS: Say and use the number names in order in familiar contexts such as number rhymes, songs, stories, counting games and activities (first to five, then ten, then twenty and beyond). Recite the number names in order, continuing the count forwards or backwards from a given number. **Begin to use the vocabulary involved in adding and subtracting. Use language such as more or less, greater or smaller, to compare two numbers** and say which is more or less, and say a number which lies between two given numbers. Estimate a number in the range that can be counted reliably, then check by counting. **Begin to relate addition to combining two groups of objects, counting all the objects. Begin to relate subtraction to 'taking away'** and counting how many are left.

Unit	Topic	Objectives: children will be taught to...
7	Counting Comparing and ordering numbers	● **Count reliably up to 10 everyday objects** (first to 5, then 10, then beyond). ● **Use language such as more or less, greater or smaller, to compare two numbers** and say which is more or less, and say a number which lies between two given numbers.
8	Counting Adding and subtracting	● **Begin to use the vocabulary involved in adding and subtracting.** ● **Find one more or one less than a number from 1 to 10.**
9	Shape and space Reasoning	● Begin to name solids such as a cube, cone, sphere... and flat shapes such as a circle, triangle, square, rectangle. ● Use a variety of shapes to make models, pictures and patterns, and describe them. ● Talk about, recognise and recreate patterns: for example, simple repeating or symmetrical patterns in the environment. ● Make simple estimates and predictions: for example, of the number of cubes that will fit in a box or strides across the room.
10	Counting Measures, including time	● Begin to recognise 'none' and 'zero' in stories, rhymes and when counting back. ● Begin to understand and use the vocabulary of time. ● Sequence familiar events. ● Begin to know the days of the week in order.
11	Counting Money and 'real life problems'	● Recite the number names in order, continuing the count forwards or backwards from a given number. ● Begin to relate addition to counting on. ● **Say and use the number names in order in familiar contexts** such as number rhymes, songs, stories, counting games and activities (first to five, then ten, then twenty and beyond). ● **Use language such as more or less, greater or smaller, to compare two numbers** and say which is more or less, and say a number which lies between two given numbers. ● **Use developing mathematical understanding to solve problems** involving counting and comparing in a practical or role play context. ● Begin to use the vocabulary related to money; begin to recognise coins, including the £1 and £2 coins, and use them in role-play to pay and give change.
12	Assess and review	

UNIT 1

ORGANISATION (5 LESSONS)

LEARNING OUTCOMES	ORAL AND MENTAL STARTER	WHOLE-CLASS TEACHING ACTIVITY	PLENARY
LESSON 1 • Recite the number names in order, continuing the count forwards or backwards from a given number. • **Count reliably up to 10 everyday objects** (first to 5, then 10).	ONE, TWO, THREE: Counting in ones.	STARTING AT ONE: Counting objects up to 5.	Counting in ones.
LESSON 2 • **Say and use the number names in order in familiar contexts** such as number rhymes, songs, stories, counting games and activities (first to five, then ten). • **Count reliably up to 10 everyday objects** (first to 5, then 10).	...FOUR, FIVE: Counting in ones.	FROM THE TOY BOX: Counting objects.	Feedback from activities.
LESSON 3 • **Say and use the number names in order in familiar contexts** such as number rhymes, songs, stories, counting games and activities (first to five, then ten). • **Count reliably up to 10 everyday objects** (first to 5, then 10).	ONE, TWO, THREE: Counting in ones.	MORE FROM THE TOY BOX: Counting objects.	Feedback from activities.
LESSON 4 • **Say and use the number names in order in familiar contexts** such as number rhymes, songs, stories, counting games and activities (first to five, then ten). • **Count reliably up to 10 everyday objects** (first to 5, then 10).	COUNTING IN ONES: Counting in ones to 5, then 10.	WASH DAY: Sorting and counting objects.	Feedback from activities. Counting to 5, then 10
LESSON 5 • **Say and use the number names in order in familiar contexts** such as number rhymes, songs, stories, counting games and activities (first to five, then ten). • **Count reliably up to 10 everyday objects** (first to 5, then 10).	SHOW ME: Counting in ones to 10. Children then show a number by holding up a given number of fingers.	MARY'S GARDEN: Counting activities using the rhyme 'Mary, Mary, quite contrary'.	Feedback from activities.

ORAL AND MENTAL SKILLS **Say and use the number names in order in familiar contexts** such as number rhymes, songs, stories, counting games and activities (first to five, then ten). **Count reliably up to 10 everyday objects** (first to 5, then 10). Recite the number names in order, continuing the count forwards or backwards from a given number.

Lessons 1, 2 and 4 are presented in full, with Lessons 3 and 5 in grid format.

RESOURCES

Selection of counting rhymes such as 'One, two, three, four five', 'One, two, buckle my shoe'; shopping bag; three teddy bears; cut-outs of fish; garden canes; string; magnets; plastic fish tank. **Group activities:** assorted counting objects such as socks, shells, cubes, beads, buttons, conkers, toy cars/animals, dominoes; plastic washing-up bowls or large ice-cream cartons; blue paper; crayons.

PREPARATION

Choose some counting rhymes which involve counting to 10. Make some cardboard fish in different shapes and sizes. Cover each fish in wrapping paper, clip a paper-clip to the mouth end and put them in the fish tank. Make 'fishing rods' with garden canes and string. Attach a magnet to each string. Place three bears in the shopping bag.

LEARNING OUTCOMES

ORAL AND MENTAL STARTER
● **Say and use the number names in order in familiar contexts** such as number rhymes, songs, stories, counting games and activities (first to five, then ten).
● Recite the number names in order, continuing the count forwards or backwards from a given number.

WHOLE-CLASS TEACHING ACTIVITY
● Recite the number names in order, continuing the count forwards or backwards from a given number.
● **Count reliably up to 10 everyday objects** (first to 5, then 10).

ORAL AND MENTAL STARTER

ONE, TWO, THREE: Teach the class the rhyme 'One, two, three, four, five, once I caught a fish alive...'. Ask the children to join in. Show them how to count on their fingers as you repeat the rhyme.

WHOLE-CLASS TEACHING ACTIVITY

STARTING AT ONE: Explain that the lesson is about counting. Say: *We have just been counting in ones to 10.* Ask the children to count up to 5. *Hold up one finger when you say 1, hold up two fingers when you say 2.* Continue to 5. *Count along with me: 1, 2, 3, 4, 5.* Show the children the shopping bag: *I've some special friends in my bag.* Take out the bears one at a time, counting each one. *How many bears are there? Let's count them.* Touch each bear as you count with the children. Say: *My bears like fishing.* Show the children the 'fishing rods' and the fish tank. Count out five fish and place them in the tank. Explain that the bears are going to catch fish. Count out the fish as they are caught: *1, 2, 3, 4, 5 fish.* Tell the children they are going to do some counting activities. Talk about the group activities.

GROUP ACTIVITIES

1. Place a variety of counting items such as socks, shells, toy animals, toy cars, cubes, play-people, ribbons, dominoes (up to five of each sort) on the table. Working with an adult, the children sort the items into sets. Ask children to count out the number of objects in each set, touching them one by one.
2. Place the washing up bowls, fishing rods and fish on the table. Give each child a rod and ask them to 'catch' the fish. They place their fish in front of them, then count the number of fish they have caught, touching them one by one.
3. Give each child a sheet of blue paper and some crayons. Ask them to draw a fish tank and then draw different numbers of fish inside it.

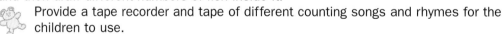 Provide a tape recorder and tape of different counting songs and rhymes for the children to use.

DIFFERENTIATION

Less able: use numbers 1–3, then extend to 5.
More able: use numbers 1–5, then extend to 10.

PLENARY

Repeat the rhyme 'One, two, three, four, five'. Display five fish in a line. *Let's count the fish together.* Count each fish, touching them one by one. Say: *Can you count the fish as I touch them?*

RESOURCES

Selection of counting rhymes such as 'One, two, three, four, five', 'One, two, buckle my shoe'; cardboard boxes; wrapping paper; assorted counting objects such as soft toys, cubes, beads, buttons, conkers, dolls, cars, teddy bears, books, balls. **Group activities:** selection of small boxes; washing-up bowls; fishing rods; cut-outs of fish; cubes.

PREPARATION

Cover the large and small boxes in wrapping paper. Place a selection of toys, such as one doll, two cars, three teddy bears, two books, two balls (up to a total of ten objects) in the large box.

LEARNING OUTCOMES

ORAL AND MENTAL STARTER and WHOLE-CLASS TEACHING ACTIVITY

● **Say and use the number names in order in familiar contexts** such as number rhymes, songs, stories, counting games and activities (first to five, then ten).
● **Count reliably up to 10 everyday objects** (first to 5, then 10, then beyond).

ORAL AND MENTAL STARTER

...FOUR, FIVE: Recite the rhyme: 'One, two, three, four, five'. Ask the children to hold up one hand. Show them how to touch each finger as they count up to 5. Say: *All count together up to 5. 1, 2, 3, 4, 5.* Ask all the boys to count up to 5, then all the girls.

WHOLE-CLASS TEACHING ACTIVITY

FROM THE TOY BOX: Tell the children that today's lesson is about counting. Place the toy box on a table so that all the class can see it and say: *I wonder what is in the box?* Ask individuals to come and take out one item. As the items are taken out, arrange them in a line. Say: *How many things were in the box? Let's count them.* Touch each object as you count. *How many books are there?* Repeat with different items.

GROUP ACTIVITIES

1. Place a selection of counting items on each table. Give each child a box. The children choose five items to put in their toy box. They count out the total number of items, then count how many of each.
2. Place the washing-up bowls, fishing rods and fish on the table. Give each child a rod and ask them to 'catch' the fish. They place their fish in front of them, then count the number of fish they have caught, touching them one by one.
3. Place a selection of cubes on each table. Children make towers using different numbers of cubes.

Make a treasure hunt in the sand tray by hiding a number of objects. Ask children to find them and count how many they find.

DIFFERENTIATION

Less able: work with numbers 1–5.
More able: work with numbers 1–10.

PLENARY

Take feedback from the **Group activities**.

VOCABULARY

Counting; number; one, two, three ... to ten, how many?; count; count (up) to; count in ones.

LESSON 3

RESOURCES	Selection of counting rhymes such as 'One, two, three, four, five', 'One, two, buckle my shoe'; toy box and items, eg one doll, two teddy bears, three skipping ropes, four paintbrushes (up to a total of ten items); a picture of a toy box drawn on a large sheet of paper. **Group activities:** cut-out pictures of toys from magazines; adhesive; paper; beads in different colours; threading laces; washing-up bowls; fishing rods; fish.
LEARNING OUTCOMES	**ORAL AND MENTAL STARTER** ● **Say and use the number names in order in familiar contexts** such as number rhymes, songs, stories, counting games and activities (first to five, then ten, then twenty and beyond). **WHOLE-CLASS TEACHING ACTIVITY** ● **Say and use the number names in order in familiar contexts** such as number rhymes, songs, stories, counting games and activities (first to five, then ten). ● **Count reliably up to 10 everyday objects** (first to 5, then 10).
ORAL AND MENTAL STARTER	ONE, TWO, THREE: As Lesson 1 on page 22.
WHOLE-CLASS TEACHING ACTIVITY	MORE FROM THE TOY BOX: Display the toy box at the front of the class. Say: *What was in the box yesterday? How many things did we count inside? Let's see what's in there today.* Pick out an item, for example a teddy, and place it on the table. Ask a child to come out and see if there is another teddy in the box. *How many teddies now?* Repeat until all the items have been sorted. Count the number of each item. Ask a child to touch each one as the whole class counts: *How many things were in the box today?* Display your picture of a toy box and say: *We could draw the toys in our box on the sheet. Then we would know how many are in there.* Invite children to draw items on the sheet. *Count all the toys on the sheet. Now count all the toys from the box. Have we drawn the same number?*
GROUP ACTIVITIES	**1.** Place the pictures of toys and the adhesive on the table. Give each child a sheet of paper. Ask them to draw an outline of a toy box and then choose toys to stick inside. **2.** Place a selection of beads and threading laces on the table. The children make necklaces, then count how many beads there are of each colour. **3.** Place the washing-up bowls, fishing rods and fish on the table. Give each child a rod and ask them to 'catch' the fish. They place their fish in front of them, then count the number of fish they have caught, touching them one by one. ● Ask children to check items in the role-play corner.
DIFFERENTIATION	Less able: work with numbers 1–5. More able: work with numbers 1–10.
PLENARY	Feedback from the **Group activities**. Recite 'One, two, buckle my shoe'.

LESSON 4

RESOURCES

Counting rhymes such as 'One, two, three, four, five', 'One, two, buckle my shoe'; washing line; clothes basket; items of clothing; puppet 'Miss Count'. **Group activities:** cut-out pictures of toys from magazines; adhesive; paper; plastic containers; assorted counting objects.

PREPARATION

Place the items of clothing in the clothes basket. Make or select a suitable puppet to be 'Miss Count'.

LEARNING OUTCOMES

ORAL AND MENTAL STARTER
● **Say and use the number names in order in familiar contexts** such as number rhymes, songs, stories, counting games and activities (first to five, then ten, then twenty and beyond).
● Recite the number names in order, continuing the count forwards or backwards from a given number.

WHOLE-CLASS TEACHING ACTIVITY
● **Say and use the number names in order in familiar contexts** such as number rhymes, songs, stories, counting games and activities (first to five, then ten).
● **Count reliably up to 10 everyday objects** (first to 5, then 10).

ORAL AND MENTAL STARTER

COUNTING IN ONES: Recite 'One, two, buckle my shoe'. Count in ones as a class up to 5, then 10. Ask individuals and pairs to count to 5 and then 10.

WHOLE-CLASS TEACHING ACTIVITY

WASH DAY: Peg up the washing line across the classroom. Show the children the items in the clothes basket. *Can we sort out the clothes and peg them on the line?* Invite individuals to come out to the front and select an item then peg it on the line. Ask: *Are there any more clothes?* Get children to peg out the rest of the items. Say: *How many socks are there? Can you count the T-shirts? Are there three hats?* Ask the children to count out all the items on the line. Touch each item as they count. Introduce the puppet 'Miss Count'. Say: *Miss Count likes counting in ones. She'd like to count the clothes on our washing line.* Say: *1, 2, 4, 3, 5...* Ask the children if Miss Count counted correctly. *What was wrong?* Ask the children to count correctly for Miss Count. Explain that you want the children to show you a number by holding up their fingers. *Show me three. Hold up three fingers.* Repeat using different numbers to 5, then to 10.

GROUP ACTIVITIES

1. Give the children the washing basket and clothes. Ask them to sort out the clothes, then count each set.
2. Place the pictures of toys and the adhesive on the table. Give each child a sheet of paper. Ask them to draw an outline of a toy box and then choose toys to stick inside.
3. Put out the plastic containers. Ask children to count out a different number of items into each container. Ask children how many there are in each one.
 Set up the fishing game.

DIFFERENTIATION

Less able: ask a classroom assistant to help them.
More able: extend to 10 and beyond.

PLENARY

Take feedback from the **Group activities**. Repeat counting to 5, then 10 with 'Miss Count'.

RESOURCES	Nursery rhyme: 'Mary, Mary, quite contrary'; an enlarged copy of photocopiable page 30 (Mary's garden); **Group activites:** copies of photocopiable page 26; small plastic containers; counting objects: cubes, beads, buttons; biscuit recipe ingredients.
LEARNING OUTCOMES	**ORAL AND MENTAL STARTER** ● **Say and use the number names in order in familiar contexts** such as number rhymes, songs, stories, counting games and activities (first to five, then ten). **WHOLE-CLASS TEACHING ACTIVITY** ● **Say and use the number names in order in familiar contexts** such as number rhymes, songs, stories, counting games and activities (first to five, then ten). ● **Count reliably up to 10 everyday objects** (first to 5, then 10).
ORAL AND MENTAL STARTER	SHOW ME: Count in ones to 10. Then children hold up a given number of fingers (as in the **Whole-class teaching activity** from Lesson 4 above.)
WHOLE-CLASS TEACHING ACTIVITY	MARY'S GARDEN: Recite 'Mary, Mary, quite contrary'. Ask children to look at your enlarged copy of 'Mary's garden'. *How many shells are there? How many birds?*
GROUP ACTIVITIES	**1.** Give each child a copy of photocopiable page 26 (Mary's garden). Ask them to count all the different objects in the garden. **2.** Put out the plastic containers. The children count out a different number of items into each container. Ask the children how many there are in each one. **3.** Working with an adult, children make simple biscuits. They decorate them with small sweets. ● In farm play ask children to count out the different animals and place them in fields and sheds.
DIFFERENTIATION	Less able: provide opportunities to count to 5 then 10. More able: count to 10, then beyond.
PLENARY	Feedback from the **Group activities**. Use 'Miss Count' to count out the objects in Mary's garden.

UNIT 1

Mary's garden

UNIT 2

ORGANISATION (5 LESSONS)

LEARNING OUTCOMES	ORAL AND MENTAL STARTER	WHOLE-CLASS TEACHING ACTIVITY	PLENARY
LESSON 1 • **Say and use the number names in order in familiar contexts** such as number rhymes, songs, stories, counting games and activities (first to five, then ten). • Recite the number names in order, continuing the count forwards or backwards from a given number. • **Count reliably up to 10 everyday objects** (first to 5, then 10, then beyond).	ONE ELEPHANT WENT OUT TO PLAY: Counting objects up to 5.	MORE ELEPHANTS: Counting to 5, then 10	FINGER COUNT: Counting to 5, then 10 using fingers.
LESSON 2 • **Say and use the number names in order in familiar contexts** such as number rhymes, songs, stories, counting games and activities (first to five, then ten). • Recite the number names in order, continuing the count forwards or backwards from a given number. • **Count reliably up to 10 everyday objects** (first to 5, then 10, then beyond).	ONE, TWO, BUCKLE MY SHOE: Counting to 5, then 10.	DOTTY WASHING: Children match dotty cards to numeral cards.	SHOW ME: Children show a specific number.
LESSON 3 • Recite the number names in order, continuing the count forwards or backwards from a given number.	COUNTING IN ONES: Counting in ones to 5, then 10.	BLAST OFF: Children count down from 10 to 0.	FINGER COUNT: Children use fingers to count.
LESSON 4 • Recite the number names in order, continuing the count forwards or backwards from a given number. • **Count reliably up to 10 everyday objects** (first to 5, then 10, then beyond).	FINGER COUNT: Counting in ones to 5, then 10.	CLAP AND COUNT: Children clap and count out numbers.	Children recite a number rhyme.
LESSON 5 • Recite the number names in order, continuing the count forwards or backwards from a given number. • Count reliably in other contexts, such as clapping sounds.	FINGER COUNT: Counting in ones to 5, then 10.	COUNT OUT: Children count out and rearrange up to ten items.	CLAP AND COUNT:Children clap and count out numbers.

ORAL AND MENTAL SKILLS Recite the number names in order, continuing the count forwards or backwards from a given number. **Count reliably up to 10 everyday objects** (first to 5, then 10, then beyond). **Say and use the number names in order in familiar contexts** such as number rhymes, songs, stories, counting games and activities (first to five, then ten).

Lessons 1, 2 and 3 are presented in full, with Lessons 4 and 5 in grid format.

UNIT 2

LESSON 1

RESOURCES
Elephants and spider's web templates (page 17); Velcro; thick card; sticky labels.
Group activities: elephant cards; (1–10) spinner; sets of dotty cards (1 to 5) (page 18); labelled containers; selection of counting items.

PREPARATION
Make sufficient enlarged copies of the elephants and spider's web template sheet (page 17). Cut out ten elephants and mount them on card. Attach Velcro to the backs of the elephants and the spider's web. Also make six sets of elephant cards (ten in each set).

Stick coloured spots (1–10) on each card. Photocopy page 18 and mount the dotty cards on card. Draw spots (1–10) on to labels and stick these on the containers.

LEARNING OUTCOMES
ORAL AND MENTAL STARTER and WHOLE-CLASS TEACHING ACTIVITY
● **Say and use the number names in order in familiar contexts** such as number rhymes, songs, stories, counting games and activities (first to five, then ten).
● Recite the number names in order, continuing the count forwards or backwards from a given number.
● **Count reliably up to 10 everyday objects** (first to 5, then 10, then beyond).

ORAL AND MENTAL STARTER

VOCABULARY
Counting; number; one, two, three... to ten; how many?; count; count (up) to; count on (from, to); count back (from, to); count in ones.

ONE ELEPHANT WENT OUT TO PLAY: Sing the rhyme. Next, show the children the elephant cut-outs and the spider's web. Recite the rhyme again. Ask the children to place the elephants (up to five) on the web. *How many elephants are on the web? Count the elephants.*

WHOLE-CLASS TEACHING ACTIVITY

MORE ELEPHANTS: Explain that the lesson is about counting, first to 5, then to 10. Recite the number names in order with the children. Place different amounts of elephants, up to five, on the web. Ask the class and individuals to count the elephants. Repeat using ten elephant cards. Ask the children to place the elephants on the web in order. Count them with the children. The children hold up their fingers as they count. Ask questions such as: *What comes before 3? What comes after 2?*

GROUP ACTIVITIES

1. Place sets of elephant cards on the table with spots face up. Children take turns to spin the spinner. They match the number of spots on the dice to those on the elephant. The child with the most elephant cards wins.
2. Place two sets of dotty cards on the table. Children match the spots on the cards.
3. Place the labelled containers and a selection of counting items on the table. Children count out items to match the labels.

Ask children to count and match items in the role-play area, for example cups and saucers, knives and forks.

DIFFERENTIATION

Less able: reduce the number range to 3, then 5.
More able: extend the number range to 10.

PLENARY

FINGER COUNT: Children count to 5, then 10, using their fingers.

LESSON 2

RESOURCES
See Lesson 1. Also washing line; pegs; enlarged set of dotty cards (1–10) (page 18).

PREPARATION
See Lesson 1. Peg up the washing line at the front of the class.

LEARNING OUTCOMES
ORAL AND MENTAL STARTER
● Recite the number names in order, continuing the count forwards or backwards from a given number.
● **Say and use the number names in order in familiar contexts** such as number rhymes, songs, stories, counting games and activities (first to five, then ten).

WHOLE-CLASS TEACHING ACTIVITY
● **Say and use the number names in order in familiar contexts** such as number rhymes, songs, stories, counting games and activities (first to five, then ten).
● Recite the number names in order, continuing the count forwards or backwards from a given number.
● **Count reliably up to 10 everyday objects** (first to 5, then 10, then beyond).

ORAL AND MENTAL STARTER
ONE, TWO, BUCKLE MY SHOE: Say the rhyme. Children count to 5, then 10, using their fingers. Ask individuals and pairs to show a given number by holding up their fingers.

VOCABULARY
Counting; number; one, two, three... to ten; how many?; count; count (up) to; count on (from, to); count back (from, to); count in ones.

WHOLE-CLASS TEACHING ACTIVITY
DOTTY WASHING: Remind the children of when they pegged up the washing in Unit 1, Lesson 4 (page 24). Explain that now they are going to use dotty cards. Show them the enlarged dotty cards: *How many dots on this card?* Ask the class and individuals to count. Arrange the cards on the washing line in order, from 1 to 5. *This card has one dot, this card two.* Continue to five. Point to a card and ask: *How many dots?* Repeat with different numbers. Extend to ten and repeat the activity. Count together along the number line.

GROUP ACTIVITIES

Choose from the **Group activities** in Lesson 1, page 28.
Organise a class treasure hunt with children looking for a given number of objects.

DIFFERENTIATION
Less able: work with number spots to 5 then 10
More able: work with number spots then numerals to 10.

PLENARY
SHOW ME: Ask the children to hold up a given number of fingers. Say: *Show me seven fingers.* Ask children to come and count out a given number of objects. Say: *Count out nine cubes.* Repeat using numbers 1 to 10.

RESOURCES

Set of large numeral cards (0–10) (page 12); cut-outs of fish; washing line; pegs; one large and six small sets of dotty cards (1–10) (page 18). **Group activities:** zigzag books; elephant cards; spinner; crayons.

PREPARATION

Stick gummed spots onto the back of the fish. Make zigzag books with five spaces each side, one book per child. Write the numerals 1–10 at the top of each page with the corresponding number of dots.

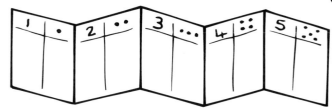

LEARNING OUTCOMES

ORAL AND MENTAL STARTER

● Recite the number names in order, continuing the count from a given number.
● **Say and use the number names in order in familiar contexts** such as number rhymes, songs, stories, counting games and activities (first to five, then ten).

WHOLE-CLASS TEACHING ACTIVITY

● Recite the number names in order, continuing the count forwards or backwards from a given number.

VOCABULARY

Counting; number; one, two, three ... to ten; how many?; count; count (up) to; count on (from, to); count back (from, to); count in ones.

ORAL AND MENTAL STARTER

COUNTING IN ONES: Say the rhyme 'One, two three, four, five'. Count in ones from 1 to 5. Repeat with numbers from 1 to 10.

WHOLE-CLASS TEACHING ACTIVITY

BLAST OFF: Explain that when a rocket is launched the people at space control count back in ones instead of counting forward: *Try it. Count back from 5 to 1: 5, 4, 3, 2, 1.* Repeat counting from 10 to 1. Say: *The people count back from 10 to 0, then the rocket is launched.* Ask everybody to count back from 10 to 0. Invite pairs and individuals to count forward from 0 to 5, then back. Repeat using 0 to 10. Peg the numeral cards on the washing line. Hand out the dotty cards and ask the children to match these to the numeral cards and peg them on the line. Then count in ones to 10, pointing to each number.

GROUP ACTIVITIES

1. Give each child a zigzag book. Point out the numbers and spots on each page. Ask children to draw items on the page to make their own number books.
2. Place sets of dotty cards on the table. Ask children to find cards from 1 to 10.
3. Place sets of elephant cards on the table with spots face up. Children take turns to spin the spinner (1–10). They match the number of spots on the dice to those on the elephant. The child with the most elephant cards wins.

 Ask the children to count out pencils, cups, and so on during the day.

DIFFERENTIATION

Less able: count forwards and backwards from 1 to 5, then extend to 10.
More able: encourage children to count beyond 10.

PLENARY

FINGER COUNT: to 10. Count back from 5 then 10.

RESOURCES	Appropriate resources for the **Group activities**, see Lesson 3, page 30.
LEARNING OUTCOMES	**ORAL AND MENTAL STARTER** ● Recite the number names in order, continuing the count forwards or backwards from a given number. **WHOLE-CLASS TEACHING ACTIVITY** ● Count reliably in other contexts, such as clapping sounds. ● Recite the number names in order, continuing the count forwards or backwards from a given number.
ORAL AND MENTAL STARTER	FINGER COUNT: To 10. Count on in ones from 1 to 5, then to 10.
WHOLE-CLASS TEACHING ACTIVITY	CLAP AND COUNT: Children clap and count out the number you say. Start with numbers to 5, then to 10. Children clap and count at the same time. Say: *Clap and count to four.* Repeat using different numbers. Ask the class, pairs and individuals to clap and count.
GROUP ACTIVITIES	Choose from the activities in Lesson 3 on page 30. ● Set up a range of musical instruments for children to use to count out the beat.
DIFFERENTIATION	Less able: limit counting to 10. More able: encourage children to count to 20.
PLENARY	Sing 'One elephant went out to play'. Ask the children to come and carry out the actions.

RESOURCES	Selection of counting items; puppet 'Miss Count'. **Group activities:** Choose appropriate resources from Lesson 3, page 30.
LEARNING OUTCOMES	**ORAL AND MENTAL STARTER** ● Recite the number names in order, continuing the count forwards or backwards from a given number. **WHOLE-CLASS TEACHING ACTIVITY** ● **Count reliably up to 10 everyday objects** (first to 5, then 10, then beyond). ● Recite the number names in order, continuing the count forwards or backwards from a given number.
ORAL AND MENTAL STARTER	FINGER COUNT: To 10. Count back in ones from 5 to 0, then from 10.
WHOLE-CLASS TEACHING ACTIVITY	COUNT OUT: Ask the children to count out ten items and place them in a pile in front of them on the table. Explain that when you say a number, you want them to count out that number of objects to show you. Say: *Count out 3. Arrange these objects in a line. How many are there now?* Repeat using numbers to 10. Ask the children to arrange their objects in different ways, such as spread out, touching, stacked up. Finally, use 'Miss Count' to count forwards and backwards. Ask the children to listen for counting mistakes.
GROUP ACTIVITIES	Choose from the activities in Lesson 3 on page 30. ● Make a classroom number book including the numbers of windows, doors, etc.
DIFFERENTIATION	Less able: limit counting to 10. More able: encourage children to count to 20.
PLENARY	Repeat 'Clap and count' from the **Whole-class teaching activity** in Lesson 4 above.

UNIT 3

ORGANISATION (5 LESSONS)

	LEARNING OUTCOMES	ORAL AND MENTAL STARTER	WHOLE-CLASS TEACHING ACTIVITY	PLENARY
LESSON 1	● **Use language such as circle or bigger to describe the shape and size of solids and flat shapes.** ● Begin to name solids such as a cube, cone, sphere... and flat shapes such as a circle, triangle, square, rectangle. ● Use a variety of shapes to make models, pictures and patterns, and describe them.	COUNT OUT: Children count out various amounts of items.	SHAPE BOX: 2-D and 3-D shape recognition.	Feedback from group activities. Children pick out a shape and say whether it belongs to the 2-D or 3-D shape family.
LESSON 2 +3	● **Use language such as circle or bigger to describe the shape and size of solids and flat shapes.** ● Begin to name solids such as a cube, cone, sphere... and flat shapes such as a circle, triangle, rectangle. ● Use a variety of shapes to make models, pictures and patterns, and describe them.	CLAP AND COUNT: Children clap and count out numbers.	TRIANGLE OR NOT?: 2-D and 3-D shape recognition.	Feedback from group activities.
LESSON 4	● **Use language such as circle or bigger to describe the shape and size of solids and flat shapes.** ● Begin to name solids such as a cube, cone, sphere... and flat shapes such as a circle, triangle, square, rectangle. ● Use a variety of shapes to make models, pictures and patterns, and describe them.	ONE ELEPHANT WENT OUT TO PLAY: Children recite this number rhyme and add role-play.	ODD ONE OUT: Sorting and matching activities.	GUESS THE SHAPE Children match shapes.
LESSON 5	● **Use language such as circle or bigger to describe the shape and size of solids and flat shapes.** ● Begin to name solids such as a cube, cone, sphere... and flat shapes such as a circle, triangle, square, rectangle. ● Use a variety of shapes to make models, pictures and patterns, and describe them.	COUNT FORWARD AND BACK: Counting up to and back from 20.	ODD ONE OUT. Recognising which shape is the odd one out in a set.	Feedback from activities.

ORAL AND MENTAL SKILLS **Say and use the number names in order in familiar contexts** such as number rhymes, songs, stories, counting games and activities (first to five, then ten, then twenty and beyond). Recite the number names in order, continuing the count forwards or backwards from a given number. **Count reliably up to 10 everyday objects** (first to 5, then 10, then beyond). Count reliably in other contexts, such as clapping sounds.

Lessons 1 and 2 are given in full, with Lesson 3 extending Lesson 2. Lessons 4 and 5 are provided in grids.

RESOURCES

Selection of items for counting; collection of different-sized 2-D shapes (circle, square, rectangle, triangle) and 3-D shapes (cubes, cuboids, spheres, cylinders); large container or storage box; wrapping paper. **Group activities:** recycled materials; selection of 3-D shapes for printing with; paints; thick cardboard; strips of card.

PREPARATION

Cover the container or storage box with wrapping paper to make a 'shape box'. Place the 2-D and 3-D shapes inside. (Note that 2-D shapes should technically have no thickness at all. Therefore, use the thinnest 2-D shapes possible for practical work, such as plastic templates, card or laminated paper.) Make labels saying 'The 3-D shape family' and 'The 2-D shape family'. Cut the strips of card to fit around a child's head. Set up the printing table.

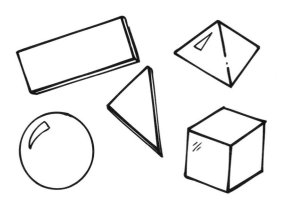

LEARNING OUTCOMES

ORAL AND MENTAL STARTER
● Recite the number names in order, continuing the count forwards or backwards from a given number.
● **Count reliably up to 10 everyday objects** (first to 5, then 10, then beyond).

WHOLE-CLASS TEACHING ACTIVITY
● **Use language such as circle or bigger to describe the shape and size of solids and flat shapes.**
● Begin to name solids such as a cube, cone, sphere... and flat shapes such as a circle, triangle, square, rectangle...
● Use a variety of shapes to make models, pictures and patterns, and describe them.

<table>
<tr><td>

VOCABULARY

Solid shape; hollow shape; 3-D shape; cube; cuboid; sphere; flat; flat shape; face; 2-D shape; circle; triangle; square; rectangle.

</td></tr>
</table>

ORAL AND MENTAL STARTER

COUNT OUT: Ask individuals, with or without help from the class, to count out a given number of items. Ask the children to arrange the items in different ways.

WHOLE-CLASS TEACHING ACTIVITY

SHAPE BOX: Show the children the 'shape box' and explain that it contains different types of shapes. Say: *There are two families of shapes – 3-D shapes and 2-D shapes.* Tell the children that the shapes in the box have all got muddled up. Pick out a 3-D shape and say, for example: *This is a cylinder.* Ask individuals to come and pick out other members of the cylinder family. Repeat with cubes, spheres and cuboids. Say: *All these shapes belong to the 3-D family.* Display the shapes on a nearby table or cupboard top. Repeat this process using the 2-D shapes. Display them near the 3-D shapes. Show and read out the labels. *Where shall we put the label for the 3-D shape family?* Repeat for the 2-D label.

GROUP ACTIVITIES

1. Place an assortment of recycled 3-D materials on the table. Ask the children to use these to make models.
2. Give each child a strip of card. Ask them to decorate their cards by printing with the 3-D shapes. Make these into shape hats.
3. Place a selection of 2-D and 3-D shapes on the table. Ask children to sort them into the two shape families.
Put out the large construction apparatus for children to build models.

DIFFERENTIATION

Less able: provide lots of practical activities in handling and matching shapes.
More able: encourage children to name the families and their shapes.

PLENARY

Feedback from the **Group activities**. Ask individuals to pick out a shape and say whether it belongs to the 2-D or 3-D family.

LESSON 2 + 3

RESOURCES

Collection of 2-D and 3-D shapes; tray; sorting rings; labels. **Group activities:** printing materials.

PREPARATION

Place the 2-D and 3-D shapes in the tray. Make labels saying 'triangles', 'not triangles', etc. Cut the strips of card to fit around a child's head. Set up the printing table.

LEARNING OBJECTIVES

ORAL AND MENTAL STARTER
● Recite the number names in order, continuing the count from a given number.
● Count reliably in other contexts, such as clapping sounds.

WHOLE-CLASS TEACHING ACTIVITY
● **Use language such as circle or bigger to describe the shape and size of solids and flat shapes.**
● Begin to name solids such as a cube, cone, sphere... and flat shapes such as a circle, triangle, square, rectangle...
● Use a variety of shapes to make models, pictures and patterns, and describe them.

VOCABULARY

Solid shape; hollow shape; 3-D shape; cube; cuboid; sphere; flat; flat shape; face; 2-D shape; circle; triangle; square; rectangle; not triangles ....

ORAL AND MENTAL STARTER

CLAP AND COUNT: Ask the children to clap and count a given number.

WHOLE-CLASS TEACHING ACTIVITY

TRIANGLE OR NOT?: Explain that these two lessons are about sorting and matching shapes. Display in front of the class the tray of 2-D and 3-D shapes. Remind the children of the shape names. Select a triangle. *Does this belong to the 2-D or the 3-D shape family? What is its special name?* Ask individuals to come and find a shape that is the same as the triangle. Say: *These all belong to the triangle family.* Place the triangles in the sorting ring and ask: *Are there any more triangles? Can the other shapes go in the sorting ring?* Ask the children to place those shapes that are not triangles outside the sorting ring. Read and place the labels. *All the shapes in the sorting ring are triangles. The shapes outside the ring are not triangles.*

GROUP ACTIVITIES

1. Place a selection of 2-D and 3-D shapes on the table. Ask the children to sort them into the two shape families.
2. In pairs, children sort a selection of either 2-D or 3-D shapes. Each pair then chooses one shape, sorts their selection and places the respective shapes inside a sorting ring. All other shapes are placed outside the sorting ring.
3. Give each child a strip of card. Ask them to decorate their cards by printing with the 3-D shapes. Make these into shape hats.

Place an assortment of recycled 3-D materials on the table. Ask the children to make models.

DIFFERENTIATION

Less able: ask a classroom assistant to support them.
More able: encourage children to extend their vocabulary.

PLENARY

Feedback from the **Group activities**.

LESSON 3

Repeat Lesson 2, but focus on 3-D shapes such as a cylinder.

LESSON 4

RESOURCES	Selection of 2-D and 3-D shapes; Blu-Tack; flip chart; feely bag; tray. **Group activities:** sorting ring; recycled materials.
LEARNING OUTCOMES	**ORAL AND MENTAL STARTER** ● **Say and use the number names in order in familiar contexts** such as number rhymes, songs, stories, counting games and activities (first to five then ten). **WHOLE-CLASS TEACHING ACTIVITY** ● **Use language such as circle or bigger to describe the shape and size of solids and flat shapes.** ● Begin to name solids such as a cube, cone, sphere... and flat shapes such as a circle, triangle, square, rectangle... ● Use a variety of shapes to make models, pictures and patterns, and describe them.
ORAL AND MENTAL STARTER	ONE ELEPHANT WENT OUT TO PLAY: Sing this song. Children can add appropriate actions.
WHOLE-CLASS TEACHING ACTIVITY	ODD ONE OUT: Attach two triangles and one circle to the flip chart. Explain the term 'odd one out': *Which one is the odd one out? Why have you chosen that shape?* Repeat using different 2-D and 3-D shapes, sizes and colours. Extend to four shapes then five. Invite individuals to choose the shapes for the game.
GROUP ACTIVITIES	**1.** Children play the 'Odd one out' game. A classroom assistant can choose the shapes and lead the game. **2.** In pairs, children sort a selection of 2-D or 3-D shapes. Each pair then chooses one shape and places these inside a sorting ring. All other shapes are placed outside the sorting ring. **3.** Place an assortment of recycled 3-D materials on the table. Ask children to make models. ● Set up a table for picture making using 2-D and 3-D shapes.
DIFFERENTIATION	Less able: limit the number of shapes used. More able: encourage children to identify and name 2-D and 3-D shapes.
PLENARY	GUESS THE SHAPE: Place three to five shapes in the feely bag. Place a set of matching shapes on the tray. *I want you to feel the shape in the bag. Can you tell which shape it is? Look at the shapes on the tray to help you.* Repeat several times.

LESSON 5

RESOURCES	Selection of 2-D and 3-D shapes; Blu-Tack; flip chart; tray; feely bag. **Group activities:** sorting rings, camera, adult helpers.
LEARNING OUTCOMES	**ORAL AND MENTAL STARTER** ● Recite the number names in order, continuing the count forwards or backwards from a given number. **WHOLE-CLASS TEACHING ACTIVITY** ● **Use language such as circle or bigger to describe the shape and size of solids and flat shapes.** ● Begin to name solids such as a cube, cone, sphere... and flat shapes such as a circle, triangle, square, rectangle... ● Use a variety of shapes to make models, pictures and patterns, and describe them.
ORAL AND MENTAL STARTER	COUNT FORWARD AND BACK: to and from 5, then 10, then 20.
WHOLE-CLASS TEACHING ACTIVITY	ODD ONE OUT: Play as in Lesson 4 above. Use three then extend to four and five shapes. Use 2-D and 3-D shapes. Explain that 2-D and 3-D shapes can be seen everywhere. Look for shapes in the classroom. Ask children to look for shapes in the playground, in school, at home etc. The class can make a 'Shapes everywhere' book. Show children shapes found in different cultures – for example in material, decorations in buildings, and so on.
GROUP ACTIVITIES	**1.** Organise a shape walk around the school with the children. Take photographs of the shapes found. **2.** Children play 'Guess the shape'. Ask a classroom assistant to support the children. **3.** In pairs, children sort a selection of 2-D or 3-D shapes. Each pair then chooses one shape and places these inside a sorting ring. All other shapes are placed outside the sorting ring. ● Set up a table for picture making using 2-D and 3-D shapes.
DIFFERENTIATION	Less able: limit the number of shapes used. More able: encourage children to identify and name 2-D and 3-D shapes.
PLENARY	Feedback from the **Group activities**.

UNIT 4

ORGANISATION (5 LESSONS)

LEARNING OUTCOMES	ORAL AND MENTAL STARTER	WHOLE-CLASS TEACHING ACTIVITY	PLENARY
LESSON 1 ● **Say and use the number names in order in familiar contexts** such as number rhymes, songs, stories, counting games and activities (first to five, then ten, then twenty and beyond).	TEN GREEN BOTTLES: Children recite this rhyme.	COUNT ON/COUNT BACK: Children count up to and back from 10.	Feedback from activities.
LESSON 2 +3 ● **Use language such as more or less, taller or shorter, wider or narrower.** ● **Compare quantities** by making direct comparisons of two, then three, lengths.	MORE GREEN BOTTLES: Children count bottles as they are placed on a 'wall'.	TALL BOTTLE, SHORT BOTTLE: Children compare different shapes.	Feedback from activities.
LESSON 4 ● **Use language such as longer or shorter to compare two quantities,** then more than two, by making direct comparisons of lengths.	SHOW ME: Children hold up a given number of fingers or a numeral card.	MOUSE TAILS: Comparing lengths.	Feedback from activities.
LESSON 5 ● **Use language such as more or less to compare two quantities** by filling and emptying containers.	SHOW ME: Children show a specific number of fingers or items.	FILL IT UP: Comparing capacity.	Feedback from activities.

> **ORAL AND MENTAL SKILLS** **Say and use the number names in order in familiar contexts** such as number rhymes, songs, stories, counting games and activities (first to five, then ten, then twenty and beyond). **Count reliably up to 10 everyday objects** (first to 5, then 10, then beyond). **Use language such as more or less to compare two quantities.**

Lessons 1 and 2 are given in full, with Lesson 3 extending Lesson 2. Lessons 4 and 5 are provided as grids.

RESOURCES

Green card; bottle templates; Blu-Tack; objects for counting such as pencils, straws, toy cars, animals. **Group activities:** labelled containers; cups; saucers; plates; spoons; cubes.

PREPARATION

Cut out ten green card bottles of different shapes and sizes, eg long, short, narrow, wide. Attach them to the wall. On the sticky labels, draw numerals and pictures of objects such as 6 pairs of scissors, 10 straws. Stick the labels on some of the containers. Put relevant items inside – make the number of items either more or less than the amount on the label.

LEARNING OUTCOMES

ORAL AND MENTAL STARTER
● **Say and use the number names in order in familiar contexts** such as number rhymes, songs, stories, counting games and activities (first to five, then ten, then twenty and beyond).

WHOLE-CLASS TEACHING ACTIVITY
● **Say and use the number names in order in familiar contexts** such as number rhymes, songs, stories, counting games and activities (first to five, then ten, then twenty and beyond).
● **Use language such as more or less to compare two quantities.**

VOCABULARY

Count;
number; zero,
one, two,
three, four,
five, six,
seven, eight,
nine, ten...;
how many?;
count to;
count (up) to;
count back;
count back
from; count
back to; start
from; start
with; start at;
the same
number as; as
many as;
more; less.

ORAL AND MENTAL STARTER

TEN GREEN BOTTLES: Draw the children's attention to the bottles on the wall. Ask the class to count them. Explain that as you sing the song 'Ten green bottles' you will ask someone to come out and take a bottle off the wall when the song says so. *How many bottles were there at the start? How many are left?*

WHOLE-CLASS TEACHING ACTIVITY

COUNT ON/COUNT BACK: Explain that today's lesson is about counting up to 10 and counting back from 10. Put out a selection of everyday objects. Ask: *Is 5 more than 2? Is 7 less than 10?* Say: *Count out five cubes. Now count out three beads. Are there more beads than cubes?* Repeat using different numbers and objects. Say: *Count out three pencils. Count out more cubes than pencils.* Ask individuals to tell you the number of each item they have counted.

GROUP ACTIVITIES

1. Give children the labelled containers and ask them to check the number of items.
2. Ask the children to set the table for Teddy's tea time. Get them to count out cups, saucers, plates, spoons etc for a given number of teddies. Ask the children to make the tea party for more or less teddies and set places as appropriate.
3. Place a selection of cubes on the table. Ask each child to make a tower of cubes. They count their cubes, then make towers of more and less cubes.

 Ask the children to carry out a stock check of the role-play café.

DIFFERENTIATION

Target the counting carefully with children working with numbers up to five, up to ten and above ten.

PLENARY

Feedback from the **Group activities**.

RESOURCES

Cut-outs of ten green bottles (see Lesson 1, page 36); card 'bricks'; *Seven Dizzy Dragons and Other Maths Rhymes*, Sue Atkinson et al (Cambridge University Press). **Group activities:** ribbons; string; pencils; straws; bamboo canes; paper; selection of clothes such as socks, T-shirts, trousers, shorts, that are long, short, wide, thin etc; washing line; pegs.

PREPARATION

Paint some pieces of card to look like 'bricks'.

LEARNING OUTCOMES

ORAL AND MENTAL STARTER

● **Say and use the number names in order in familiar contexts** such as number rhymes, songs, stories, counting games and activities (first to five, then ten, then twenty and beyond).
● **Count reliably up to 10 everyday objects** (first to 5, then 10, then beyond).
● **Use language such as more or less to compare two quantities.**

WHOLE-CLASS TEACHING ACTIVITY
● **Use language such as more or less, taller or shorter, wider or narrower....**
● **Compare quantities** by making direct comparisons of two, then three, lengths.

VOCABULARY

Short; tall;
high; low;
wide; long;
short; longer;
shorter; taller;
higher;
compare.

ORAL AND MENTAL STARTER

MORE GREEN BOTTLES: Make a wall using the cardboard 'bricks'. Ask the children to count the bottles as they are placed on the wall. Say: *How many are there now? Are there more than four? Are there less than ten?* Sing 'Ten green bottles'.

WHOLE-CLASS TEACHING ACTIVITY

TALL BOTTLE, SHORT BOTTLE: Point to the bottles on the wall and ask: *Are all the bottles the same? How are they different?* Explain that some of the bottles are tall/short/narrow/wide. Point to a bottle: *Is this bottle tall or short?* Invite the children to point to a bottle that is shorter than it. Repeat, focusing on different attributes of the bottles.

GROUP ACTIVITIES

1. Place a selection of ribbons, paper and string on the table. Children choose one item, then find something that is wider or narrower than it.
2. Give children a collection of clothes. Ask them to peg them out in sets, such as things that are wide, things that are short, and so on.
3. Give each child an object such as a piece of ribbon or a bamboo cane. Ask them to find an item that is longer or taller than their item.
Ask the children to build model garages or bridges wide enough for two toy cars, tall enough for a toy double-decker bus, etc.

DIFFERENTIATION

Less able: limit the range of vocabulary used.
More able: extend the range of vocabulary.

PLENARY

Feedback from the **Group activities**. Ask individuals to come out and point to wide, tall, narrow and short bottles. Read the poem 'Playing opposites' from *Seven Dizzy Dragons*.

LESSON 3

Repeat Lesson 2 to reinforce the comparative language.

LESSON 4

RESOURCES	Sets of individual numeral cards for each child (page 12) (optional); identical cardboard mice with different length string tails. **Group activities:** cut-outs of mice; adhesive; string; ribbon; wool; lace; straw; paper; pencils; crayons; beads; Learning Links.
LEARNING OUTCOMES	**ORAL AND MENTAL STARTER** ● **Count reliably up to 10 everyday objects** (first to 5, then 10, then beyond). **WHOLE-CLASS TEACHING ACTIVITY** ● **Use language such as longer or shorter to compare two quantities,** then more than two, by making direct comparisons of lengths.
ORAL AND MENTAL STARTER	SHOW ME: Hand out the numeral cards. Ask children to hold up a given number of fingers or a numeral card.
WHOLE-CLASS TEACHING ACTIVITY	MOUSE TAILS: Show children one of the mice. *Does it have a long tail or a short tail?* Pick up another mouse: *Look at the length of the tails. Are they the same length? Which mouse has the longer tail?* Repeat by comparing two different tails. Include mice that have tails that are the same length.
GROUP ACTIVITIES	**1.** Place string, ribbon, wool and lace on the table. Give each child two mice. Ask them to attach tails to the mice. Children decide on the length of the tails. Encourage them to compare tails. **2.** Give each child a straw, paper and mark-making resources. They draw lines that are longer, shorter or the same length as their straw. **3.** Place a selection of beads or Learning Links on the table. Invite the children to use them to make crowns for their friends. Compare the lengths. ● Provide a range of materials for children to make kites with different length tails.
DIFFERENTIATION	Less able: compare two objects. More able: compare two, then three and four objects.
PLENARY	Feedback from the **Group activities**.

LESSON 5

RESOURCES	A selection of counting items; containers such as plastic bottles, beakers, small boxes, yoghurt pots, plant pots, jugs, egg cups; water; counters or cubes etc for counting. **Group activities:** conkers; shells; buttons.
LEARNING OUTCOMES	**ORAL AND MENTAL STARTER** ● **Count reliably up to 10 everyday objects** (first to 5, then 10, then beyond). **WHOLE-CLASS TEACHING ACTIVITY** ● **Use language such as more or less to compare two quantities** by filling and emptying containers.
ORAL AND MENTAL STARTER	SHOW ME: Ask the children to hold up their fingers or count out items when you say a number. *Count out six cubes. Count out nine counters. How many cubes? How many counters?*
WHOLE-CLASS TEACHING ACTIVITY	FILL IT UP: Explain that you are going to compare two containers by filling them with water. Hold up the empty containers. Ask: *Which holds more?* Pour water into one of the containers. *Is it full?* Now pour water into the second container. *Which one holds the most?* Repeat using dry materials.
GROUP ACTIVITIES	**1.** Set out a range of different containers and filling items. Ask the children to pick two containers and see which holds the most. **2.** Set out a range of containers such as yoghurt pots and items such as conkers, shells, buttons. Children fill the container with each item in turn. **3.** Carry out as 2 above but use different containers and water. ● Provide opportunities for 'free play' in the sand and water.
DIFFERENTIATION	Less able: compare two objects. More able: compare two, then three and four objects.
PLENARY	Feedback from the **Group activities**.

UNIT 5

ORGANISATION (5 LESSONS)

	LEARNING OUTCOMES	ORAL AND MENTAL STARTER	WHOLE-CLASS TEACHING ACTIVITY	PLENARY
LESSON 1	● Begin to recognise 'none' and 'zero' when counting. ● Recite the number names in order, continuing the count forwards or backwards from a given number. ● **Recognise numerals 1 to 9,** then 0 and 10.	FINGER COUNT: Children count up to 10 using their fingers, then start from different numbers.	COUNT ON/COUNT BACK: Counting on and back activities.	Feedback from activities. Children say which number comes before or after a given number.
LESSON 2	● **In practical activities and discussion, begin to use the vocabulary involved in adding.** ● **Find one more than a number.**	ONE MORE: Children add one more.	AND ANOTHER: Children add 1 up to 10.	Children recite the rhyme 'One man went to mow'.
LESSON 3	● **In practical activities and discussion, begin to use the vocabulary involved in adding.** ● **Find one more than a number.**	PLAYFUL ELEPHANTS: Children recite a counting rhyme.	ONE MORE ELEPHANT: Children add 1 up to 10.	Feedback from activities.
LESSON 4 +5	● **In practical activities and discussion, begin to use the vocabulary involved in adding.** ● **Find one more than a number.**	SING IT AGAIN: Children recite counting rhymes.	ADD ONE MORE: Children add on one more to a number.	ADD ONE MORE: Children repeat the Whole-class teaching activity.

ORAL AND MENTAL SKILLS Say and use the number names in order in familiar contexts such as number rhymes, songs, stories, counting games and activities (first to five, then ten, then twenty and beyond). **Recite the number names in order, continuing the count forwards or backwards from a given number. Begin to use the vocabulary involved in adding. Find one more or one less than a number from 1 to 10.**

Lessons 1, 2 and 3 are given in full. Lessons 4 and 5 are presented as one grid.

RESOURCES

Set of large numeral cards to 10 (page 12). **Group activities:** blank number tracks (page 13); individual sets of numeral cards (page 12); cardboard cut-outs of dogs; dice (1–6); cardboard spots; selection of different containers; counting items.

LEARNING OUTCOMES

ORAL AND MENTAL STARTER
● **Say and use the number names in order in familiar contexts** such as number rhymes, songs, stories, counting games and activities (first to five, then ten, then twenty and beyond).
● Recite the number names in order, continuing the count forwards or backwards from a given number.

WHOLE-CLASS TEACHING ACTIVITY
● Begin to recognise 'none' and 'zero' when counting.
● Recite the number names in order, continuing the count forwards or backwards from a given number.
● **Recognise numerals 1 to 9,** then 0 and 10.

VOCABULARY

Count; number;
number line;
zero, one, two,
three, four,
five, six,
seven, eight,
nine, ten...;
how many?;
count
to; count (up)
to; count back;
count back
from; count
back to; start
from; start
with; start at;
before; after;
more than;
less than;
bigger than;
smaller than.

ORAL AND MENTAL STARTER

FINGER COUNT: Ask the class to count up to 10 using their fingers. Then count back from 10. Tell the children that you want them to start from a number and count up to 10. For example: *Start at 3, count up to 10.* Repeat using different starting and stopping numbers.

WHOLE-CLASS TEACHING ACTIVITY

COUNT ON/COUNT BACK: Explain that today's lesson is about counting on and back. Shuffle the large numeral cards. Choose one and ask: *What is this number?* Repeat using different cards. Ask: *Which number comes first?* Give out the cards to individual children. *Who has 0?* Ask children to come out in order and stand at the front. Say: *This is a number line. Our number line starts at zero and goes up to 10.* Point to children in the line. Ask the class to recite the numbers from 0 to 10 together. Ask: *Which number comes before 3? Which number comes after 9? Which number comes between 5 and 7?*

GROUP ACTIVITIES

1. In pairs, each child has a number track (page 13) and a set of numeral cards. They take turns to pick a card and place it at the appropriate place on the number track.
2. Place the cut-outs of the dogs, the cardboard spots and dice (1–6) on the table. Each child has a dog. In turn, children throw the dice and collect the corresponding number of spots. The first child to get ten spots on their dog wins.
3. Each child chooses a container and a counting item. They fill their container, then count how many of the item fitted inside.

Draw out a hopscotch grid on the playground or make one with large carpet tiles for inside so the children can play to familiarise themselves with the order of numbers.

DIFFERENTIATION

Children work with numbers up to 5, 10 and above. Make sure the items are appropriate for the numbers the children are using, for example, lots of dried peas fill a small tube!

PLENARY

Feedback from the **Group activities**. Ask the children to make a number line using the numeral cards. Point to a number. *Which number comes before...? Which number comes after...?* Explain that you can change the order of the number line to count back to 0.

RESOURCES

The song 'One man went to mow'; chairs. **Group activities:** cubes; peg boards; pegs; selection of small pots or containers; counting items.

PREPARATION

Label the pots or containers from 1 to 10. Add a corresponding number of items to each pot. Set out the chairs in rows to make a 'bus'.

LEARNING OUTCOMES

ORAL AND MENTAL STARTER
● **Say and use the number names in order in familiar contexts** such as number rhymes, songs, stories, counting games and activities (first to five, then ten, then twenty and beyond).
● Recite the number names in order, continuing the count forwards or backwards from a given number.
● **Find one more than a number from 1 to 10.**

WHOLE-CLASS TEACHING ACTIVITY
● **Begin to use the vocabulary involved in adding.**
● Begin to recognise 'none' and 'zero' in stories, rhymes and when counting.
● **Find one more than a number from 1 to 10.**

ORAL AND MENTAL STARTER

ONE MORE: Sing the song 'One man went to mow' with children adding the actions. Point out that there is one more man each time. Ask the children to finger add by holding up one finger and then holding up 'add one more': *1 add 1 more is 2*. Continue until ten fingers are being held up.

WHOLE-CLASS TEACHING ACTIVITY

AND ANOTHER: Explain that the lesson is about counting and adding on one more. Point out the chairs to the children and explain that they are like a bus. Say: *There are no people on the bus then one gets on*. Ask a child to sit in a chair. *How many are on the bus?* Repeat until all the seats are full. Emphasise the sums involved by saying: *1 add 1 more makes 2, 2 add 1 more makes 3, 3 add 1 more makes 4, 4 add 1 more makes 5.* Continue to 10.

GROUP ACTIVITIES

1. Place cubes on the table. Children make a staircase starting with one cube and adding one more each time.
2. Give each child a peg board and pegs. Ask them to build up a pattern by adding one more each time.
3. Place some number pots on the table each containing a different number of items from 1 to 10. Children add one more item to each pot, then count the number of items.

 Set up a 'bus' for role-play.

DIFFERENTIATION

Less able: work with numbers to five, then ten.
More able: work with numbers to ten, then beyond.

PLENARY

Sing the song 'One man went to mow'.

RESOURCES

Copies of the elephants and spider's web (page 17); flip chart; Blu-Tack; marker pen; label saying 'Add one more'. **Group activities:** cubes; peg boards; pegs; selection of small pots or containers; counting items.

LEARNING OUTCOMES

ORAL AND MENTAL STARTER
● **Say and use the number names in order in familiar contexts** such as number rhymes, songs, stories, counting games and activities (first to five, then ten, then twenty and beyond).

WHOLE-CLASS TEACHING ACTIVITY
● **Begin to use the vocabulary involved in adding.**
● **Find one more than a number.**

ORAL AND MENTAL STARTER

PLAYFUL ELEPHANTS: Sing the song 'One elephant went out to play' with role-play.

WHOLE-CLASS TEACHING ACTIVITY

ONE MORE ELEPHANT: Explain that today's session is about counting and adding on one more. Display the spider's web. Place one elephant on the spider's web: *If I add one more elephant, how many altogether?* Repeat until there are ten elephants. Show and read the label 'Add one more'. Write on the flip chart: 1 add 1 more is 2. Build up a table: 2 add 1 more is 3, etc. Ask children to tell you the number sentence each time.

LESSON 3

GROUP ACTIVITIES

Use the activities given for Lesson 2 on page 42.

DIFFERENTIATION

Less able: work with numbers up to three then five.
More able: work with numbers up to five, then up to ten.

PLENARY

Feedback from the **Group activities**. *What is 3 add 1 more? What is 8 add 1 more?*

LESSON 4 + 5

RESOURCES

Counting rhymes; large number line; sets of numeral cards (page 12). **Group activities:** dice (1–6); cubes; crayons; counters; (1–10) spinners; copies of photocopiable page 44 (Add one more).

LEARNING OUTCOMES

ORAL AND MENTAL STARTER

● **Say and use the number names in familiar contexts** such as number rhymes, songs, stories, counting games and activities (first to five, then ten, then twenty and beyond).
● **Begin to use the vocabulary involved in adding.**
● **Find one more or one less than a number from 1 to 10.**

WHOLE-CLASS TEACHING ACTIVITY

● **Begin to use the vocabulary involved in adding.**
● **Find one more than a number from 1 to 10.**

VOCABULARY
Count; number; zero, one, two, three, four, five, six, seven, eight, nine, ten...; how many?; count to; count (up) to; count back; count back from; count back to; start from; start with; start at; before; after.

ORAL AND MENTAL STARTER

SING IT AGAIN: Sing 'One elephant went out to play' or 'One man went to mow'.

WHOLE-CLASS TEACHING ACTIVITY

ADD ONE MORE: Give each pair a set of numeral cards to spread in front of them. Say a number. The children add one more and hold up the numeral card. Start with 1 add 1, then 2 add 1, then use random order. Refer to the number line and ask more questions.

GROUP ACTIVITIES

1. Children throw the dice in turn. They collect the number of cubes then add one more.
2. In pairs, the children take turns to spin the spinner. They collect the number of counters then add one more. Children record their work by drawing the counters.
3. Give each child a copy of photocopiable page 44 (Add one more) to complete.
Set up a 'number bingo' game with children covering the numbers on their cards which are one more than the number given by the caller.

DIFFERENTIATION

Less able: ask a classroom assistant to support them.
More able: work with numbers beyond 10.

PLENARY

Repeat 'Add one more' from the **Whole-class teaching activity**.

LESSON 5

Repeat Lesson 4 but this time, during the **Whole-class teaching activity**, throw a dice. Ask children, in pairs, to use their fingers to add the next number and then to hold up the correct numeral card. Ask children to add more than one, for example, *7 add 2 more.*

UNIT 5

Add one more

add one more

add one more

add one more

add one more

add one more

add one more

UNIT 6: Assess & Review

Choose from the following activities. Opportunities are provided for you to review all the key objectives introduced in the first half term. You will need to decide which children to work with during the group activities.

RESOURCES

Numeral cards for each child; a selection of objects for counting; interlocking cubes; sets of 3-D and 2-D shapes; pieces of ribbon of different lengths and widths; a selection of containers such as jugs, boxes; water, sand and dry items for comparing capacity.

ORAL AND MENTAL STARTER

ASSESSMENT

● Can the children: **Say and use the number names in order in familiar contexts? Count reliably up to 10 everyday objects?**
RHYMES: Recite the rhyme '1, 2, 3, 4, 5, once I caught a fish alive'.
COUNTING: Put out a selection of objects to count. Ask the children to count with you as you touch each object. Start by counting from 1 to 5, then 1 to 10. Observe and record who counts with confidence and who needs more practice. Allow individual children opportunities to count objects 1 to 5, then 1 to 10 while you observe who is doing this confidently and correctly, counting in the right order and giving a number name to each object.

GROUP ACTIVITIES

ASSESSMENT

● Can the children: **Recognise numerals 1 to 9? Use language such as more or less to compare two numbers or quantities? Find one more than a number from 1 to 10? Use the vocabulary involved in adding? Use language such as circle or bigger to describe the shape and size of solids and flat shapes? Use language such as longer or shorter to compare two lengths by making direct comparison? Use language such as more or less to compare capacity by direct comparison?**
RECOGNISE NUMERALS 1 TO 9: Arrange the individual numeral cards in order on the table. Ask children to point to the number you say.
COMPARE TWO QUANTITIES: Count out a number of cubes (1–5). Ask children to count how many there are. Count out a smaller number of cubes. Ask: *Are there more or less cubes?* Repeat using greater or larger to compare quantities. Repeat using a different quantity (1– 10). Go on to...
ADD ONE MORE: Use examples from Lessons 2, 3, 4 or 5 of Unit 5, pages 41–43, or make up some similar ones.
SHAPE SORT: Ask children to sort a selection of 2-D and 3-D shapes. Say: *Are all the shapes the same? What are these shapes called? Do they belong to the 2-D or 3-D family?* Can the children find a shape, such as a rectangle, a cube or a triangle? Check that children are able to use the appropriate language correctly.
COMPARING LENGTH: Use the 'Mouse tails' activity in Lesson 4 of Unit 4, page 39, or make up a similar activity.
COMPARING CAPACITY: Use the whole class and group activities in Lesson 5 of Unit 4, page 39, or make up some similar ones.

UNIT 7

ORGANISATION (5 LESSONS)

LEARNING OUTCOMES	ORAL AND MENTAL STARTER	WHOLE-CLASS TEACHING ACTIVITY	PLENARY
LESSON 1 ● **Count reliably up to 10 everyday objects** (first to 5, then 10, then beyond).	WASH DAY: Recognising numbers from 0–20.	ALL TENS: Counting objects in different arrangements (conservation).	Identifying mistakes in a counting sequence.
LESSON 2 ● **Use language such as more or less, greater or smaller, to compare two numbers** and say which is more or less, and say a number which lies between two given numbers.	LINE THEM UP: Recognising numbers greater or smaller than another number.	COMPARING NUMBERS: Recognising numbers greater or smaller than another number.	Comparing the amount of objects in various containers.
LESSON 2+3 ● **Use language such as more or less, greater or smaller, to compare two numbers** and say which is more or less, and say a number which lies between two given numbers.	WASH DAY: Identifying numbers that have been placed in the wrong order.	MISSING NUMBERS: Finding missing numbers in a sequence.	ORDER IT: Ordering numbers.
LESSON 5 ● **Use language such as more or less, greater or smaller, to compare two numbers** and say which is more or less, and say a number which lies between two given numbers.	ORDER IT: Number recognition.	MORE AND LESS: Finding numbers that are more or less than another number.	ORDER IT: Number recognition.

ORAL AND MENTAL SKILLS Say and use the number names in order in familiar contexts such as number rhymes, songs, stories, counting games and activities (first to five, then ten, then twenty and beyond). Recite the number names in order, continuing the count forwards or backwards from a given number.

Lessons 1, 2 and 3 are given in full. Lesson 4 repeats Lesson 3, and Lesson 5 is provided as a grid.

RESOURCES

A washing basket; clothes line; pegs, cardboard cut-outs of clothes with numerals from 0 to 20; selection of counting objects such as cubes, acorns, counters, buttons; puppet 'Miss Count'. **Group activities:** blank 2 × 5 and 5 × 5 grids; counters; (1–10) spinners; dice (1–6).

VOCABULARY

Count; number; zero, one, two, three... to ten; how many?; count (up) to; count back (from, to); start from; start with; start at; before; after; more than; less than; bigger than; smaller than.

LEARNING OUTCOMES

ORAL AND MENTAL STARTER
● **Say and use the number names in order in familiar contexts** such as number rhymes, songs, stories, counting games and activities (first to five, then ten, then twenty and beyond).

WHOLE-CLASS TEACHING ACTIVITY
● **Count reliably up to 10 everyday objects** (first to 5, then 10, then beyond).

ORAL AND MENTAL STARTER

WASH DAY: Hang up the washing line across the classroom. Hand the cut-out clothes to individuals and say: *Look at the number on your clothes. Who has 0?* Ask the children to come and peg their clothes onto the washing line in order. Say: *Count from 0 to 20. Now count back.*

WHOLE-CLASS TEACHING ACTIVITY

ALL TENS: Ask the children to count out ten objects and arrange them in a line. *Count your objects by moving each one as you count. Now touch each one.* Ask them to arrange their objects in different ways, such as in a circle, in a row from top to bottom, left to right, in a pile etc and then to count them again. *How many did you start with? How many are there now? Are there any more? Are there any less? Can you arrange them in a different way?* Make sure the children understand that the arrangement of objects does not alter the count (ie. conservation).

GROUP ACTIVITIES

1. Give each pair a large, blank 2 × 5 grid, some counters and a spinner. The children take turns to spin the spinner. They collect the appropriate number of counters and place them on their grid. The first child to fill all ten spaces is the winner.

2. Take children on a counting walk around the school. Count and record objects in the environment such as the number of classes, teachers, litter bins, wash-basins.

3. Play 'number bingo'. Give each child some counters and a blank 5 × 5 grid with the numerals 1–10 written in random order. Children shake the dice (numerals 1–6) and place the correct number of counters on the card.

 Set out some musical instruments with some simple pictorial music showing how many times to beat the drum, shake the tambourine, etc.

DIFFERENTIATION

Less able: use dice with spots.
More able: work with numbers up to 20.

PLENARY

Use 'Miss Count' to listen to children count to 10 then 20. Count with Miss Count making errors, such as pointing to one object but saying two numbers, missing out an object, counting correctly but incorporating a wrong number. Ask children to identify the mistakes. *Who can show us how to count correctly?* Invite individuals to demonstrate.

RESOURCES

Number line; cubes; two collections of items, eg cups and saucers, pencils and erasers, shoes and socks. **Group activities:** counting objects; trays or plates; dice (1–6); counters.

LEARNING OUTCOMES

ORAL AND MENTAL STARTER
● **Say and use the number names in order in familiar contexts** such as number rhymes, songs, stories, counting games and activities (first to five, then ten, then twenty and beyond).

WHOLE-CLASS TEACHING ACTIVITY
● **Use language such as more or less, greater or smaller, to compare two numbers** and say which is more or less, and say a number which lies between two given numbers.

VOCABULARY
The same number as; bigger; smaller; biggest; largest; smallest; more; less; few; most; least; order; first; last; before; after; next; between.

ORAL AND MENTAL STARTER

LINE THEM UP: Point to the class number line. Count on and back to 10 then 20. Ask questions: *Which is bigger – 5 or 10?* Say: *10 is bigger than 5. Which is less, 0 or 9? 0 is less than 9. Which number comes after 17? Give me a number between 11 and 15.*

WHOLE-CLASS TEACHING ACTIVITY

COMPARING NUMBERS: Remind the children how they added one more (Unit 5, Lesson 2, page 42). Demonstrate by making a staircase of cubes, adding one more each time. For each step, ask: *How many now? What will be the next number when we have added one more?* Repeat using a different pattern of steps, such as adding 2 each time. Next, say:

Count out seven cubes. Now count out 11. Is 7 more or less than 11? Count out nine cubes. Now make a collection which is bigger. How many have you counted out? Repeat using 'bigger than', 'more than', 'less than' and 'the same as'.

GROUP ACTIVITIES

1. Children build 'staircases' in different steps.
2. Ask children to count out a given number of objects onto a tray or plate. They then make another collection that is 5 bigger, 7 less, the same number.
3. In pairs, one child throws the dice and takes that number of counters. Their partner attempts to throw the same number to match it.

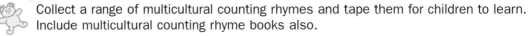 Collect a range of multicultural counting rhymes and tape them for children to learn. Include multicultural counting rhyme books also.

DIFFERENTIATION

Less able: limit the numbers up to 10.
More able: extend by asking how many more/less. Use simple recording.

PLENARY

Ask children to count collections of objects, eg cups and saucers, girls and boys, pencils and erasers. *Are there more, less or the same number of items? How many more/less?*

LESSON 3 + 4

RESOURCES

The poem 'What turkey doing?' by John Agard (*Counting Rhymes*, compiled by John Foster, OUP); cut-out number clothes (0–20); washing line; pegs; number line with some numerals missing; flip chart; marker pen. **Group activities:** containers; sets of objects; sets of dotty cards (page 18); sets of numeral cards (page 12); copies of photocopiable page 50 (Missing numbers); small numeral cards.

PREPARATION

Place a number of objects into various containers. Make sets of small numeral cards for the children to place on photocopiable page 50.

LEARNING OUTCOMES

ORAL AND MENTAL STARTER
● **Say and use the number names in order in familiar contexts** such as number rhymes, songs, stories, counting games and activities (first to five, then ten, then twenty and beyond).

WHOLE-CLASS TEACHING ACTIVITY
● **Use language such as more or less, greater or smaller, to compare two numbers** and say which is more or less, and say a number which lies between two given numbers.

ORAL AND MENTAL STARTER

WASH DAY: Read the poem 'What turkey doing?'. Ask the children to join in. Arrange the cut-out clothes on the washing line in the wrong order. Ask the children to look and count to find the 'wrong' numbers. *Is 11 more than 9? Is 15 less than 20?* Invite individuals to rearrange the numeral clothes correctly.

WHOLE-CLASS TEACHING ACTIVITY

MISSING NUMBERS: Explain that these lessons are about missing numbers. Show the children the number line with the missing numerals and ask: *Which numbers are missing? Which numbers should come between 4 and 7?* Write the numbers on the line as the children give them. Then say: *Give me three numbers less than 7. Tell me two numbers that are more than 12.*

VOCABULARY

Missing numbers; number line; number track; in order; in a different order; arrange; rearrange; place; put; change; change over; what comes next?; what comes before?; what comes after?; what comes in between?; more than; greater than; less than; smaller than; more; less.

GROUP ACTIVITIES

1. Give children the containers with the objects. Ask them to sort the containers into ascending then descending order, according to how many objects they have in them.

2. Shuffle the set of dotty cards. Children count the dots, then arrange the cards in ascending order. Repeat using descending order.

3. Ask children to sort a set of numeral cards to make a number track in ascending then descending order. Give more able children photocopiable page 50 (Missing numbers) to complete.

Hide numeral cards around the room. Ask children to spot the numbers, then arrange them in order.

DIFFERENTIATION

Less able: work with objects and put groups into ascending order.

More able: use photocopiable page 50 (Missing numbers).

PLENARY

ORDER IT: Write some numbers on the flip chart. *Which number comes first? What comes next? Which number goes in between?* Ask children to give you the correct order and write it on the flip chart.

LESSON 4

Repeat Lesson 3 to practise the skills of ordering and identifying missing values in the sequence. In the **Whole-class teaching activity**, work in reverse order, from 20–0.

RESOURCES	The poem 'What turkey doing?' (*Counting Rhymes*, John Foster, OUP); individual sets of numeral cards 0–20; enlarged copy of photocopiable page 51 (More and less); dice (1–6). **Group activities:** dice; spinners; pencils; copies of photocopiable pages 50 and 51 (Missing numbers and More and less); small numeral cards; sets of dotty cards (page 18); sets of numeral cards (page 12).
LEARNING OUTCOMES	**ORAL AND MENTAL STARTER** ● **Say and use the number names in order in familiar contexts** such as number rhymes, songs, stories, counting games and activities (first to five, then ten, then twenty and beyond). ● Recite the number names in order, continuing the count forwards or backwards from a given number. **WHOLE-CLASS TEACHING ACTIVITY** ● **Use language such as more or less, greater or smaller, to compare two numbers** and say which is more or less, and say a number which lies between two given numbers.
ORAL AND MENTAL STARTER	ORDER IT: Recite the poem 'What turkey doing?' as in Lessons 3 and 4. Hand out the numeral cards to 20. Ask children to hold up their numbers. *Who has a number less than 5? More than 9? In between 3 and 8?* Ask children to arrange themselves into a number line. Count to see if in they are in the correct order. Redeal the cards and repeat.
WHOLE-CLASS TEACHING ACTIVITY	MORE AND LESS: Remind the children of Lessons 3 and 4 on missing numbers. Display the enlarged copy of 'More and less'. With the class, throw the dice. Write this number in the first column. With the children, decide on a number that is more and less than that number to complete the other columns.
GROUP ACTIVITIES	**1.** Provide dice, spinners, pencils and copies of photocopiable page 51 (More and less) for each child to complete. **2.** Shuffle the set of dotty cards. Children count the dots, then arrange the cards in ascending order. Repeat using descending order. **3.** Children sort a set of numeral cards to make a number track in ascending then descending order. Give each child a copy of photocopiable page 50 (Missing numbers) to complete using the small numeral cards. ● Set out a selection of counting games such as Snakes and Ladders.
DIFFERENTIATION	Less able: children make sets of objects showing numbers greater/less than. More able: children find and record their own numerals that are greater/fewer, more/less than.
PLENARY	Repeat 'Order it'.

Missing numbers

1		3	4	5	6		8	9	10

	2	3		5	6	7			10

			4			7		9	10

	3			6			9		

Make your own missing numbers.

UNIT 7

More and less

Throw the dice. What is your number?
Complete the table:

My number is	more	less
9 2	12 5	3 1

Spin the 1–10 spinner and fill in this table:

My number is	fewer	greater
3 7	0 6	9 8

UNIT 8

ORGANISATION (5 LESSONS)

LEARNING OUTCOMES	ORAL AND MENTAL STARTER	WHOLE-CLASS TEACHING ACTIVITY	PLENARY
LESSON 1 • **Say and use the number names in order in familiar contexts** such as number rhymes, songs, stories, counting games and activities (first to five, then ten, then twenty and beyond).	TEN TEDDIES: Children recite numbers using the context of a rhyme.	TEDDIES' PARTY: Counting out items for a specific purpose.	Feedback from activities. Reinforcement of more and less.
LESSON 2 +3 • **Begin to use the vocabulary involved in adding and subtracting.** • **Find one more or one less than a number from 1 to 10.**	GRIBBIT!: Taking away and adding activities.	ONE MORE, ONE LESS: Finding a number more or less than a given number.	Children add one more to a given number.
LESSON 4 +5 • **Begin to use the vocabulary involved in adding and subtracting.** • **Find one more or one less than a number from 1 to 10.**	ONE MORE TEDDY: Finding numbers more or less than another number.	ONE MORE GAME: Finding numbers more and less.	Reinforcement of one more and one less.

ORAL AND MENTAL SKILLS Say and use the number names in order in familiar contexts such as number rhymes, songs, stories, counting games and activities (first to five, then ten, then twenty and beyond). Recite the number names in order, continuing the count forwards or backwards from a given number. **Begin to use the vocabulary involved in adding and subtracting.**

Lessons 1 and 2 are given in full. Lesson 3 repeats Lesson 2. Lessons 4 is given in full. Lesson 5 repeats Lesson 4.

RESOURCES

The rhyme 'Ten little teddies jumping on the bed'; numeral cards (1–20); teddy bears or teddy bear counters; paper plates, spoons, knives, forks, biscuits, packets of crisps, sweets; paper hats. **Group activities:** skittles; soft ball; counters; cubes; dice (1–6); spinners; copies of photocopiable page 51 (More and less).

PREPARATION

Set up the skittles in an appropriate area. Mark a line with chalk or tape.

LEARNING OUTCOMES

ORAL AND MENTAL STARTER
● Recite the number names in order, continuing the count forwards or backwards from a given number.

WHOLE-CLASS TEACHING ACTIVITY
● **Say and use the number names in order in familiar contexts** such as number rhymes, songs, stories, counting games and activities (first to five, then ten, then twenty and beyond).

ORAL AND MENTAL STARTER

TEN TEDDIES: Ask the children to count up to 10 starting at 3, then count back. Repeat using different starting points, then extend to 20. Recite the rhyme 'Ten little teddies'. Invite individuals to come out and 'be' the teddies. Give them a number card to hold as they say the rhyme. Ask: *How many are left? Count the teddies. If there are three teddies and one goes, how many will be left?*

WHOLE-CLASS TEACHING ACTIVITY

TEDDIES' PARTY: Explain that the teddy bears want to have a party. *If ten teddies are invited, how many plates would we need? How many beakers, paper hats, spoons?* Ask the children to arrange the teddies in a space and count out the items. Explain that each teddy needs two biscuits, a packet of crisps and three sweets. Ask children to count out the items for each teddy. *How many of each item are there? Are there more crisps than paper hats? Are there fewer sweets than biscuits? Are there the same number of teddies as beakers?*

GROUP ACTIVITIES

1. Set up the skittles in a space. Children take turns to throw a soft ball to see how many skittles they can knock down. They keep their score using counters or cubes.

2. Place dice, spinners and counters on the table. Give each child a copy of photocopiable page 51 (More and less). Children throw the dice and spin the spinner, find numbers more and less and record their answers on the sheet.

3. Place a number of teddies on the table. Children organise a picnic for the teddies and decide how many items they would require. A classroom assistant can support the children.

 Arrange a teddy bears' picnic and include children in planning and making the food.

DIFFERENTIATION

Less able: limit numbers to 10.
More able: work with numbers up to 20 and beyond.

PLENARY

Feedback from the **Group activities**. Ask questions to reinforce more and less – for example: *If I knocked down two skittles then one more, how many would I have knocked down altogether? If there are five teddies at the picnic, how many plates do I need? If I spin the spinner and get to 10, which number is 1 more/1 less?*

LESSON 2 + 3

RESOURCES

Rhyme 'Five little speckled frogs'; Frogs and lily pads (page 14); cardboard 'pond'; Blu-Tack; number line; copies of photocopiable page 51 (More and less) plus an enlarged copy; flip chart; dice (1–10); collection of items such as counters, pegs, coins, cubes, pencils, crayons; labelled containers with numbers on (up to 10). **Group activities:** dominoes; sets of numeral cards (page 12).

PREPARATION

Colour, laminate and cut-out the frogs and lily pads from page 14 (you will need five frogs). Create a pond background using a piece of blue card. Stick Blu-Tack on the backs of the shapes and attach them to the 'pond'. Make copies of photocopiable page 51 (More and less). Make an enlarged copy on to card.

LEARNING OUTCOMES

ORAL AND MENTAL STARTER

● Recite the number names in order, continuing the count forwards or backwards from a given number.

● **Say and use the number names in order in familiar contexts** such as number rhymes, songs, stories, counting games and activities (first to five, then ten, then twenty and beyond).

WHOLE-CLASS TEACHING ACTIVITY
● **Begin to use the vocabulary involved in adding and subtracting.**
● **Find one more or one less than a number from 1 to 10.**

VOCABULARY

More; and; add; make; sum; total; altogether; score; take (away); leave; how many are left/left over?; how many have gone?; one more; one less; how many more to make?; how many more is... than...?; how many fewer is... than...?; difference between.

ORAL AND MENTAL STARTER

GRIBBIT!: Recite 'Five little speckled frogs'. Display the five frogs and lily pads on the pond. Invite individuals to come and take away a frog. *How many frogs were there altogether? How many are gone? How many are left?* Get the children to hold up one finger. Ask them to add 1. *How many more?* Repeat until the children are showing ten fingers.

WHOLE-CLASS TEACHING ACTIVITY

ONE MORE, ONE LESS: Ask children to count in ones using the number line. Say: *What is one more/less?* Attach the enlarged copy of 'More and less' to the flip chart. Throw the dice. Ask the children to find one more and one less using the number line. Say: *I am thinking of a number. It is one more than 9. What is it?* Use different examples. Repeat with one less.

GROUP ACTIVITIES

1. Place dice, spinners and counters on the table. Give each child a copy of photocopiable page 51 (More and less). Children find numbers more and less and record their answers on the sheet.
2. Place a set of dominoes on the table. Ask children to find all the dominoes that show a number of spots that are one more or one less.
3. Spread out two sets of numeral cards face up on the table. Ask children to pick up two cards. If a card shows one more than the other, then the child takes both cards. The winner is the child who collects the most pairs of cards.

 Find a selection of counting rhymes and songs that include one more and one less.

DIFFERENTIATION

Less able: limit numbers to 10.
More able: encourage children to record their answers.

PLENARY

Ask the children to add one more to a given number in their heads. *How many altogether?* Write the number on the flip chart. Repeat 'Ten little teddies'.

LESSON 3

Repeat Lesson 2 to reinforce this important concept and give lots of experience of more/less.

RESOURCES

Large number line; flip chart; marker pen; dice; the rhyme 'Ten little teddies'.
Group activities: appropriate resources from Lessons 2 and 3.

LESSON 4 +5

LEARNING OUTCOMES

ORAL AND MENTAL STARTER

● **Say and use the number names in order in familiar contexts** such as number rhymes, songs, stories, counting games and activities (first to five, then ten, then twenty and beyond).
● **Begin to use the vocabulary involved in adding and subtracting.**

WHOLE-CLASS TEACHING ACTIVITY

● **Begin to use the vocabulary involved in adding and subtracting.**
● **Find one more or one less than a number from 1 to 10.**

VOCABULARY

More; and; add; make; sum; total; altogether; score; take away; leave; how many are left/left over?; how many have gone?; one more; one less; how many more to make...?; how many more is... than...?; how many fewer is... than...?; difference between.

ORAL AND MENTAL STARTER

ONE MORE TEDDY: Recite the rhyme 'Ten little teddies'. Ask individuals to be teddies. Say: *Hold up ten fingers, take one away. How many now?* Continue until all fingers have been used. Point to the number line. *What is one less than 6? One less than 3? What is one more than 1?*

WHOLE-CLASS TEACHING ACTIVITY

ONE MORE GAME: Explain that the lesson is about one more and one less. Introduce 'one more'. Draw a 3 × 2 grid. Select six numbers from 1–10 and write these randomly inside the grid. Throw a dice. Read the number, then ask the children to: *Add one more.* Cross out the numeral if it appears in the grid. Repeat using one less.

GROUP ACTIVITIES

Choose from the **Group activities** in Lessons 2 and 3.

DIFFERENTIATION

Less able: consolidate work on one more.
More able: extend numbers to 20 and beyond.

PLENARY

Repeat 'Ten little teddies'. Ask: *What is one more than 6? One less than 10?* and so on.

LESSON 5

Repeat Lesson 4.

UNIT 9

ORGANISATION (5 LESSONS)

	LEARNING OUTCOMES	ORAL AND MENTAL STARTER	WHOLE-CLASS TEACHING ACTIVITY	PLENARY
LESSON 1	● Begin to name solids such as a cube, cone, sphere... and flat shapes such as a circle, triangle, square, rectangle. ● Use a variety of shapes to make models, pictures and patterns, and describe them.	COUNT UP AND COUNT BACK: Children count up to and back to a given number.	GUESS MY SHAPE. Sorting and naming 3-D shapes.	Feedback from activities. Reinforcing the properties of shapes.
LESSON 2	● Begin to name solids such as a cube, cone, sphere... and flat shapes such as a circle, triangle, square, rectangle. ● Use a variety of shapes to make models, pictures and patterns, and describe them.	COMPARE ME: Children show a number of fingers or numeral card to compare a given number.	GUESS MY SHAPE: Sorting and naming 3-D shapes.	Feedback from activities. Repeat 'Guess my shape'.
LESSON 3	● Begin to name solids such as a cube, cone, sphere... and flat shapes such as a circle, triangle, square, rectangle.	ONE ELEPHANT WENT OUT TO PLAY: Reciting the number names within a rhyme.	FEELY SHAPES: Sorting and naming 2-D and 3-D shapes.	Children play 'I spy' referring to shapes.
LESSON 4	● Talk about, recognise and recreate patterns: for example, simple repeating patterns in the environment.	COUNT AROUND: Children count in ones.	MAKE A PATTERN: Recognising patterns.	Children copy a counting and clapping pattern.
LESSON 5	● Make simple estimates and predictions: for example, of the number of cubes that will fit in a box or strides across the room.	GUESS IT: Estimating then counting.	GUESS WHAT: Children make simple estimates.	Feedback from activities.

ORAL AND MENTAL SKILLS Recite the number names in order, continuing the count forwards or backwards from a given number. **Use language such as more or less, greater or smaller, to compare two numbers** and say which is more or less, and say a number which lies between two given numbers. **Say and use the number names in order in familiar contexts** such as number rhymes, songs, stories, counting games and activities (first to five, then ten). Estimate a number in the range that can be counted reliably, then check by counting.

Lessons 1 and 4 are given in full, with Lessons 2, 3 and 5 as grids.

RESOURCES

A large selection of 2-D and 3-D shapes of different sizes and colours; wrapping paper; sorting rings; thick card. **Group activities:** picture postcards; shape dominoes.

PREPARATION

Cover a selection of the 2-D and 3-D shapes in wrapping paper to make them into 'parcels'. Keep some shapes unwrapped. Make appropriate labels saying 'triangles', 'circles' etc and 'cubes', 'cylinders' ... and 'not a triangle', 'not a cube' etc. Cut the picture postcards up to make jigsaw puzzles.

LEARNING OUTCOMES

ORAL AND MENTAL STARTER

● Recite the number names in order, continuing the count forwards or backwards from a given number.

WHOLE-CLASS TEACHING ACTIVITY

● Begin to name solids such as a cube, cone, sphere... and flat shapes such as a circle, triangle, square, rectangle...

● Use a variety of shapes to make models, pictures and patterns, and describe them.

VOCABULARY

Solid shape; hollow shape; cube; cuboid; pyramid; sphere; face; flat face; curved face; round; edge; straight edge; curved edge; corner; flat; circle; triangle; square; rectangle; star; side; line; straight line; curved line; point; thick; thin.

ORAL AND MENTAL STARTER

COUNT UP AND COUNT BACK: Recite the rhyme 'One, Two, Three, Four' (from *Counting Rhymes*, adapted by John Foster, OUP). Ask children to count up to 5 and back, then to 10, then 20.

WHOLE-CLASS TEACHING ACTIVITY

GUESS MY SHAPE: Explain that you want to find out which shapes are in the 'parcels' without unwrapping them. Pick up a cube and ask: *Is it a flat shape or a solid shape? Does it belong to the 2-D or 3-D family?* Say: *It's a solid shape. It belongs to the 3-D family. Does it roll?* Ask the children to count the number of faces. *Are all the faces the same shape? Which shape has all its faces the same shape?* Encourage the children to guess the name of the shape. Point to the selection of unwrapped shapes. *Can you see the same shape here?* Ask a child to come out and match the shapes. Ask another child to unwrap the shape to see if they are the same. Say: *It is a cube. It is a solid shape. All the faces are the*

same. *A cube belongs to the 3-D shape family.* Repeat with other 3-D shapes. Work together to make a set of cubes using the sorting rings. Put the cube in one ring and place the label that says 'cubes' beside it. Choose a child to pick a shape that is not a cube: *Does it go in the ring? Why can't it go in? What is it called?* Place it in another ring and say: *This is not a cube. It is a cylinder. What is special about the cubes? What is special about the cylinder?* Keep sorting the shapes and placing them in the relevant ring.

GROUP ACTIVITIES

1. Place a selection of 2-D shapes on the carpet. Ask children to sort them into set rings and label them using the name cards, for example 'triangle'/'not a triangle'. Ask the children how they know it is a triangle shape.

2. Place a selection of 3-D shapes on the table. Children sort them into rings and label them using the name cards.

3. Give each child a postcard jigsaw. Ask them to assemble the picture.

4. Give children a set of shape dominoes. Ask them to match the shapes on each end of the dominoes.

5. Place a selection of 2-D and 3-D shape parcels on the table. Working with a classroom assistant, the children play 'Guess my shape' as described in the **Whole-class teaching activity** above.

6. Give children an assortment of 3-D shapes. Ask them to find those shapes that roll/do not roll.

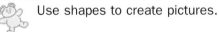 Use shapes to create pictures.

DIFFERENTIATION

Less able: limit the number of shapes used. Use lots of practical sorting and matching before pictorial representation.

More able: use a range of 2-D and 3-D shapes.

PLENARY

Feedback from the **Group activities**. Ask the class and individuals to name a shape, then reinforce its properties.

LESSON 2

RESOURCES	As in Lesson 1, page 56, plus numeral cards (optional) (page 12).
LEARNING OUTCOMES	**ORAL AND MENTAL STARTER** ● **Use language such as more or less, greater or smaller, to compare two numbers** and say which is more or less, and say a number which lies between two given numbers. **WHOLE-CLASS TEACHING ACTIVITY** ● Begin to name solids such as a cube, cone, sphere... and flat shapes such as a circle, triangle, square, rectangle... ● Use a variety of shapes to make models, pictures and patterns, and describe them.
ORAL AND MENTAL STARTER	COMPARE ME: Ask children to show a number of fingers or a numeral card that is more, less, greater, smaller than a given number.
WHOLE-CLASS TEACHING ACTIVITY	GUESS MY SHAPE: Play as in Lesson 1 using the 2-D shape parcels. With the children, work together to sort the triangles from the rest of the shapes. Go on to sort squares and rectangles.
GROUP ACTIVITIES	Choose from the activities in Lesson 1. ● Model-making with 3-D shapes.
DIFFERENTIATION	Less able: limit the number of shapes used. Use lots of practical sorting and matching before pictorial representation More able: use a range of 2-D and 3-D shapes.
PLENARY	'Guess my shape'. Reinforce the shape's properties and differences to other shapes.

LESSON 3

RESOURCES	As in Lesson 1, page 56, plus a feely bag; tray.
LEARNING OUTCOMES	**ORAL AND MENTAL STARTER** ● **Say and use the number names in order in familiar contexts** such as number rhymes, songs, stories, counting games and activities (first to five, then ten). **WHOLE-CLASS TEACHING ACTIVITY** ● Begin to name solids such as a cube, cone, sphere... and flat shapes such as a circle, triangle, square, rectangle...
ORAL AND MENTAL STARTER	ONE ELEPHANT WENT OUT TO PLAY: Sing the rhyme.
WHOLE-CLASS TEACHING ACTIVITY	FEELY SHAPES: Display some 2-D and 3-D shapes. Describe the properties of various shapes and ask the children to show or name them. Place three to five shapes (2-D and 3-D) in a feely bag. Put a corresponding set of shapes on a tray. Choose a shape, but keep it inside the feely bag. Describe it. The children match it to a shape on the tray. Repeat with children feeling and describing the shapes for others to match.
GROUP ACTIVITIES	Choose from the activities in Lesson 1. ● Create a collage with 2-D and 3-D shapes.
DIFFERENTIATION	Less able: support children by displaying the shapes in the feely bag so that they can see them. Show children the shape and ask them to find one that matches. More able: use a wider range of shapes.
PLENARY	Play 'I spy' with shapes. Display 2-D and 3-D shapes. Say: *I spy a shape. It has four sides. The sides are all the same length. It is a flat shape. What is it?*

LESSON 4

RESOURCES

Different-coloured beads; threading lace; wrapping paper; multicultural artefacts; patterned fabrics; a tie; necklaces; percussion instruments. **Group activities:** 2-D and 3-D shapes.

PREPARATION

Select items that have a clear repeating pattern.

LEARNING OUTCOMES

ORAL AND MENTAL STARTER
● Recite the number names in order, continuing the count forwards or backwards from a given number.

WHOLE-CLASS TEACHING ACTIVITY
● Talk about, recognise and recreate patterns: for example, simple repeating patterns in the environment.

VOCABULARY

VOCABULARY

Pattern; make; build; size; bigger; larger; smaller; match; repeating pattern; shape; circle; triangle; square; rectangle; star; cube; pyramid; sphere; cone; before; after; beside; next to; between; middle; answer; right; wrong.

ORAL AND MENTAL STARTER

COUNT AROUND: Recite the rhyme 'One, Two, Three, Four' from Lesson 1, page 57. Ask children to count in ones around the class with you.

WHOLE-CLASS TEACHING ACTIVITY

MAKE A PATTERN: Explain that the lesson is about patterns. Thread a red then a blue bead on a lace and ask: *How can I make a pattern for my necklace?* Place another red and blue bead on the lace. *Now I've made a red and blue pattern with the beads. What comes next?*

Show the children the wrapping paper: *Can you see a pattern?* Ask individuals to point out the patterns on the wallpaper, material and tie. Explain that there are different patterns all around us. Show the children the musical instruments. Beat the drum four times, then tap the triangle four times. Repeat. *What comes next to continue my musical pattern?* Repeat using different numbers of beats. Invite the children to continue your patterns.

GROUP ACTIVITIES

1. Give children beads and lace. They make a pattern using two different-coloured beads. Extend to three colours.

2. Place sets of 2-D shapes on the table. Ask children to make patterns using colour, size and shape. Use one, then extend to two or three criteria.

3. Ask children to copy a pattern using different sizes of 2-D and 3-D shapes.

 Set up an interactive pattern display including musical instruments and multicultural artefacts. Ask children to find, copy and make different patterns using a range of resources. Encourage children to bring items from home to add to the display.

DIFFERENTIATION

Less able: limit to one, then two attributes.
More able: ask children to identify, then copy a pattern. Limit to one, then two attributes.

PLENARY

Read 'Birds in the birdcage' from *Counting Rhymes*. Do a clapping pattern. Children listen then copy it, eg, clap, clap-clap, clap, clap-clap. Then do clap, nod, clap, nod. Recite the number names in order, continuing the count forwards or backwards from a given number.

RESOURCES	Cubes; flip chart; marker pen; different-sized and shaped containers such as beakers, egg cups, yoghurt pots, empty sweet containers. **Group activities:** counting items; sets of numeral cards (page 12); sets of cards showing various amounts of items.
LEARNING OUTCOMES	**ORAL AND MENTAL STARTER** ● Estimate a number in the range that can be counted reliably, then check by counting. **WHOLE-CLASS TEACHING ACTIVITY** ● Make simple estimates and predictions: for example, of the number of cubes that will fit in a box or strides across the room.
ORAL AND MENTAL STARTER	GUESS IT: Ask a child to take some cubes from a pile. *Look at your cubes. How many are there? Let's count to see if you were correct.* Repeat.
WHOLE-CLASS TEACHING ACTIVITY	GUESS WHAT: Hold some cubes in your hand. *Estimate (Guess) how many cubes I have in my hand.* Write some guesses on the flip chart. *James estimated ten, Laura five, Kezia estimated 20. Let's count to see who gave the nearest estimate.* Count the cubes. *There are nine cubes. James estimated ten. He was nearest.* Show children the containers. *How many beads would fit in here?* Children estimate then count out.
GROUP ACTIVITIES	**1.** Put out groups of various counting items. Children estimate how many there are in each group, then check by counting. **2.** Children estimate how many objects they can hold in their hand, how many strides it takes to cross the room, etc. They then check their estimates. **3.** Spread out the numeral and item cards face down on the table. Children turn over two cards to see whether the numeral and amount of objects match. ● Count around. Ask children to guess who will say a given number. Change the starting and finishing numbers.
DIFFERENTIATION	Less able: use numbers up to 10. More able: use numbers to 20 and beyond.
PLENARY	Feedback from the **Group activities**: how close are their guesses?

UNIT 10

ORGANISATION (5 LESSONS)

	LEARNING OUTCOMES	ORAL AND MENTAL STARTER	WHOLE-CLASS TEACHING ACTIVITY	PLENARY
LESSON 1	● Begin to recognise 'none' and 'zero' in stories, rhymes and when counting.	FIND ME: Children identify different numbers.	COUNT BACK: Children count backwards to 0.	Say 'Ten little teddies' with role-play.
LESSON 2	● Begin to understand and use the vocabulary of time. ● Sequence familiar events.	NEXT DOOR NUMBERS: Children find a numeral card near a given number.	TICK TOCK: Introducing time vocabulary.	Discuss everyday and occasional events.
LESSON 3	● Begin to know the days of the week in order.	FINGER ADD AND SUBTRACT: Combining/taking away two numbers.	WEEKLY MENU: Days of the week, using *The Very Hungry Caterpillar*.	Reinforce days of the week vocabulary.
LESSON 4	● Begin to know the days of the week in order.	FINGER ADD AND SUBTRACT: Combining/taking away two numbers.	MR WOLF'S WEEK: Children focus on the 'weekend'.	Compiling a weekly weather chart.
LESSON 5	● Begin to understand and use the vocabulary of time. Sequence familiar events.	SHOW ME ADD: Children add by counting on from one number to the next.	BIRTHDAY PARTY: Identifying special times.	Birthday graph to highlight months.

ORAL AND MENTAL SKILLS **Recognise numerals 1 to 9**, then 0 and 10. **Use language such as more or less, greater or smaller, to compare two numbers** and say which is more or less, and say a number which lies between two given numbers. **Begin to relate addition to combining two groups of objects,** counting all the objects. Begin to relate addition to counting on. **Begin to relate subtraction to 'taking away'** and counting how many are left.

Lessons 1, 2 and 3 are given in full. Lessons 4 and 5 are provided as grids.

RESOURCES

Individual sets of numeral cards (page 12); number track (0–10) (page 13); enlarged copy of photocopiable page 65 (Blast off); the rhyme 'Ten little teddies jumping on the bed'.
Group activities: copies of photocopiable page 65 (Blast off) and 66 (Slippery snake); carpet tiles numbered from 1–10; dice (0–5); counters.

LEARNING OUTCOMES

ORAL AND MENTAL STARTER
● **Recognise numerals 1 to 9,** then 0 and 10.
● **Use language such as more or less, greater or smaller, to compare two numbers** and say which is more or less, and say a number which lies between two given numbers.

WHOLE-CLASS TEACHING ACTIVITY
● Recite the number names in order, continuing the count forwards or backwards from a given number.
● Begin to recognise 'none' and 'zero' in stories, rhymes and when counting.

VOCABULARY

Number; zero, one, two, three... to twenty and beyond; none; how many?; count; count (up) to; count back (from, to).

ORAL AND MENTAL STARTER

FIND ME: Give each child a set of numeral cards. Ask them to hold up given numbers. Hold up a card and say: *Tell me the number.* Ask individuals to say which number it is. Say: *Tell me a number that comes before/after/next to this one.* Repeat using different numbers.

WHOLE-CLASS TEACHING ACTIVITY

COUNT BACK: Draw the children's attention to the number track and ask them to count from 0 to 10. Explain that today's lesson is about counting back. Point to 10. Say: *All count back from 10 as I point to the numerals: 10, 9, 8, 7, 6, 5, 4, 3, 2, 1, 0.* Discuss what happens when a rocket is launched. Say: *Count down (back) from 10 to 0.* Display the enlarged copy of photocopiable page 65 (Blast off). Explain that to launch the rocket, the children must join the numbers by counting down from 10 to 0. Join a few numbers as examples. Ask: *Where does the countdown start? Which number comes next?*

GROUP ACTIVITIES

1. Give each child a copy of photocopiable page 65 (Blast off) to complete.
2. Ask the children to place numbered carpet tiles in order from 10–0.
3. Give each pair counters, a 0–5 dice and a copy of photocopiable page 66 (Slippery snake). Each child takes a turn to throw the dice and move down the snake starting from 10. The first child to reach 0 wins. Children have to throw the correct number of throws at the end, eg if on 2, they must throw a 2.

 Record songs and rhymes that count down from 5 or 10 to 0, such as 'Ten green bottles' and encourage children to join in.

DIFFERENTIATION

Less able: ask an adult to support them. Start with 5 to 0, then 10–0.
More able: extend to 20 and beyond.

PLENARY

Recite 'Ten little teddies jumping on the bed'. Ask children to join in with role-play.

RESOURCES

Individual sets of numeral cards (page 12); a collection of objects such as pyjamas, toothbrush, school bag, sandwich box, birthday card, festival cards, calendar, clock, pictures of items or activities used or carried out at different times of the day, such as a cereal advert, children going to school etc; camera; *The Owl Who Was Afraid of the Dark* by Jill Tomlinson (Mammoth). **Group activities:** paper; pencils; zigzag books; jigsaws showing different times.

PREPARATION

Cut out pictures from newspapers and magazines that show different activities that occur during the day. Make zigzag books. Make simple jigsaws showing different times.

LEARNING OUTCOMES

ORAL AND MENTAL STARTER

● **Recognise numerals 1 to 9,** then 0 and 10.
● **Use language such as more or less, greater or smaller, to compare two numbers** and say which is more or less, and say a number which lies between two given numbers.

WHOLE-CLASS TEACHING ACTIVITY

● Begin to understand and use the vocabulary of time.
● Sequence familiar events.

ORAL AND MENTAL STARTER

NEXT-DOOR NUMBERS: Give each child a set of numeral cards. Ask them to find a number that comes before/after/in between two numbers.

WHOLE-CLASS TEACHING ACTIVITY

TICK TOCK: Explain that today's lesson is about time. Display the collection of objects. Say: *We use these at different times in the day.* Pick out an object, such as the toothbrush. *When do we use a toothbrush?* Encourage children to use the appropriate vocabulary. Ask the children to tell you when the other objects are used. Introduce special times such as birthdays, festivals, weekends, holidays. (Be sensitive to religious observances.) Remind children of particular times in the day: morning, evening, breakfast-time, lunchtime, teatime, playtime, bedtime, hometime. Explain that throughout the day you are going to take photographs of the children carrying out different tasks. These can be made into a display of their day.

VOCABULARY

Time; day; week; month; birthday; holiday; special days: Christmas, Diwali, Ramadan... Mother's Day, Father's Day; morning; afternoon; evening; night; clock; watch; hands; breakfast; lunch; school time; bedtime; dinnertime; playtime; hometime; months of the year: January, February, March...; before; after; next.

GROUP ACTIVITIES

1. Working with a classroom assistant, each child makes their own time line for their day – such as getting up, having breakfast, coming to school.
2. Give each child a zigzag book. Ask them to draw activities they do at home on one side and activities they do at school on the other.
3. Give each child a jigsaw showing different times. Ask them to complete these and describe what is happening.

 Read *The Owl Who Was Afraid of the Dark* to the children.

DIFFERENTIATION

Less able: limit the activities to morning/school time and evening.
More able: children can make timelines for their day during the week and at weekends.

PLENARY

Recap with the children the activities they have been doing that day. Encourage them to consider which things happen every day (for example, taking the register) and which things only happen on certain days (for example, PE).

LESSON 3

RESOURCES

The Very Hungry Caterpillar by Eric Carle (Puffin); flip chart; marker pen; flashcards showing the days of the week; weekly menu chart. **Group activities:** zigzag books.

PREPARATION

Make flashcards saying 'Sunday', 'Monday' etc. Make seven-page zigzag books. Create a menu card on a large sheet of paper by writing the days of the week in a column down the left-hand side. Prepare copies for the children to complete.

LEARNING OUTCOMES

ORAL AND MENTAL STARTER
- **Begin to relate addition to combining two groups of objects,** counting all the objects.
- **Begin to relate subtraction to 'taking away'** and counting how many are left.

WHOLE-CLASS TEACHING ACTIVITY
- Begin to know the days of the week in order.

VOCABULARY
Time; day; week; month; birthday; holiday; special days: Christmas, Diwali, Ramadan... Mother's Day, Father's Day; morning; afternoon; evening; night; clock; watch; hands; breakfast; lunch; school time; bedtime; dinnertime; playtime; hometime; months of the year: January, February, March...; before; after; next.

ORAL AND MENTAL STARTER

FINGER ADD AND SUBTRACT: Ask children to hold up their fingers to show you the answers to adding and subtracting questions: *5 take away 0. 6 add 4. 3 add 1 more, how many altogether? 7 subtract 7, how many are left?*

WHOLE-CLASS TEACHING ACTIVITY

WEEKLY MENU: Read *The Very Hungry Caterpillar* to the class. Explain that the caterpillar ate different food each day of the week. Hold up the flashcards and read out the days. Ask the class to recite them. *What did the caterpillar eat on Monday?* On the flip chart write what the caterpillar ate on each day. Show the children the enlarged copy of the menu card. Point out the days of the week and explain that we eat different foods on different days. *What could we eat on Sunday? What could we have on Wednesday?* Ask individuals for ideas and create a weekly menu.

GROUP ACTIVITIES

1. Give each child a menu sheet. Ask them to draw on their choices of food and drink for each day of the week.
2. Give each child a zigzag book. Write one day of the week on each page. Ask children to think of their own foods for the hungry caterpillar.
3. Working with a classroom assistant, children make a weekly calendar for the classroom showing activities for each day.

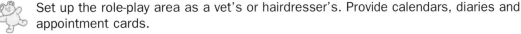 Set up the role-play area as a vet's or hairdresser's. Provide calendars, diaries and appointment cards.

DIFFERENTIATION

Less able: ask an adult to support them.
More able: encourage them to use the vocabulary of time.

PLENARY

Recite the days of the week. Feedback from the **Group activities** to reinforce vocabulary.

RESOURCES	*Mr Wolf's Week* by Colin Hawkins (Mammoth); different sorts of diaries; weather chart. **Group activities:** zigzag books; paper; pencils; crayons.
LEARNING OUTCOMES	**ORAL AND MENTAL STARTER** ● **Begin to relate addition to combining two groups of objects,** counting all the objects. ● **Begin to relate subtraction to 'taking away'** and counting how many are left. **WHOLE-CLASS TEACHING ACTIVITY** ● Begin to know the days of the week in order.
ORAL AND MENTAL STARTER	FINGER ADD AND SUBTRACT: Play as in Lesson 3, page 63.
WHOLE-CLASS TEACHING ACTIVITY	MR WOLF'S WEEK: Read the story to the class. *What happened in Mr Wolf's week?* Ask children what they do in the week. Refer to activities in school such as swimming, assembly etc. *Why is the weekend special? Which days make the weekend?* Ask individuals what they do at weekends. Explain that some people record what happens on different days such as weather people or newspaper reporters. Say that some people write a diary so that they remember what they should be doing on each day. Show the children different diaries.
GROUP ACTIVITIES	**1.** Give each child a zigzag book. Ask them to draw activities they do during the week, including weekends. **2.** Working with an adult, children make a timeline of their week. **3.** Working with an adult, the group makes a weekly calendar for the classroom and records special times for each day. ● Place a calendar, weather chart and newspapers in the role-play area and classroom for the children to use and refer to.
DIFFERENTIATION	Less able: ask an adult to support them. More able: encourage them to record in their own way.
PLENARY	Start making a weather chart to record the weather on each day of the week. Ask the children to listen to or watch weather reports on the radio/television.

RESOURCES	Birthday and festival cards; party invitations; model of a birthday cake; candles; Mother's day/Father's day cards; calendar. **Group activities:** thin card; pencils; crayons.
LEARNING OUTCOMES	**ORAL AND MENTAL STARTER** ● Begin to relate addition to counting on. **WHOLE-CLASS TEACHING ACTIVITY** ● Begin to understand and use the vocabulary of time.
ORAL AND MENTAL STARTER	SHOW ME ADD: Explain that you are going to say a number. The children must hold this number in their heads. You will then give another number. The children must add that number to the first by counting on. Children show you the answer by holding up their fingers.
WHOLE-CLASS TEACHING ACTIVITY	BIRTHDAY PARTY: Explain that there are special times during the year. *There are festivals, birthdays, special days for parents and children. What happens when it is someone's birthday? Why is it a special time?* Show the children the cards, cake and candles. Ask: *Who is 4? Who is 5?* Explain that those who are 5 are older than those who are 4. *You were all born before the 4-year olds.* Explain that birthdays and some festivals are on the same date each year but not the same day. Tell the children that they are going to make their own 'passport' showing their name, age, and birth month. Show the children the calendar and point out the months of the year.
GROUP ACTIVITIES	**1.** Children make their own 'passports' by drawing sketches of themselves on thin card and adding the appropriate age and dates. **2.** Place candles, cards and party invitations on the table. Ask children to sort the items for children who are 4, 5 and 6. **3.** Children write party invitations for a class tea party giving the day, date, starting and finishing time. ● Arrange a class party.
DIFFERENTIATION	Less able: use the support of an adult helper to act as scribe. More able: find how many children are born in each month.
PLENARY	Feedback from the **Group activities**. Make a graph to show the months of the children's birthdays.

Blast off

10 9 8 7 6 5 4 3 2 1 0

Join the numbers for the countdown:

10
9
8
7
6
5
4
3
2
1
0

Fill in the missing numbers:

10 __ 8 7 __ 5 __ __ 2 1 __

Slippery snake

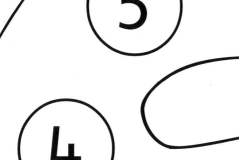

UNIT 11

ORGANISATION (5 LESSONS)

LEARNING OUTCOMES	ORAL AND MENTAL STARTER	WHOLE-CLASS TEACHING ACTIVITY	PLENARY
LESSON 1 ● Recite the number names in order, continuing the count forwards or backwards from a given number. ● Begin to relate addition to counting on.	COUNT ON: Counting on to 10, then 20.	MORE COUNTING ON: Counting on from one amount to another.	COUNT ON: Children count on several numbers.
LESSON 2 ● **Say and use the number names in order in familiar contexts** such as number rhymes, songs, stories, counting games and activities (first to five, then ten, then twenty and beyond). ● **Use language such as more or less, greater or smaller, to compare two numbers** and say which is more or less, and say a number which lies between two given numbers. ● **Use developing mathematical ideas and methods to solve practical problems** involving counting and comparing in a real or role play context.	COUNT ON, COUNT BACK.	MORE OR LESS: Counting and comparing different items.	Feedback from activities. Children recite a number rhyme.
LESSON 3 ● **Use developing mathematical ideas and methods to solve practical problems** involving counting and comparing in a real or role play context. ● Begin to use the vocabulary related to money. Sort coins, including the £1 and £2 coins, and use them in role play to pay and give change.	FINGER ADD AND SUBTRACT.	BUYING BUNS: Recognising different denominations of coins.	Feedback from activities.
LESSON 4 + 5 ● **Use developing mathematical ideas and methods to solve practical problems** involving counting and comparing in a real or role play context. ● Begin to use the vocabulary related to money. Sort coins, including the £1 and £2 coins, and use them in role play to pay and give change.	FINGER ADD AND SUBTRACT.	SWEET SHOP: Problem-solving using a money context.	Feedback from activities.

ORAL AND MENTAL SKILLS Say and use the number names in order in familiar contexts such as number rhymes, songs, stories, counting games and activities (first to five, then ten, then twenty and beyond). Recite the number names in order, continuing the count forwards or backwards from a given number. **Begin to use the vocabulary involved in adding and subtracting. Begin to relate addition to combining two groups of objects,** counting all the objects. **Begin to relate subtraction to 'taking away'** and counting how many are left.

Lessons 1, 2 and 3 are given in full. Lessons 4 and 5 are provided as a grid.

RESOURCES

The rhyme 'One little man in a flying saucer'; flip chart; marker pen; a selection of counting items such as counters, beans, teddy bear counters, cubes; empty containers.
Group activities: dice (1–6); (1–10) spinners; individual number tracks 0–20 (page 13); cubes; paper; pencils.

LEARNING OUTCOMES

ORAL AND MENTAL STARTER
● **Say and use the number names in order in familiar contexts** such as number rhymes, songs, stories, counting games and activities (first to five, then ten, then twenty and beyond).
● Recite the number names in order, continuing the count forwards or backwards from a given number.

WHOLE-CLASS TEACHING ACTIVITY
● Recite the number names in order, continuing the count forwards or backwards from a given number.
● Begin to relate addition to counting on.

VOCABULARY

Number; zero, one, two, three... to twenty and beyond; none; how many?; count; count (up) to; count back (from, to); after; next to; between; in the middle of.

ORAL AND MENTAL STARTER

COUNT ON: Sing the rhyme 'One little man in a flying saucer'. Count on from 0 to 10, then 0 to 20.

WHOLE-CLASS TEACHING ACTIVITY

MORE COUNTING ON: Explain that today's lesson is about counting on. Begin a number count with the class. *Start at 0 and count on to 10. Start at 5 and count on to 20.* Repeat, using different numbers to start and finish. Count out a number of teddy bear counters, say four, into a container. *How many are in the container? 4. Place three more on the table. How many teddy bears are there altogether? 4 count on 3. 4 – 5, 6, 7. 4 count on 3 makes 7.* Repeat using different numbers. Write the number sentences on the flip chart each time.

GROUP ACTIVITIES

1. In pairs, children take turns to throw the dice. They take the appropriate number of teddy bear counters and place them in a container. The next child throws the dice and repeats the activity. The children count the total number of teddy bears collected by counting on.
2. Give each pair a spinner and a number track (0–20). One child spins the spinner and places a counter on the number track accordingly . The second child spins again and counts on by moving the counter. The children continue until they reach 20.
3. Children work in pairs and count out ten cubes. One child places a number of cubes in a container, then five more. The children count on to find the total. They record their work using pictures and numerals.

 Place different dice and counting games such as Snakes and Ladders or Ludo out on a table for children to use.

DIFFERENTIATION

Less able: ask an adult to support them.
More able: encourage them to record in their own way.

PLENARY

COUNT ON: Several numbers starting and finishing at a given number.

LESSON 2

RESOURCES

Set of large numeral cards to 10 (page 12); flip chart; marker pen; egg cartons.
Group activities: a selection of everyday objects such as balls, beakers, straws, coloured bricks, toy cars, play people, sweets, egg boxes, chocolate eggs; paper; crayons; a variety of counting objects such as sweets, egg cartons, coins, money boxes, etc.

PREPARATION

Place some sweets in a bag, some toy eggs in an egg carton, some coins in a money box etc. Prepare labels saying 'How many more sweets to make 11 altogether?', 'How many more eggs to fill the box?', 'How much more to make 10p?' for the children to solve.

LEARNING OUTCOMES

ORAL AND MENTAL STARTER
● Recite the number names in order, continuing the count forwards or backwards from a given number.

WHOLE-CLASS TEACHING ACTIVITY
● **Say and use the number names in order in familiar contexts** such as number rhymes, songs, stories, counting games and activities (first to five, then ten, then twenty and beyond).
● **Use language such as more or less, greater or smaller, to compare two numbers** and say which is more or less, and say a number which lies between two given numbers.
● **Use developing mathematical ideas and methods to solve practical problems** involving counting and comparing in a real or role play context.

ORAL AND MENTAL STARTER

COUNT ON/COUNT BACK. As in Unit 5, Lesson 1, page 41.

WHOLE-CLASS TEACHING ACTIVITY

MORE OR LESS?: Say to the children: *Are there more boys than girls in our class? How can we find out?* Ask all the boys to line up in a row, then all the girls. Match a boy to a girl and ask: *Are there more boys than girls? Are there fewer girls than boys?* Write two numbers on the flip chart, such as 5 and 1. *What can you tell me about these numbers?* Encourage the children to compare using vocabulary such as 'bigger', 'smaller', 'fewer', 'more', 'less', 'greater than'. Repeat with other numbers. Write a number, such as 9, on the flip chart and say: *Give me a number that is greater than 9.* Show the children the egg carton and say: *How many eggs go in this box?* Count out six balls and place them in the box: *If I take out three balls, how many are left?* Repeat using different numbers.

GROUP ACTIVITIES

1. In pairs, children find different ways of making 6. They record their answers by drawing pictures.
2. Show the children the objects and labels you have prepared. Ask them to try to solve the problems you have written using actual objects. A classroom assistant can give support.
3. Play Kim's game. Place a variety of items (up to five, then ten) on the table. Children take turns to remove items. The other children say how many items are missing and what they are.

 Set up a 'bus' or 'train' as part of the role-play area.

How many more sweets to make 11?

How many eggs to fill the box?

Five people on the bus. Two more get on. How many altogether?

VOCABULARY

Compare; count; how many more to make...?; total; altogether; makes; leaves; before; after; less; take away; zero, nought; how did you work it out?; arrange; rearrange; explain; record; work out; different way.

DIFFERENTIATION

Less able: ask an adult to support them.
More able: encourage them to record using symbols.

PLENARY

Feedback from the **Group activities**. Sing 'Five little speckled frogs'. Ask: *How many frogs have gone? How many are left?*

RESOURCES

Real and plastic coins. **Group activities:** purses; a selection of money boxes; money dice (1p, 2p, 5p, 10p) (blank over the two sides not used); sorting rings.

PREPARATION

Fill some purses with varying amounts and denominations of coins. Prepare labels saying 15p, 12p, 10p, 9p.

LEARNING OUTCOMES

ORAL AND MENTAL STARTER
● **Begin to use the vocabulary involved in adding and subtracting.**
● **Begin to relate addition to combining two groups of objects,** counting all the objects.
● **Begin to relate subtraction to 'taking away'** and counting how many are left.

WHOLE-CLASS TEACHING ACTIVITY
● **Use developing mathematical ideas and methods to solve practical problems** involving counting and comparing in a real or role play context.
● Begin to use the vocabulary related to money. Sort coins, including the £1 and £2 coins, and use them in role play to pay and give change.

VOCABULARY
Money; coin; pence; penny; pound; price; cost; buy; sell; spend; spent; pay; change; costs more; costs less; how much?

ORAL AND MENTAL STARTER

FINGER ADD AND SUBTRACT: Play as in Unit 10, Lesson 3, page 63.

WHOLE-CLASS TEACHING ACTIVITY

BUYING BUNS: Sing 'Five currant buns in the baker's shop'. Role-play with 'real' money: *How many buns can I buy for 3p? How much would four buns cost?* Place a selection of coins on each table. Explain that you want children to work in pairs and sort out the coins. Ask: *How many coins do you have? Who has a £2 coin? Who has some 10p coins? Which coins are silver? Which coins are copper? Which is the largest coin?* Explain that you want the children to find the coin and hold it in the air. Say: *Show me 10p. Show me 5p. Show me 4p. Show me a coin greater than 10p. Is a £2 coin worth more than a £1 coin?*

GROUP ACTIVITIES

1. Give children the money boxes and the labels. The children take turns to roll the money dice and fill their money boxes with the correct amount.
2. Give children an assortment of coins. Ask them to sort these into sorting rings.
3. Place purses on each table. Ask children to sort the number of coins in each purse then count how much there is in each purse.

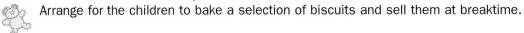   Arrange for the children to bake a selection of biscuits and sell them at breaktime.

DIFFERENTIATION

Less able: use amounts to 5p, then 10p.
More able: use amounts up to £1.00.

PLENARY

Feedback from the **Group activities**.

LESSON 4 + 5

RESOURCES	Real and plastic money; assortment of sweets; labels saying 1p, 2p, 3p etc. **Group activities:** paper; crayons; purses containing various amounts and denominations of coins; role-play area set up as a shop; a selection of money boxes; real and plastic coins; labels saying 15p, 12p, 10p, 9p; money dice; sorting rings.
LEARNING OUTCOMES	**ORAL AND MENTAL STARTER** ● **Begin to use the vocabulary involved in adding and subtracting.** ● **Begin to relate addition to combining two groups of objects,** counting all the objects. ● **Begin to relate subtraction to 'taking away'** and counting how many are left. **WHOLE-CLASS TEACHING ACTIVITY** ● **Use developing mathematical ideas and methods to solve practical problems** involving counting and comparing in a real or role play context. ● Begin to understand and use the vocabulary related to money. Sort coins, including the £1 and £2 coins, and use them in role play to pay and give change.
ORAL AND MENTAL STARTER	FINGER ADD AND SUBTRACT. Play as in Unit 10, Lesson 3, page 63.
WHOLE-CLASS TEACHING ACTIVITY	SWEET SHOP: Show the children the selection of sweets. Explain that some of the sweets are 1p or 2p each, while with some you can have two sweets for 1p. Display the price labels and read them with the children. Ask the children to choose sweets to the value of 2p. Say: *What else could you have for 2p?* Repeat using different amounts. Ask children to sort the coins on their table. Say: *Count out 3p. Is there a 3p coin? How can we make 3p? Are there any more ways?*
GROUP ACTIVITIES	Choose from these activities over the two lessons: **1.** In pairs, children make up a mix of ten sweets using different varieties. They draw their choice and place coins to show the prices. **2.** Working with an adult, children make different amounts of money such as 5p, 8p, 4p and 10p. **3.** Give children the money boxes and the labels. The children take turns to roll the money dice (1p, 2p, 5p, 10p) and fill their money boxes with the correct amount. **4.** Give children an assortment of coins. Ask them to sort these into sorting rings. **5.** Place purses on each table. Ask the children to sort the number of coins in each purse, then count how much there is in each purse. **6.** Children work in the role-play shop. ● Organise a jumble sale in the home corner. Ask children to make price labels for the items.
DIFFERENTIATION	Less able: work with amounts to 5p then 10p. More able: work with amounts up to 20p then 50p.
PLENARY	Feedback from activities.

UNIT 12: Assess & Review

Choose from the following activities. During the group activities some of the children will be working with you on practical tasks.

RESOURCES

Numeral cards for each child; a selection of objects for counting; interlocking cubes; a selection of 2-D and 3-D shapes.

ORAL AND MENTAL STARTER

ASSESSMENT

● Can the children: **Say and use the number names in order in familiar contexts? Find one more or one less than a number from 1 to 10?**
NUMBERS IN CONTEXT: Sing 'One elephant went out to play'. Say the rhyme 'One, two, buckle my shoe'. Ask the children to count with you in ones from 0–5, then 0–10, then back from 5–0 and 10–0. Observe and record who counts with confidence and who needs more practice. Allow individual children opportunities to count forwards and backwards while you observe who is doing this confidently.
ONE MORE, ONE LESS: Say a number. The children hold up that number of fingers then show you one more. Repeat with different numbers and use one less. Observe and record who finds one more and one less confidently and who needs more practice. Ask individuals to find one more and one less than a given number.

GROUP ACTIVITIES

ASSESSMENT

● Can the children: **Recognise numerals 1 to 9? Use language such as more or less, greater or smaller to compare two numbers? Count reliably up to 10 everyday objects? In practical activities and discussion, begin to use the vocabulary involved in adding and subtracting. Begin to relate addition to combining two groups of objects,** counting all the objects? **Begin to relate subtraction to 'taking away'?** Begin to name solids and flat shapes? Talk about, recognise and recreate patterns? **Use developing mathematical ideas and methods to solve practical problems?**
FROM 1 TO 9: Children pick out a numeral card that you say. Point to a numeral card and ask children to read the number. Use numbers from 1–9.
COMPARE TWO QUANTITIES: Use examples from the Whole-class teaching activity and Group activities in Unit 7, Lessons 2, 3, 4, and 5, pages 47–49 or make up some similar ones.
STARTING TO ADD AND TAKE AWAY: Say a number. The children hold up that number of fingers on one hand. Then say another number for them to hold up that number of fingers on the other hand. *How many altogether?* Now explain that when you say a number you want the children to hold up that number of fingers. When you say another number you want them to take away that number of fingers. Say: *5 take away 4. How many are left? 8 subtract 8. How many are left?*
SHAPES AND PATTERNS: Say the name of a shape for the children to hold up. *Does it belong to the 2-D or 3-D family?* Hold up a shape. *Find a shape the same as this. What's the name of this shape?* Make a pattern using cubes (two colours, such as red and blue). *Can you copy my pattern?* Use the same colour cubes. Make a pattern using two shapes, for example circle, triangle, circle. *Can you continue my pattern?* Ask children if they can make a pattern of their own.

TERM 2

Counting, recognising, comparing and ordering numbers are focused on during the spring term. Opportunities are provided for children to develop, consolidate and demonstrate their mathematical knowledge, skills and understanding and some recording is introduced. The use of mathematical vocabulary for teaching and learning is emphasised. Work is given to develop children's understanding of money and 'real life' problems.

In 'Shape and space' children are encouraged to talk about, recognise and recreate patterns, including those from different cultures. Practical activities to develop positional language are given.

In 'Measures' children compare the length, mass and capacity of two quantities to gain a thorough understanding before extending to three or more. Time lessons include daily routines and telling the time is introduced with o'clock.

TERM 2 PLANNING GRID

ORAL AND MENTAL SKILLS: Say and use the number names in order in familiar contexts such as number rhymes, songs, stories, counting games and activities (first to five, then ten, then twenty and beyond). Recite the number names in order, continuing the count forwards or backwards from a given number. Order a given set of numbers: for example, the set of numbers 1 to 6 given in random order. Count reliably in other contexts, such as clapping sounds or hopping movements. **Recognise numerals 1 to 9**, then 0 to 10, then beyond 10. Begin to recognise 'none' and 'zero' in stories, rhymes and when counting. **Begin to use the vocabulary involved in adding and subtracting.** Begin to understand and use the vocabulary of time. **Begin to relate addition to combining two groups of objects,** counting all the objects. **Begin to relate subtraction to 'taking away'** and counting how many are left. Work out by counting how many more are needed to make a larger number. Sort coins, including the £1 and £2 coins.

Unit	Topic	Objectives: children will be taught to...
1	Counting Comparing and ordering numbers	● **Say and use the number names in order in familiar contexts** such as number rhymes, songs, stories, counting games and activities (first to five, then ten, then twenty and beyond). ● Recite the number names in order, continuing the count forwards or backwards from a given number. ● **Count reliably up to 10 everyday objects** (first to 5, then 10, then beyond) ● **Use language such as more or less, greater or smaller, to compare two numbers** and say which is more or less, and say a number which lies between two given numbers. ● Order a given set of numbers: for example, the set of numbers 1 to 6 given in random order. ● **Compare two numbers** and say which is more or less, and say a number which lies between two given numbers.
2	Counting Adding and subtracting	● Count reliably in other contexts, such as clapping sounds or hopping movements. ● **Begin to use the vocabulary involved in adding and subtracting.** ● **Find one more or one less than a number from 1 to 10.** ● **Begin to relate addition to combining two groups of objects,** counting all the objects. ● **Begin to relate subtraction to 'taking' away** and counting how many are left.
3	Shape and space Reasoning	● Put sets of objects in order of size. ● **Use language such as circle or bigger to describe the shape and size of solids and flat shapes.** ● **Use everyday words to describe position:** for example, follow and give instructions about positions. ● **Talk about, recognise and recreate patterns:** for example, simple repeating or symmetrical patterns from different cultures. ● Sort and match objects, pictures or children themselves, justifying the decisions made.
4	Counting Measures	● **Use language longer or shorter, heavier or lighter, more or less to compare two quantities,** then more than two, by making direct comparisons of lengths. ● Estimate a number in the range that can be counted reliably, then check by counting. ● Begin to understand and use the vocabulary of time. ● Sequence familiar events. ● Begin to know the days of the week in order.
5	Counting Adding and subtracting Money and 'real life' problems	● **Say and use the number names in order in familiar contexts** (first to five, then ten, then twenty and beyond). ● Recite the number names in order, continuing the count forwards or backwards from a given number. ● Count reliably in other contexts, such as clapping sounds or hopping movements. ● **Recognise numerals 1 to 9,** then 0 and 10, then beyond 10. ● Order a given set of selected numbers, for example, the set of numbers 1 to 6 given in random order. ● **Begin to use the vocabulary involved in adding and subtracting.** ● **Begin to relate addition to combining two groups of objects,** counting all the objects. ● **Begin to relate subtraction to 'taking away'** and counting how many are left. ● Begin to understand and use the vocabulary related to money. Sort coins, including the £1 and £2 coins, and use them in role play to pay and give change. ● Solve simple problems or puzzles in a practical context and respond to 'What could we try next?'. ● **Use developing mathematical ideas and methods to solve practical problems** involving counting and comparing in a real or role play context.
6	Assess and review	

ORAL AND MENTAL SKILLS: Recognise numerals 1 to 9, then 0 and 10, then beyond 10. Recite the number names in order, continuing the count forwards or backwards from a given number. **Say and use the number names in order in familiar contexts** such as number rhymes, songs, stories, counting games and activities (first to five then ten, then twenty and beyond). Order a given set of numbers. **Begin to relate addition to combining two groups of objects,** counting all the objects. **Begin to relate subtraction to 'taking away'** and counting how many are left. Begin to recognise 'none' and 'zero' in stories, rhymes and when counting. Order a given set of numbers: for example, the set of numbers 1 to 6 given in random order. Count in twos. Count reliably in other contexts, such as clapping sounds or hopping movements. **Find one more or one less than a number from 1 to 10. Begin to use the vocabulary involved in adding and subtracting. Use language such as more or less, greater or smaller, to compare two numbers** and say which is more or less, and say a number which lies between two given numbers. Begin to understand and use ordinal numbers in different contexts. Find a total by counting on when one group of objects is hidden. Begin to know the days of the week in order. Count in twos. Count in tens.

Unit	Topic	Objectives: children will be taught to...
7	Counting and reading numbers Comparing and ordering numbers	● **Recognise numerals 1 to 9,** then 0 and 10, then beyond 10. ● **Count reliably up to 10 everyday objects** (first to 5, then 10, then beyond), giving just one number name to each object. ● Order a given set of numbers: for example, the set of numbers 1 to 6 given in random order. ● **Use language such as more or less, greater or smaller, to compare two numbers** and say which is more or less, and say a number which lies between two given numbers. ● Order a given set of selected numbers: for example, the set 2, 5,1, 8, 4
8	Counting and reading numbers Adding and subtracting	● Count in twos. ● **Begin to use the vocabulary involved in adding and subtracting.** ● Begin to relate addition to counting on. ● Remove a smaller number from a larger and find out how many are left by counting back from the larger number. ● Begin to find out how many have been removed from a larger group of objects by counting up from a number. ● **Begin to relate addition to combining two groups of objects.**
9	Shape and space Reasoning	● Put sets of objects in order of size. ● **Use language such as circle or bigger to describe the shape and size of solids and flat shapes.** ● **Use everyday words to describe position.** ● Talk about, recognise and recreate patterns. ● Sort and match objects, pictures or children themselves, justifying the decisions made.
10	Counting and reading numbers Measures, including time	● **Use language such as heavier or lighter, full or empty, taller or shorter to compare two quantities,** then more than two by making direct comparisons of masses, capacity, length. ● Begin to understand and use the vocabulary of time. ● Begin to read o'clock time.
11	Counting and reading numbers Adding and subtracting Money and 'real life' problems	● Recite the number names in order, continuing the count forwards or backwards from a given number. ● Count in tens. ● **Begin to use the vocabulary involved in adding and subtracting.** ● **Begin to relate addition to combining two groups of objects,** counting all the objects. ● Begin to relate addition to counting on. ● Find a total by counting on when one group of objects is hidden. ● Separate (partition) a given number of objects into two groups. ● Select two groups of objects to make a given total. ● **Begin to relate subtraction to 'taking away'** and counting how many are left. ● Remove a smaller number from a larger and find how many are left by counting back from the larger number. ● Work out by counting how many more are needed to make a larger number. ● **Use developing mathematical ideas and methods to solve practical problems** involving counting and comparing in a real or role play context. ● Begin to understand and use the vocabulary related to money. Sort coins, including £1 and £2 coins, and use them in role-play to pay and give change.
12	Assess and review	

UNIT 1

ORGANISATION (5 LESSONS)

	LEARNING OUTCOMES	ORAL AND MENTAL STARTER	WHOLE-CLASS TEACHING ACTIVITY	PLENARY
LESSON 1	● **Say and use the number names in order in familiar contexts** such as number rhymes, songs, stories, counting games and activities (first to five, then ten, then twenty and beyond). ● Recite the number names in order, continuing the count forwards or backwards from a given number. ● **Count reliably up to 10 everyday objects** (first to 5, then 10, then beyond)	COUNT ON IN ONES: Children count on from a given number.	COUNT AROUND: Children count individually around the classroom.	Children count back from a given number.
LESSON 2 +3	● **Use language such as more or less, greater or smaller, to compare two numbers** and say which is more or less, and say a number which lies between two given numbers.	COUNT AROUND: Children count individually around the classroom.	WASH DAY: Comparing and ordering numbers.	Count back.
LESSON 4	● Order a given set of numbers: for example, the set of numbers 1 to 6 given in random order. ● **Compare two numbers** and say which is more or less, and say a number which lies between two given numbers.	COUNTING RHYMES: Children recite popular counting rhymes.	ORDER IT: Ordering and comparing numbers 1–10.	Feedback from activities. Children hold up fingers in response to questions.
LESSON 5	● **Use language such as more or less, greater or smaller, to compare two numbers** and say which is more or less, and say a number which lies between two given numbers. ● Order a given set of numbers: for example, the set of numbers 1 to 6 given in random order.	SHOW ME: Children hold up numeral cards in response to various questions.	ORDER IT: Children compare and order numbers 0–10.	Comparing and ordering numbers.

ORAL AND MENTAL SKILLS **Say and use the number names in order in familiar contexts** such as number rhymes, songs, stories, counting games and activities (first to five, then ten, then twenty and beyond). Recite the number names in order, continuing the count forwards or backwards from a given number. Order a given set of numbers: for example, the set of numbers 1 to 6 given in random order.

Lessons 1, 2 and 4 are given in full. Lesson 3 extends what has been taught in Lesson 2. Lesson 5 is provided in outline.

RESOURCES

A selection of favourite counting rhymes. **Group activities:** collection of counting items; sorting rings or paper plates; Frogs and lily pads (page 14); 0–10 number tracks (page 13).

PREPARATION

Choose some counting rhymes that involve counting on or back in ones such as 'Five little speckled frogs', 'Ten green bottles', 'One, two, three, four, five'. Make the required photocopies.

LEARNING OUTCOMES
ORAL AND MENTAL STARTER
● **Say and use the number names in order in familiar contexts** such as number rhymes, songs, stories, counting games and activities (first to five, then ten, then twenty and beyond).
● Recite the number names in order, continuing the count forwards or backwards from a given number.

WHOLE-CLASS TEACHING ACTIVITY
● **Say and use the number names in order in familiar contexts** such as number rhymes, songs, stories, counting games and activities (first to five, then ten, then twenty and beyond).
● Recite the number names in order, continuing the count forwards or backwards from a given number.
● **Count reliably up to 10 everyday objects** (first to 5, then 10, then beyond).

VOCABULARY

Counting; number, one, two, three..., to twenty; how many?; count; count (up) to; count on (from, to); count back (from, to).

ORAL AND MENTAL STARTER

COUNT ON IN ONES: Children count together to 5, then 10 and beyond. Now say a number and ask the children to count on from that number. *2 count on 3 is 5. 1 count on 2 is 3. What is 4 count on 1?* Repeat with numbers to total 10. Ask both the whole class and individuals to count on.

WHOLE-CLASS TEACHING ACTIVITY

COUNT AROUND: Explain that this lesson is about counting. Together recite some counting rhymes such as 'One, two, three, four, five' and 'Five little speckled frogs'. Count together in ones to 10, then 20 and beyond. Now say that you are all going to play 'Count around'. Explain that you want the children to count individually around the class with you. Start from 1, counting to 5. Count around the class until all the children have taken part. Repeat, counting to 10, then 20. Say: *I am going to ask someone to start counting in ones. When I clap my hands that person stops and picks another child to carry on the count.* Children count to 5, then 10. Now ask the children to count out objects in the classroom: *How many windows are there? Count how many adults you can see. How many tables are there altogether?* Point out other items in the classroom and invite individuals to count and give the answer.

GROUP ACTIVITIES

1. Place a set of counting items on the table. Each child sorts and counts a collection of objects first to 5, then to 10, onto a plate or into a sorting ring.
2. Place the lily pads and frogs on the table. Each childs counts out five lily pads and five frogs. Sing the rhyme 'Five little speckled frogs'.
3. Give each child some assorted counting items and an individual number track showing the numerals 0–10. The child puts an appropriate number of items in each section of the number track.

 Children count the number of hops, skips, jumps, etc in a PE lesson.

DIFFERENTIATION

More/Less able: Target the counting carefully, making sure the number range is appropriate for individual children.

PLENARY

Count down from 5 to 1, then 10 to 0. Ask children to count back several numbers from a given number. *Start at 5, count back 3: 5 – 4, 3, 2.* Invite individuals to give the starting number for the count back.

LESSON 2 + 3

RESOURCES
Two washing lines; pegs; a clothes 'basket'; cut-outs of clothes, for example, socks, T-shirts, shorts, jeans, jumpers. **Group activities:** paper plates; containers; dice (1–6); (1–10) spinners; selection of items such as socks, cars, soft toys, books, laces, play-people, gloves, buttons.

PREPARATION
Cut out templates of clothes, mount them on card and laminate. Place them in the 'basket'.

LEARNING OUTCOMES

ORAL AND MENTAL STARTER
● **Say and use the number names in order in familiar contexts** such as number rhymes, songs, stories, counting games and activities (first to five, then ten, then twenty and beyond).
● Recite the number names in order, continuing the count forwards or backwards from a given number.

WHOLE-CLASS TEACHING ACTIVITY
● **Use language such as more or less, greater or smaller, to compare two numbers** and say which is more or less, and say a number which lies between two given numbers.

ORAL AND MENTAL STARTER
COUNT AROUND: Play as in Lesson 1, page 76. Ask the children to count in ones around the class with you. Start from 1 and count to 5, then 10. Count around the class until all the children have taken part. Explain that they are going to carry on a count around the class. Repeat, starting at a different number.

WHOLE-CLASS TEACHING ACTIVITY
WASH DAY: Explain that the lesson is about comparing and ordering numbers. Talk about the special order in which we say numbers. Select a few children to demonstrate by reciting the count from 1 to 5, then up to 10 and 20. Next, hang a washing line across the classroom. Ask a child to select a given number of cut-out clothes and peg them onto the washing line. When they have been pegged up, ask the rest of the class to count out the number of items. Invite another child to peg up another set of clothes. Ask the children to check whether there are more clothes in one set or the other. Then, using these sets, focus on individual items, asking questions such as: *Are there fewer socks than T-shirts?* Select children to count and say the number of socks and then make the number of them less or more; greater or smaller.

GROUP ACTIVITIES
1. Children sort out two sets of the same object and place them on plates or in containers. They count and say the number of objects in each set and identify which has more or less; is greater or smaller.
2. Hang up the washing line. Children add washing to the line and compare the number of items, for example two socks, five T-shirts.
3. Give children a number of items and ask them to make it more or less, greater or smaller than the given amount.
4. Children throw a dice (1–6) and collect that number of items. The first child to collect ten items is the winner.
5. In pairs, each child spins a (1–10) spinner. The other child counts out that number of objects.
6. Place a selection of items on the table, for example socks, cars, soft toys, books, laces, play-people, gloves, buttons. Give the children a plastic container and ask them to find all the similar items, for example all the cars. Get them to count how many cars they have collected. Compare the sets by counting.

VOCABULARY

Number; zero, one, two, three... to twenty and beyond; how many?; count; count (up) to; count on (from, to); count back (from, to); count in ones; more; less; the same number as; greater; fewer; smaller; less; most; biggest; largest; greatest; fewest; smallest; least; compare; order.

Ask the children to count out sets during PE lessons and outside play, for example, three hoops, nine balls, hop ten times, do five jumps.

DIFFERENTIATION

Less able: work with numbers to 5, then 10.
More able: work with numbers to 10, then 20 and beyond. Encourage them to use a range of vocabulary to compare quantities.

PLENARY

Select a few children to describe and demonstrate their activities. Count back together from 10 to 0, then from 20. Next, ask individuals to continue a count down from 10 to 0. Repeat, starting and stopping at different numbers.

LESSON 3

Repeat as for Lesson 2, but choose different **Group activities** from those used previously.

RESOURCES

Flip chart; marker pen; washing line; pegs; cut-out clothes (from Lesson 2, page 77).
Group activities: individual sets of numeral cards (page 12); 3 × 2 number grids; flashcards; counters; small plastic containers; selection of counting items; sets of dominoes; (1–6) spinners.

PREPARATION

Make the required number of blank 3 × 2 number grids. Write random numerals (1–10) inside them. Write the words 'less than', 'more than', 'greater than' and 'fewer than' on the flashcards. Label the spinner with numerals from 1–6. Label the containers 1–6. Hang up the washing line. Write numerals from 1–10 on the clothes to make a number line.

LEARNING OUTCOMES

ORAL AND MENTAL STARTER
● **Say and use the number names in order in familiar contexts** such as number rhymes, songs, stories, counting games and activities (first to five, then ten, then twenty and beyond).
● Recite the number names in order, continuing the count forwards or backwards from a given number.

WHOLE-CLASS TEACHING ACTIVITY
● Order a given set of numbers: for example, the set of numbers 1 to 6 given in random order.
● **Compare two numbers** and say which is more or less, and say a number which lies between two given numbers.

ORAL AND MENTAL STARTER

COUNTING RHYMES: Use the rhymes suggested in Lesson 1, page 76. Then play 'Carry on counting' as in Unit 7, Lesson 2, page 104.

WHOLE-CLASS TEACHING ACTIVITY

ORDER IT: Write the numbers 1–6 on the flip chart. Ask: *What number comes next?* Select the cut-out clothes numbered 1–10 and hand these out randomly to individuals. *Look carefully at the numbers on the clothes. Let's hang the clothes on the washing line in order to make a number line. Which number comes first?* Ask the child holding number 1 to peg it on the line. *Which number comes next?* Continue to 10.

Tell the children you will be asking them questions and you want them to hold up their fingers to show you the answer. Demonstrate by asking for a number fewer than 6, and hold up, say, five fingers. Say: *5 is a number fewer than 6.* Repeat using different vocabulary for adding and subtracting, for example: *...more than 4, ...less than 8.*

GROUP ACTIVITIES

1. Set out the numeral cards, 3 × 2 grids with numbers 1–10, and the flashcards. Each child chooses a grid and places it in front of them. The starting number for each child is 10. Each child turns over a flashcard ('fewer than' etc) and reads it out. Then the child turns over a numeral card. If the answer is shown on their grid, the child covers that number with a counter (children only cover one number at a time). They take turns until one child has covered all the numbers on the grid.

2. In pairs, children choose six containers numbered 1–6. Each child spins the (1–6) spinner, then counts out and places the correct number of items in the appropriate container.

3. Children sort the dominoes into those that have a greater or fewer number of spots on one end than the other.

 In farm or animal play ask the children: *Are there a greater number of cows than sheep? Fewer play-people than animals?*

DIFFERENTIATION

Less able: use numbers in the range 0–10.
More able: use numbers in the range 0–20, then beyond.

PLENARY

Take feedback from the **Group activities**. Repeat the second part of the **Whole-class teaching activity,** with the children holding up the appropriate numbers of fingers in response to your questions.

RESOURCES	Flip chart; marker pen; individual sets of numeral cards (page 12); washing line; pegs; cut-out number clothes (from Lesson 4, page 78). **Group activities:** cubes; trays; coins; packs of playing cards.
LEARNING OUTCOMES	**ORAL AND MENTAL STARTER** ● Order a given set of numbers: for example, the set of numbers 1 to 6 given in random order. **WHOLE-CLASS TEACHING ACTIVITY** ● **Use language such as more or less, greater or smaller, to compare two numbers** and say which is more or less and say a number which lies between two given numbers. ● Order a given set of numbers: for example, the set of numbers 1 to 6 given in random order.
ORAL AND MENTAL STARTER	SHOW ME: Hand out the numeral cards. Say: *Show me the number that comes before 7. Show me the number that comes after 1. Show me the number that comes between 3 and 5.* Children hold up a card to show their answers.
WHOLE-CLASS TEACHING ACTIVITY	ORDER IT: Hand out the cut-out clothes (0–10) randomly. *When we start to count, what number do we usually start with?* Explain that counting can start from anywhere, so you are going to choose a starting number and the children are going to work out where the clothes should be placed on the washing line. Choose a number, say, 6. The child holding 6 comes out and pegs it on the line. *Who has 2? Does it come before or after 6? Is it a greater or smaller number than 6?* Repeat until all the numbers have been pegged up.
GROUP ACTIVITIES	**1.** Ask the children to make towers of cubes (limit them to less than 20). They count the number of cubes in each tower and arrange them in ascending order. **2.** Children sort a tray of coins into sets of 1ps, 2ps, 5ps, etc. They count and compare each set then put them in ascending order. **3.** Give children one suit of a shuffled pack of playing cards. They sort the cards into order: *What comes before, after, in between?* ● Children count and compare the number of coins in the role-play shop.
DIFFERENTIATION	Less able: use numbers in the range 0–10. More able: use numbers in the range 0–20 and beyond.
PLENARY	Write the numbers 0–20 on the flip chart. Ask: *What comes before 10? Give me a number bigger than 2. Tell me a number more than 15.*

UNIT 2

ORGANISATION (5 LESSONS)

LEARNING OUTCOMES	ORAL AND MENTAL STARTER	WHOLE-CLASS TEACHING ACTIVITY	PLENARY
LESSON 1 ● Count reliably in other contexts, such as clapping sounds or hopping movements.	FINGER COUNT: Children count from 0–20.	COUNT THE BEAT: Children count objects and sounds.	Children recite counting rhymes.
LESSON 2 ● **Begin to use the vocabulary involved in adding and subtracting.** ● **Find one more or one less than a number from 1 to 10.**	COUNT ON, COUNT BACK: Children count forwards then backwards.	ONE MAN WENT TO MOW: Children consider what is one more and one less than a given number.	Children respond to number questions.
LESSON 3 ● **Begin to use the language involved in adding and subtracting.** ● **Find one more or one less than a number from 1 to 10.**	COUNT AND CHANGE: Children count on to a given number then count back, first to 10, then to 20.	ONE MORE, ONE LESS: One more, one less activities.	Feedback from activities.
LESSON 4 ● **Begin to use the vocabulary involved in adding and subtracting.** ● **Begin to relate addition to combining two groups of objects,** counting all the objects.	COUNT AND CHANGE: Children count on to a given number then count back, first to 10, then to 20	TWO INTO ONE: Children combine two sets.	FINGER ADD: Children combine two numbers.
LESSON 5 ● **Begin to use the vocabulary involved in adding and subtracting.** ● **Begin to relate subtraction to 'taking' away'** and counting how many are left.	FINGER ADD AND SUBTRACT: Children use their fingers to show one more and one less.	TAKE IT AWAY: Children take away various amounts from a pile of cubes.	FINGER ADD AND SUBTRACT: Up to 10.

ORAL AND MENTAL SKILLS   Recite the number names in order, continuing the count forwards or backwards from a given number. **Find one more or one less than a number from 1 to 10.**

Lessons 3 and 4 are provided in full, with Lessons 1, 2 and 5 given in outline.

RESOURCES	The song 'Alice the camel has 10 humps'; selection of counting objects; bucket; musical instruments such as a triangle, tambourine, drum; counting rhymes. **Group activities:** cubes; beads; plastic plant pots; dice (1–6); matchboxes; small counting items.
LEARNING OUTCOMES	**ORAL AND MENTAL STARTER** ● Recite the number names in order, continuing the count forwards or backwards from a given number. **WHOLE-CLASS TEACHING ACTIVITY** ● Count reliably in other contexts, such as clapping sounds or hopping movements.
ORAL AND MENTAL STARTER	FINGER COUNT: Children count aloud, holding up their fingers from 0 to 10, then to 20.
WHOLE-CLASS TEACHING ACTIVITY	COUNT THE BEAT: Arrange the children in a circle and sing 'Alice the camel has 10 humps'. Say: *Look carefully and count the number of objects I drop into the bucket. How many did you count?* Start with numbers to 5, then to 10. *Now close your eyes and count when you hear something drop into the bucket. How many did you hear?* Repeat both activities several times. Show the children the musical instruments. Say: *Count the number of beats played on the drum.* Invite individual children to play the instruments (one at a time). Ask the class and individuals to give the number of beats counted.

GROUP ACTIVITIES	1. In pairs, children repeat the **Whole-class teaching activity**, this time counting cubes into plastic plant pots. Repeat the activity using beads. 2. Children take turns to throw a dice and carry out that number of hops, skips, strides, claps, etc, as directed by an adult helper. 3. Children place a set of similar objects into a matchbox, then count how many items are inside. Repeat using a different set of objects. ● During an outdoor or indoor play activity, an adult gives children a number of jumps, hops, claps, skips etc. to count and carry out.
DIFFERENTIATION	Less able: consolidate counting using numbers to 10. More able: extend to 20 and beyond.
PLENARY	Recite other counting rhymes such as 'One, two, three, four, five' and 'One, two, buckle my shoe'.

LESSON 2

RESOURCES	The songs 'One man went to mow' and 'Alice the camel has 10 humps'; soft toy dog; set of numeral cards (page 12). **Group activities:** beads; egg boxes; dice (1–6); individual sets of numeral cards (page 12).
LEARNING OUTCOMES	**ORAL AND MENTAL STARTER** ● Recite the number names in order, continuing the count forwards or backwards from a given number. **WHOLE-CLASS TEACHING ACTIVITY** ● **Begin to use the vocabulary involved in adding and subtracting.** ● **Find one more or one less than a number from 1 to 10.**
ORAL AND MENTAL STARTER	COUNT ON/COUNT BACK: Starting at a given number, ask the children to count on several numbers. *Start at 10, count on 2. 10 – 11, 12. 10 count on 2 is 12.* Then try: *Start at 9, count back 4: 9, 8, 7, 6, 5. 9 count back 4 is 5.*
WHOLE-CLASS TEACHING ACTIVITY	ONE MAN WENT TO MOW: Sing this song. Ask children to come out for each verse, so that the class can see that one more is being added each time. Give out the set of numeral cards in random order. *Who has number 1? Come out and start our number line. What is one more than 1?* When you say a number, ask individuals to give a number that is one more. The child with that card comes out and continues the number line. Repeat the activity with one less.
GROUP ACTIVITIES	1. Place a bead in a section of the egg box. The children count how many beads. Add another bead in the next section: *How many now?* Continue to six, then find one less. 2. Throw the dice and ask the children to count the number of spots. *What would one more spot be?* Repeat, asking: *What is one less?* 3. Give each child a set of numeral cards (0–10). Choose a number from a set of numeral cards and ask the children to find the card that is one more than your card. Repeat using one less. ● Ask children to find one more item when working in the role-play area.
DIFFERENTIATION	Less able: add one more to 5, then find one less from 5. More able: add one more using numbers to 10. Repeat with one less.
PLENARY	Sing 'Alice the camel'. Children count one less on their fingers each time. *What comes before 6? What comes after 9? What is one more then 2? What is one less than 7?*

LESSON 3

RESOURCES
Set of numeral cards (1–10) (page 12); flip chart; marker pen; pointer; flashcards; large foam dice (1–6). **Group activities:** cubes; star cards (see below).

PREPARATION
Select a suitable counting rhyme. Make flashcards saying '1 more' and '1 less'. Make a selection of 'star cards' by sticking 1–10 stars onto rectangular cards.

LEARNING OUTCOMES
ORAL AND MENTAL STARTER
● Recite the number names in order, continuing the count forwards or backwards from a given number.
● **Find one more or one less than a number from 1 to 10.**

WHOLE-CLASS TEACHING ACTIVITY
● **Begin to use the vocabulary involved in adding and subtracting.**
● **Find one more or one less than a number from 1 to 10.**

LESSON 4

VOCABULARY

Counting; number, one, two, three... to twenty; how many?; count; count (up) to; count on (from, to); count back (from, to); one more; one less; order; before; after; next; add; more; one more; one less; count; sort.

ORAL AND MENTAL STARTER

COUNT AND CHANGE: Hold up a numeral card from 1 to 10. Start the count with the class. Continue counting until the displayed number is reached. Then count back to 1. Repeat the activity with one child at a time counting in ones until the number is reached. Another child counts back to 1. Repeat several times, allowing individuals to choose numeral cards.

WHOLE-CLASS TEACHING ACTIVITY

ONE MORE, ONE LESS: Recite a counting rhyme, for example 'Monsters' (see 'Counting rhymes' in *First Verses*, compiled by John Foster, Oxford University Press). Ask five children to act out the rhyme. Repeat the rhyme, counting the number of monsters left after each verse. Next, write a number line to 10 on the flip chart. Use a pointer and point to 4. *One more than 4 is 5. 5 is the number after 4. One less than 4 is 3. 3 is the number before 4.* Explain that you will be saying some numbers and you want the children to say the number which is one more. Repeat with one less, then a combination of one more and one less. Show the children the flashcards. Throw the foam dice and say the number. Hold up a flashcard and ask individuals to say the number that is one more or one less as appropriate.

GROUP ACTIVITIES

1. Give pairs a '1 more' flashcard and place it on the table. The children take turns to throw a dice and collect an amount of cubes that is one more than the number on the dice.
2. In pairs, children take a star card. They count the number of stars, then find the card that has one more or one less star than their card.
3. Children build pairs of towers that have one more or one less than each other.
 Using the farm play items, ask children to count the number of sheep in the field and add one more, count the number of cows and make it one less, and so on.

DIFFERENTIATION

Less able: provide number tracks so that the children can move counters along the track.
More able: work with numbers to 10.

PLENARY

Ask the children to discuss their activities and demonstrate their answers. Repeat the counting rhyme 'Monsters' from the **Whole-class teaching activity**.

RESOURCES

Set of numeral cards (page 12); collection of small counting objects; large foam dice.
Group activities: dominoes; dice; counters; small pots such as yoghurt pots; ladybird templates (page 15); pencils; (1–6) spinners; tape recorder; some taped counting rhymes.

PREPARATION

Make the required photocopies.

LEARNING OUTCOMES

ORAL AND MENTAL STARTER

● Recite the number names in order, continuing the count forwards or backwards from a given number.
● **Find one more or one less than a number from 1 to 10**.

WHOLE-CLASS TEACHING ACTIVITY

● **Begin to use the vocabulary involved in adding and subtracting.**
● **Begin to relate addition to combining two groups of objects,** counting all the objects.

ORAL AND MENTAL STARTER

COUNT AND CHANGE: Repeat as in Lesson 3 above.

VOCABULARY

Start from; add; more; count; make; total; altogether; join; one more; one less; how many?; one less.

WHOLE-CLASS TEACHING ACTIVITY

TWO INTO ONE: Explain that the lesson is about counting and joining two sets. Tell the children to get two objects and place them on the table. Repeat with three objects. Check that each child has the correct number. Tell the children to join the sets. *How many altogether?* Check that children are joining the sets and counting all the objects. Say: *2 add 3 more makes 5 altogether.* Repeat with different numbers to 5 then to 10. Now tell the children that they are going to play a game. Explain that it involves throwing two dice to choose the numbers in each set. Demonstrate by rolling the dice, counting out the objects for each set and joining the sets. Count the number of objects altogether by touching and counting each one. Repeat with the children rolling the dice, counting the objects and joining the sets. Ask the class and individuals to count the number of objects altogether.

GROUP ACTIVITIES

1. Give out sets of dominoes. Children count both sets of spots on each domino individually, then count the number of spots altogether.
2. In pairs, one child throws a dice. The other child puts that number of counters into a pot. Children swap tasks and repeat. Both children count out the total number of counters.
3. Give each child a ladybird template. They take turns to spin a 1–6 spinner and draw that number of spots on a wing of the ladybird. Repeat for the second wing. Count how many spots altogether.

 Set up a listening table for the children with a tape recorder and a set of headphones. Tape some counting songs and rhymes where one is added or subtracted, for example 'Ten green bottles', 'One elephant went out to play'. Encourage the children to listen, recite and sing along with the songs and rhymes.

DIFFERENTIATION

Less able: give adult support to check counting, combining of sets and touch counting the total number. Limit the total of the two combined sets to 6.
More able: extend to 10 and beyond. Combine two and three sets. Involve children in checking the total amount by recounting.

PLENARY

Take feedback from the **Group activities**. Then play 'Finger Add'. Children combine two numbers, each less than 5, by holding up their hands.

RESOURCES	The song 'One elephant went out to play'; cubes; large foam dice. Group activities: counters; dice; ladybird templates (page 15).
LEARNING OUTCOMES	**ORAL AND MENTAL STARTER** ● **Find one more or one less than a number from 1 to 10.** **WHOLE-CLASS TEACHING ACTIVITY** ● **Begin to use the vocabulary involved in adding and subtracting.** ● **Begin to relate subtraction to 'taking' away** and counting how many are left.
ORAL AND MENTAL STARTER	FINGER ADD AND SUBTRACT: Children use fingers to 'add on' 1 and 'take away' 1 using numbers to 5 then 10.
WHOLE-CLASS TEACHING ACTIVITY	TAKE IT AWAY: Sing 'One elephant went out to play'. Children role-play actions. Ask each child to count out six cubes. Roll the dice and say the number that is thrown. Children take away that number of cubes from their pile. *How many are left?* Say, for example: *6 take away 3 leaves 3. 6 subtract 3 is 3.* Repeat several times. Ask individuals to say how many cubes are left.
GROUP ACTIVITIES	**1.** Each child has ten counters. In turn, they roll the dice and take that number away from their set of ten. *How many are left?* **2.** Use the ladybird templates as in Lesson 4, Group activity 3, above. **3.** Children work in pairs – both have ten counters to begin. One child throws the dice. The other takes that number of counters away. Repeat with the children swapping tasks until all counters have been taken away. ● Children work with large bricks and make towers by adding one more or subtracting one less.
DIFFERENTIATION	Less able: use counters and combine two sets to make 5, then 10. More able: use cubes to combine three sets to make 10 and beyond.
PLENARY	Sing 'One elephant went out to play' and 'Five little speckled frogs'. Play 'Finger add and subtract' with numbers limited to a total of 10 for ease of finger play.

LESSON 5

UNIT 3

ORGANISATION (5 LESSONS)

	LEARNING OUTCOMES	ORAL AND MENTAL STARTER	WHOLE-CLASS TEACHING ACTIVITY	PLENARY
LESSON 1	● Put sets of objects in order of size.	FINGER COUNT: Children hold up their fingers to show a given number.	THREE BEARS: Ordering items by comparing, using related language.	Feedback from activities.
LESSON 2	● **Use language such as circle or bigger to describe the shape and size of solids and flat shapes.** ● Put sets of objects in order of size.	COUNT ON/COUNT BACK: Children count in ones up to and back from 20.	WHAT'S THIS SHAPE?: Children match 2-D and 3-D shapes according to shape and size.	Feedback from activities.
LESSON 3	● **Use everyday words to describe position:** for example, follow and give instructions about positions.	COUNT AND SHOW: Children hold up a card in response to various questions.	POSITION IT: Children use positional language to place items.	Feedback from activities. Positional game.
LESSON 4	● **Talk about, recognise and recreate patterns:** for example, simple repeating or symmetrical patterns from different cultures.	COUNT AND CLAP: Children count and clap out numbers.	PATTERN-MAKING: Children create and recognise patterns.	Pattern detectives. Repeat 'Patterns' rhyme.
LESSON 5	● Sort and match objects, pictures or children themselves, justifying the decisions made.	COUNT AND CLAP: Children count and clap around the class.	SORT YOURSELVES: Sorting and matching. Introduce Venn diagrams.	Feedback from activities. Discuss sorting in day-to-day life.

ORAL AND MENTAL SKILLS **Count reliably up to 10 everyday objects** (first to 5, then 10). **Say and use the number names in order in familiar contexts.** Recite the number names in order, continuing the count forwards or backwards from a given number. Count reliably in other contexts, such as clapping sounds or hopping movements.

Lesson 3 is provided in full. Lessons 1, 2, 4 and 5 of this unit follow on from what has already been taught and are given in outline.

LESSON 1

RESOURCES	Four teddy bears of different sizes. **Group activities:** set of Russian dolls; three different-sized bowls, spoons, cups and saucers; Duplo; building blocks; boxes.
LEARNING OUTCOMES	**ORAL AND MENTAL STARTER** ● **Count reliably up to 10 everyday objects** (first to 5, then 10). ● **Say and use the number names in order in familiar contexts.** **WHOLE-CLASS TEACHING ACTIVITY** ● Put sets of objects in order of size.
ORAL AND MENTAL STARTER	FINGER COUNT: Children use their fingers to show a number that comes before 4, 2, 8, and so on.
WHOLE-CLASS TEACHING ACTIVITY	THREE BEARS: Introduce the three teddy bears, one at a time, in any order. Ask: *Is this bear big or small?* Introduce the second bear and let children compare them. Repeat with the third bear. Ask individuals to order the bears according to size from biggest to smallest, then vice versa. Introduce another bear: *Where does this bear fit in the order?* Muddle up the bears and invite children to arrange them in order.
GROUP ACTIVITIES	**1.** Children order a set of Russian dolls from smallest to biggest, then vice versa. **2.** Children order and match three sets of different-sized bowls, spoons, cups and saucers to the bears. **3.** Children build houses out of Duplo, building blocks or boxes for the three bears. ● Children make different-sized furniture for the three bears' house, for example, chairs, tables, beds.
DIFFERENTIATION	Less able: order three, then four objects by size. Extend to five, if appropriate. More able: work quickly through three, four, five, up to ten objects.
PLENARY	Take feedback from the **Group activities**.

RESOURCES	A large selection of different-sized 2-D and 3-D shapes; a feely bag or box. **Group activities:** trays; shape templates; biscuit recipe; baking ingredients; shape cutters; utensils; cooker; printing materials.
LEARNING OUTCOMES	**ORAL AND MENTAL STARTER** ● Recite the number names in order, continuing the count forwards or backwards from a given number. **WHOLE-CLASS TEACHING ACTIVITY** ● **Use language such as circle or bigger to describe the shape and size of solids and flat shapes.** ● Put sets of objects in order of size.
ORAL AND MENTAL STARTER	COUNT ON/COUNT BACK: Count in ones from 0 to 10, then to 20. Then count back from 10 to 0, then from 20 to 0.
WHOLE-CLASS TEACHING ACTIVITY	WHAT'S THIS SHAPE?: Give each child one of the 2-D or 3-D shapes. Place the rest in a feely bag or box. Pull out a shape and ask the children to look at their shape and see whether it is the same. *Does it belong to the 2-D or 3-D family? Is it a flat or solid shape?* If their shape is the same they hold it in the air. Observe whether children are matching the shapes correctly. Encourage individuals to name their shape. *Is it the same size? Why is it different?* Encourage the children to describe the size. Repeat with other shapes. Select a few of the same shape and invite individuals to put them in order of size.
GROUP ACTIVITIES	**1.** Children sort a collection of different-sized shapes into trays, then explain how they have sorted the objects. **2.** With adult supervision, children make a selection of shape biscuits. **3.** Children draw round shape templates of different sizes. ● Children can print using a range of different 2-D and 3-D shapes which are also different sizes.
DIFFERENTIATION	Less able: use a limited number of shapes and sizes. More able: extend the range and size of shapes.
PLENARY	Feedback from the **Group activities**.

RESOURCES
Sets of mixed cards showing spots (page 18), numerals (page 12) and objects; flip chart; marker pen; pictures of toys; Blu-Tack. **Group activities:** items such as play-people, farm and zoo animals; toy cars; egg boxes; pencils; paper.

PREPARATION
Collect catalogues or magazines, and cut out items that might be found in a toy cupboard, for example a toy car, a teddy bear, a jigsaw, a book, a teddy, a kite, a ball. Mount these on to card. On the flip chart, draw an outline to represent the inside of a toy cupboard with three or four shelves.

LEARNING OUTCOMES
ORAL AND MENTAL STARTER
● **Count reliably up to 10 everyday objects** (first to 5, then 10).

WHOLE-CLASS TEACHING ACTIVITY
● **Use everyday words to describe position:** for example, follow and give instructions about position.

VOCABULARY

Position; over; under; above; below; top; bottom; side; next to; between; middle; next to.

ORAL AND MENTAL STARTER
COUNT AND SHOW: Give each pair a set of mixed cards representing the numbers 1–10. Explain that when you say a number they must hold up a card showing that amount of spots, items or number.

WHOLE-CLASS TEACHING ACTIVITY
POSITION IT: Explain that today's lesson is about position. Point out the toy cupboard and show the children the pictures of toys. Invite the children to place the 'toys' on the shelves. Ask individuals to describe the position of the toys. *Is the teddy next to the car? Where is the ball? What is above the...? What is on the top shelf? What is below the...?*

GROUP ACTIVITIES

1. Invite children to arrange three to five items, eg play-people, farm animals or toy cars. Ask: *How can these be arranged differently?*

2. Children choose six objects and place them in an egg box. Invite them to describe the position of their objects in the egg box to an adult helper. Ask them to rearrange their items.

3. Children arrange farm or zoo animals. Invent scenarios that require the children to change their arrangements and discuss the new positions, for example: *Where have the elephants moved to? What is in the next pen?* Suggest the children draw a plan of their wildlife park or farm.

 Use the role-play area and ask the children to do a house 'makeover' by relocating items. Encourage them to describe the position of the objects.

DIFFERENTIATION

Less able: limit the number of items and language used.
More able: extend the use of language and number of items involved.

PLENARY

Feedback from the **Group activities**. Ask five children to stand in front of the class: *Who is next to...?* Give instructions to the group to line up as if they were going out to play. Give instructions to move children into new positions, eg *Samina stand in front of Harry. Henry stand between Jack and Daisy.* Repeat with the whole class at the end of the lesson.

RESOURCES	The rhyme 'Patterns' (from *Seven Dizzy Dragons and Other Maths Rhymes* by Sue Atkinson et al, Cambridge University Press); cubes; examples of patterns from other cultures, eg Rangoli patterns, mosque mosaics. **Group activities:** threading lace; beads in different colours; adult support; camera; assorted 2-D shapes; paint and objects for printing.
LEARNING OUTCOMES	**ORAL AND MENTAL STARTER** ● Count reliably in other contexts, such as clapping sounds or hopping movements. **WHOLE-CLASS TEACHING ACTIVITY** ● **Talk about, recognise and recreate simple patterns:** for example, simple repeating patterns or symmetrical patterns from different cultures.
ORAL AND MENTAL STARTER	COUNT AND CLAP: Count up to 5, 10, then 20 and beyond. Use a count then clap sequence.
WHOLE-CLASS TEACHING ACTIVITY	PATTERN MAKING: Read the rhyme 'Patterns'. Arrange the children in a circle and make a pattern with the first child sitting, the next child standing, etc. *What comes next in our pattern?* Ask the children to think of another pattern that could be made. Using two colours of cube, give alternate colours to six children. Go round and ask them to say the colour of their cube. *Which colour comes next?* Continue the pattern, handing out cubes to the rest of the class. Explain that they have been making patterns. Ask children to look for patterns in the classroom and show them examples of patterns from different cultures, for example Rangoli patterns.
GROUP ACTIVITIES	**1.** Children thread beads using two, then three colours. **2.** Take children for a walk around the school and look for patterns in the environment. Use a camera to record any patterns that are identified. These can be used for a pattern display. **3.** Assemble some different coloured 2-D shapes (eg circles, squares, triangles, rectangles). Make a repeating pattern using two different shapes but only one colour, eg red circle, red triangle, red circle, etc. Ask the children to identify the pattern. Invite them to copy your patterns then to continue a given pattern. ● Provide paint and different objects for the children to design their own patterns and print onto paper or fabric.
DIFFERENTIATION	Less able: copy a pattern using two properties, eg colour, shape, object. More able: children continue patterns or make their own. Extend to three or more properties.
PLENARY	Feedback from children who have looked for patterns in the environment. Look for more patterns in the classroom. Repeat the rhyme 'Patterns'.

RESOURCES	Flip chart; marker pen; sorting rings; selection of 2-D and 3-D shapes. **Group activities:** selection of different objects; trays; sorting rings; paper; pencils; a set of pictures mounted on card and laminated showing different methods of transport; items for the role-play café.
LEARNING OUTCOMES	**ORAL AND MENTAL STARTER** ● Recite the number names in order, continuing the count forwards or backwards from a given number. ● Count reliably in other contexts, such as clapping sounds or hopping movements **WHOLE-CLASS TEACHING ACTIVITY** ● Sort and match objects, pictures or children themselves, justifying the decisions made.
ORAL AND MENTAL STARTER	COUNT AND CLAP: Repeat as in Lesson 4, page 86. Carry on the count around the class.
WHOLE-CLASS TEACHING ACTIVITY	SORT YOURSELVES: Tell the children that they are going to play a sorting game and must all stand up. Explain that you are going to ask them to sort themselves into special groups. They must listen carefully as you tell them how to sort themselves. *I want all the boys over there and all the girls over here.* Repeat by sorting the children in different ways, such as those children who have sandwiches, school lunches, go home for lunch. Other sorting methods could include ways of travelling to school, ages, pets, favourite colours. Encourage the children to think of other ways. Explain sorting using a Venn diagram. Demonstrate with sorting rings and a selection of 2-D and 3-D shapes. Limit to one attribute.
GROUP ACTIVITIES	**1.** Children sort a selection of objects into trays. They explain the different attributes they used to sort their objects, eg made of wood, animals, have four legs, are shiny, and so on. **2.** Children sort shapes using sorting rings, then draw the shapes. **3.** Give children the transport pictures and ask them to sort them in different ways, such as type of transport, Does it have wheels? Does it fly in the air? Does it move on water? ● Set up the role-play area as a café. Children sort the cutlery, cups, saucers, plates and place mats and set the tables for the 'customers'.
DIFFERENTIATION	Less able: sort into colours, shapes, or the same type of item. Concentrate on matching with one attribute – red bead, circle, pencil. More able: children choose their own sorting criteria and explain reasons. Find and describe different ways of sorting a group of objects.
PLENARY	Feedback from **Group activities**. Relate sorting to everyday life – sorting toys, clothes for washing, shopping, matching socks, buttons and buttonholes, etc.

UNIT 4

ORGANISATION (5 LESSONS)

	LEARNING OUTCOMES	ORAL AND MENTAL STARTER	WHOLE-CLASS TEACHING ACTIVITY	PLENARY
LESSON 1	● **Use language such as longer or shorter to compare two quantities,** then more than two, by making direct comparisons of lengths.	SHOW ME: Children show a number card in response to various questions.	TWO LONG: Children compare the length of two items.	Feedback from activities. Children compare lines of different lengths.
LESSON 2	● **Use language such as heavier or lighter to compare two quantities,** then more than two, by making direct comparisons of masses.	WASHING LINE: Children peg numeral cards in sequence.	HEAVIER OR LIGHTER: Children compare the weight of various items.	Children look for 'heavy' and 'light' objects in the environment.
LESSON 3	● **Use language such as more or less to compare two quantities,** then more than two, by filling and emptying containers.	SHOW ME: Children show a number card which is one more, one less, bigger than or smaller than a given number.	CAPACITY: Children compare the capacity of various containers.	Children order various objects according to size.
LESSON 4	● Estimate a number in the range that can be counted reliably, then check by counting.	NONE: Children count from 0 to 5, then from 20.	GUESS AND COUNT: Children estimate various amounts.	Children count down from 5 to 0, then 20.
LESSON 5	● Begin to understand and use the vocabulary of time. Sequence familiar events. ● Begin to know the days of the week in order.	WHAT TIME?: Children consider what happens at various times of the day.	THE VERY HUNGRY CATERPILLAR: Children consider what happens on various days.	Children compile a food diary for a week.

ORAL AND MENTAL SKILLS Say and use the number names in order in familiar contexts. **Recognise numerals 1 to 9,** then 0 to 10. **Find one more or one less than a number from 1 to 10.** Begin to recognise 'none' and 'zero' in stories, rhymes and when counting. **Begin to use the vocabulary involved in adding and subtracting.** Begin to use the vocabulary of time.

Lesson 3 is provided in full. Lessons 1, 2, 4 and 5 are provided in outline.

LESSON 1

RESOURCES	Flip chart; marker pens; individual sets of numeral cards (page 12); a selection of 'pairs' where one object is longer than the other, for example knitting needles, socks, ribbons, pencils, card, toothbrushes, laces, strips of paper, towers of cubes, paintbrushes, string, wool; sorting trays labelled 'long' and 'short'. **Group activities:** scissors; Play-Doh; threading lace; beads.
LEARNING OUTCOMES	**ORAL AND MENTAL STARTER** ● **Recognise numerals 1 to 9,** then 0 and 10. ● **Say and use the number names in order in familiar contexts.** **WHOLE-CLASS TEACHING ACTIVITY** ● **Use language such as longer or shorter to compare two quantities,** then more than two, by making direct comparisons of lengths.
ORAL AND MENTAL STARTER	SHOW ME: Give each child a set of numeral cards. Say a number and ask the children to show the relevant numeral card. Say: *Show the card that is one more, one less, comes between, is before, comes after.*
WHOLE-CLASS TEACHING ACTIVITY	TWO LONG: Show the children the collection of objects. Pick out two related items and ask: *Which is longer?* Discuss how the objects can be compared to find out. Ask individuals to compare other matching objects and say which is shorter. Show children the labelled sorting trays and ask them to help you sort the objects into the relevant trays.
GROUP ACTIVITIES	**1.** Children match and sort objects into long and short piles. **2.** Children cut string, ribbon, paper, wool, card into short and long lengths. **3.** Children make snakes, necklaces, towers of cubes that are long and short. ● In art and design, encourage children to compare the lengths of materials, to draw and paint long and short lines or objects, or to design patterns using different lengths.
DIFFERENTIATION	Less able: compare two objects. More able: compare three or four objects using the terms 'shorter' and 'longer'.
PLENARY	Ask the children to describe some of their activities. Draw lines on the flip chart and invite the children to discuss whether they are long or short. Invite individuals to draw two different lines and compare which is long and short.

LESSON 2

RESOURCES	A set of numeral cards (page 12); washing line; pegs; shopping basket; selection of shopping items, eg tin of beans, bag of potatoes, toothbrush, cotton wool, wrapping paper; different-sized boxes; sticky tape; *The Shopping Basket* by John Burningham (Red Fox). **Group activities:** set of everyday classroom items; paper; pencils; crayons; items for a role-play post office.
LEARNING OUTCOMES	**ORAL AND MENTAL STARTER** ● **Say and use the number names in order in familiar contexts.** **WHOLE-CLASS TEACHING ACTIVITY** ● **Use language such as heavier or lighter to compare two quantities,** then more than two, by making direct comparisons of masses.
ORAL AND MENTAL STARTER	WASHING LINE: Hand out the set of numeral cards and ask the children to peg up their number card in position on the line. Tell the children to close their eyes. Remove two or three cards, then ask: *Which numbers are missing? How do you know?* Invite children to peg the numbers on the line in the correct sequence.
WHOLE-CLASS TEACHING ACTIVITY	HEAVIER OR LIGHTER: Read *The Shopping Basket* to the class. Show the children your basket full of items. Take one out and ask: *Is it heavy or light?* Invite children to find something that is lighter or heavier than the first item. Repeat with the rest of the shopping. *How do we know if an object is heavy or light?*
GROUP ACTIVITIES	**1.** Children sort the shopping objects into heavy and light items. **2.** Place the everyday classroom items on the table. Ask them to draw the outline of two shopping bags, then draw in three heavy items and three light items. **3.** Give each child a sheet of paper. Each child draws three heavy and three light items. ● Make the role-play area into a post office and provide a range of letters, parcels and balances.
DIFFERENTIATION	Less able: use a range of sorting activities to find heavy and light objects. Reinforce vocabulary. More able: make comparisons using three or four items.
PLENARY	Ask the children to look around the environment and find objects that are heavier or lighter than a given item. Get them to compare by handling.

RESOURCES

Individual sets of numeral cards (page 12); a box of sweets; plastic container; water; set of Russian dolls. **Group activities:** collection of different-shaped and sized boxes, containers and plastic bottles; measuring jugs; yoghurt pots; items for filling such as dried peas and beans, beads, pasta, cubes, conkers, shells, dry and wet sand.

PREPARATION

Make a collection of containers and items for filling. Fill the water tray, and wet a section of sand.

LEARNING OUTCOMES

ORAL AND MENTAL STARTER
● **Say and use the number names in order in familiar contexts.**
● **Recognise numerals 1 to 9,** then 0 to 10.
● **Find one more or one less than a number from 1 to 10.**
● **Begin to use the vocabulary involved in adding and subtracting.**

WHOLE-CLASS TEACHING ACTIVITY
● **Use language such as more or less to compare two quantities,** then more than two, by filling and emptying containers.

ORAL AND MENTAL STARTER

SHOW ME: Play as in Lesson 1, page 89, but this time say to the children: *Show a numeral card which is one more, one less, bigger than, smaller than that number.*

WHOLE-CLASS TEACHING ACTIVITY

CAPACITY: Show the children the box of sweets and invite them to guess whether it is full or empty. *How can we find out?* Empty out the contents. *Is it full or empty?* Half fill the box. *Is it full or empty?* Tell the children it is half full. Repeat the activity using water to fill a plastic container. Invite individual children to fill empty containers so that they are full, empty and half full. Explain that groups are going to investigate the capacity of containers using different items.

GROUP ACTIVITIES

1. Invite children to choose a box and fill it with one item. Repeat using different objects. Compare the amounts used to fill the box.
2. Set up the water tray. Ask the children to compare which containers hold more by filling jugs and bottles using different containers.
3. Set up the sand tray. Ask children to compare which containers hold more by filling buckets or plastic containers using other containers.

 Collect a range of large cardboard boxes and let the children use them in outdoor and indoor play. *How many children can fit inside standing up or sitting down? Can more boys than girls fit inside?*

DIFFERENTIATION

Less able: emphasise the language 'full', 'empty', 'more than' and 'less than'.
More able: use three or four containers and encourage the children to order them according to which holds the most, least, or the same amount.

PLENARY

Show the children the Russian dolls. Ask: *How many dolls are there?* Reveal the dolls inside. Invite children to order them according to size. *Which doll holds the most? Which holds the least?* Demonstrate using small items.

LESSON 4

RESOURCES	Flip chart; marker pen; selection of counting items; plastic bag. **Group activities:** paper bags; labels; sets of numeral cards (page 12); copies of photocopiable page 92 (Fill it); selection of different small containers; pencils.
LEARNING OUTCOMES	**ORAL AND MENTAL STARTER** ● Begin to recognise 'none' and 'zero' in stories, rhymes and when counting. **WHOLE-CLASS TEACHING ACTIVITY** ● Estimate a number in the range that can be counted reliably, then check by counting.
ORAL AND MENTAL STARTER	NONE: Sing 'There were ten in the bed' as a class. Count from 0 to 5, extend to 10, then 20.
WHOLE-CLASS TEACHING ACTIVITY	GUESS AND COUNT: Place a number of items in the plastic bag. Ask the children to guess how many there are. Draw two columns on the flip chart saying 'Our guess' and 'Our count'. Write down the guesses. Ask children to count out the correct number. Write this down. *Is it the same number, more or less than the guess?* Invite individuals to place items into the bag and then ask other children to guess the amount. Record the guesses, then count the actual amount.
GROUP ACTIVITIES	**1.** Label bags with numbers 0 to 10. Place objects inside using correct and incorrect amounts. In pairs, children check whether bags contain the correct number of items. **2.** Children sort numeral cards into descending order, then count out a number of items to match each card. **3.** Give each child a copy of photocopiable page 92 (Fill it). Children work in pairs. One child places a number of items into a small container, their partner guesses the amount, then checks to see if their guess was correct. They draw the estimate and actual number of items in the containers on the photocopiable sheet. ● Children use a programmable toy to guess the number of steps needed to reach an object. They then check.
DIFFERENTIATION	Less able: use numbers 0 to 5, then to 10. More able: use numbers 0 to 10, then to 20 and beyond.
PLENARY	Count down from 5 to 0, then down from 10, then 20. Arrange a number line in descending order from 10 to 0.

LESSON 5

RESOURCES	Pictures cut from catalogues and magazines showing objects or events which might happen or be used at different times of the day; flashcards giving days of the week plus ones saying 'yesterday', 'today', 'tomorrow', 'morning', 'afternoon', 'night'; flip chart; marker pen; washing line; pegs; calendar; diary. **Group activities:** card; felt-tipped pens; pointer; zigzag books; *The Very Hungry Caterpillar*, Eric Carle (Puffin).
LEARNING OUTCOMES	**ORAL AND MENTAL STARTER** ● Begin to understand and use the vocabulary of time. **WHOLE-CLASS TEACHING ACTIVITY** ● Begin to understand and use the vocabulary of time. ● Sequence familiar events. ● Begin to know the days of the week in order.
ORAL AND MENTAL STARTER	WHAT TIME?: Hold up the pictures one at a time and ask children to look at what it shows, eg people eating breakfast. *When does this happen?* Place the pictures into sets with the appropriate labels. *All these show things that happen at night.* Hold up the flashcards for 'today', 'tomorrow' and 'yesterday'. *What did we do yesterday? What is happening tomorrow?* Tell the children what they are going to do today.
WHOLE-CLASS TEACHING ACTIVITY	THE VERY HUNGRY CATERPILLAR: On the flip chart, record what the caterpillar ate on each day. Write: Monday – two apples, and so on. Recite the days of the week. Give out the days of the week flashcards to individual children. *What is the first day of the week? Who has the word 'Sunday'?* Peg 'Sunday' on the washing line. Invite those children with the other days to peg them on the washing line. Encourage children to match their flashcards to the order on the flip chart. Show the children a calendar and a diary and point out the days of the week. *How many days are there in a week?*
GROUP ACTIVITIES	**1.** Children make a circular chart with a movable pointer to indicate the days of the week. They illustrate each day with familiar activities. **2.** Children make picture strips to show their daily activities either at home or school. **3.** Make individual zigzag books with seven sections and ask each child to draw what the hungry caterpillar might like to eat each day of the week. ● Provide diaries and calendars in the role-play and writing areas.
DIFFERENTIATION	Less able: make sure they understand the terms 'today', 'tomorrow' and 'yesterday'. Relate the days of the week to their own experiences. More able: encourage them to learn the days of the week and the sequence.
PLENARY	Make a diary on the flip chart of things the children like to eat on different days.

Fill it

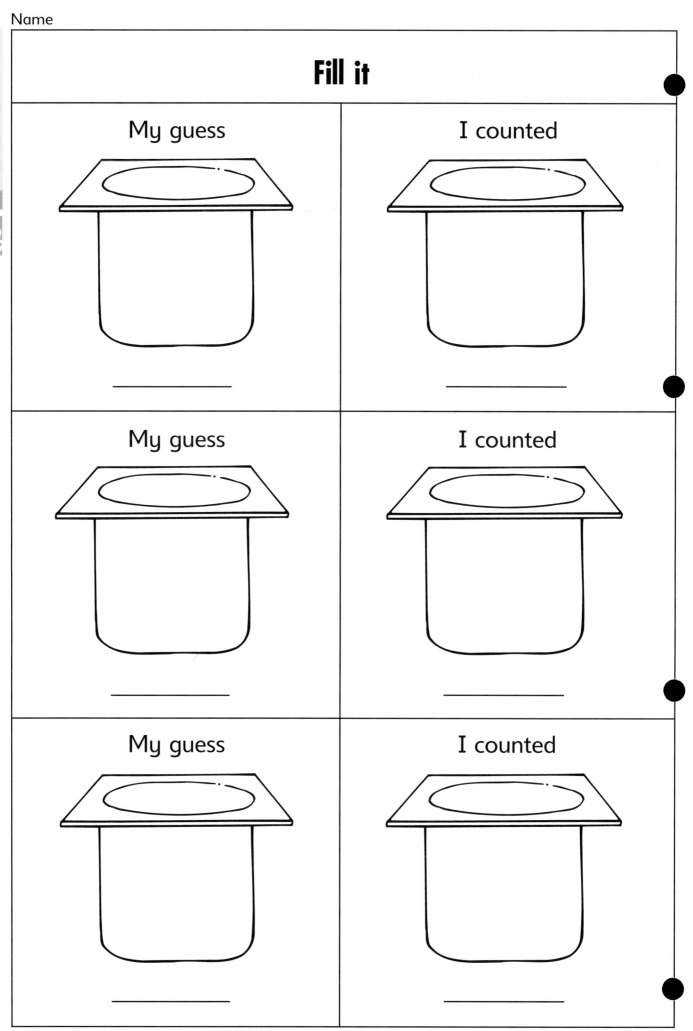

My guess	I counted
_____	_____
My guess	I counted
_____	_____
My guess	I counted
_____	_____

UNIT 5

ORGANISATION (8 LESSONS)

	LEARNING OUTCOMES	ORAL AND MENTAL STARTER	WHOLE-CLASS TEACHING ACTIVITY	PLENARY
LESSON 1	● **Say and use the number names in order in familiar contexts** (first to five, then ten, then twenty and beyond). ● Recite the number names in order, continuing the count forwards or backwards from a given number. ● Count reliably in other contexts, such as clapping sounds or hopping movements.	CARRY ON COUNTING: Children count around the class from 0–10, then up to 20 and 50.	COUNTING: Children count on from various numbers.	COUNT ON, COUNT BACK: Children count on and back from numbers.
LESSON 2	● **Recognise numerals 1 to 9,** then 0 and 10, then beyond 10. ● Order a given set of selected numbers: for example, the set of numbers 1 to 6 given in random order.	NUMBER TRACK: Children count, recognising numerals.	SHOW ME: Children order selected numbers.	Ordering numbers.
LESSON 3 +4	● **Begin to use the vocabulary involved in adding and subtracting.** ● **Begin to relate addition to combining two groups of objects,** counting all the objects. ● **Begin to relate subtraction to 'taking away'** and counting how many are left.	FINGER ADD AND SUBTRACT: Children add numbers up to 5, then repeat for taking away.	ADDING AND SUBTRACTING PROBLEMS: Problem-solving using addition and subtraction.	Feedback from activities.
LESSON 5	● Begin to understand and use the vocabulary related to money. Sort coins, including the £1 and £2 coins, and use them in role play to pay and give change.	ORDERING MONEY: Children 'peg' coins on the washing line according to value.	FIVE CURRANT BUNS: Children solve money problems.	Feedback from activities.
LESSON 6	● Begin to understand and use the vocabulary related to money. Sort coins, including the £1 and £2 coins, and use them in role play to pay and give change.	SHOW ME: Children show particular coins in response to various questions.	FIVE CURRANT BUNS IN THE BAKER'S SHOP: Children role-play situations using money.	Children order a selection of coins.
LESSON 7 +8	● Solve simple problems or puzzles in a practical context, and respond to 'What could we try next?'. ● **Use developing mathematical ideas and methods to solve practical problems** involving counting and comparing in a real or role play context.	COUNT UP: Children count how many more are needed to find a larger number.	LIGHTHOUSE KEEPER'S LUNCH: Problem-solving activities.	Feedback from activities and problem-solving questions.

> **ORAL AND MENTAL SKILLS** **Recognise numerals 1 to 9,** then 0 and 10, then beyond 10. **Say and use the number names in order in familiar contexts** (first to five, then ten, then twenty and beyond). **Begin to relate addition to combining two groups of objects,** counting all the objects. **Begin to relate subtraction to 'taking away'** and counting how many are left. Work out by counting how many more are needed to make a larger number. Sort coins, including the £1 and £2 coins.

Lessons 3 and 7 are given in full, Lessons 4 and 8 extend what has already been taught and are shown in outline. Lessons 1, 2, 5 and 6 are provided as grids.

LESSON 1

RESOURCES	Large carpet tiles with numbers 1 to 10 painted on them; quoits or plastic hoop; large number track (1 to 10). **Group activities:** individual number tracks (1 to 10) (page 13); cut-outs of rabbits and frogs; counters; cubes; dice (0–5); blank number tracks; spinners; sets of individual numeral cards (page 12).
LEARNING OUTCOMES	**ORAL AND MENTAL STARTER** ● **Say and use the number names in order in familiar contexts** such as number rhymes, songs, stories, counting games and activities (first to five, then ten, then twenty and beyond). **WHOLE-CLASS TEACHING ACTIVITY** ● **Say and use the number names in order in familiar contexts** such as number rhymes, songs, stories, counting games and activities (first to five, then ten, then twenty and beyond). ● Recite the number names in order, continuing the count forwards or backwards from a given number. ● Count reliably in other contexts, such as clapping sounds or hopping movements.
ORAL AND MENTAL STARTER	CARRY ON COUNTING: Count around the class from 1 to 10, then 0 to 10, then repeat to 20 and 50.
WHOLE-CLASS TEACHING ACTIVITY	COUNTING: Explain that you are going to make a big number track. Ask what number is needed to start and invite individuals to place the tiles in order. Place the hoop on a tile. Count and jump along the track until you reach the hoop: *Start at 4, count on to 9. How many jumps? 4, 5, 6, 7, 8, 9. 4 count on 5 makes 9.* Repeat with children placing the hoop, then jumping and counting along. Point to the large number track. *Start at 2, count on 8. 2 – 3, 4, 5, 6, 7, 8, 9, 10. 2 count on 8 is 10.* Repeat using different numbers.
GROUP ACTIVITIES	**1.** In pairs, children use table-top number tracks. One child places a counter or cube on the track, the other uses a frog or rabbit cut-out to jump and count. **2.** Use the carpet tile number track (1–10). Children throw the dice to find a starting number. They throw the dice again to find the number of jumps to add on. The first child to reach ten wins. **3.** In pairs, children use blank number tracks. They spin a spinner, count on the given number and place the appropriate numeral card on the track. ● Play dot-to-dot activities in ascending and descending order.
DIFFERENTIATION	Less able: practise counting on from a given number to 10 then 20. More able: encourage children to devise their own counting on and counting back activities.
PLENARY	COUNT ON, COUNT BACK: Change the starting number and count on to 10, then 20 and beyond. Repeat by counting back to 0.

LESSON 2

RESOURCES	Flip chart; marker pen; large number track; pointer; individual sets of numeral cards (page 12); selection of counting objects. **Group activities:** spinners; domino cards with spots and numbers on either end; number lotto cards showing numbers or spots from 1–9; 3 × 3 grids with numbers 1 to 9 placed in random order.
LEARNING OUTCOMES	**ORAL AND MENTAL STARTER** ● **Say and use the number names in order in familiar contexts** such as number rhymes, songs, stories, counting games and activities (first to five then ten, then twenty and beyond). ● **Recognise numerals 1 to 9,** then 0 and 10, then beyond 10. **WHOLE-CLASS TEACHING ACTIVITY** ● **Recognise numerals 1 to 9,** then 0 and 10, then beyond 10. ● Order a given set of numbers: for example, the set of numbers 1 to 6 given in random order.
ORAL AND MENTAL STARTER	NUMBER TRACK: Ask the whole class to count as you point to the numbers on the number track, first to 10 then 20.
WHOLE-CLASS TEACHING ACTIVITY	SHOW ME: Hand out the numeral cards. Say a number from 0 to 20 and ask the children to hold up the matching numeral card or to count out that number of objects in front of them on the table. Repeat using different numbers. Next, explain that you are going to choose a set of numbers, say 1 to 6. Say the numbers out of order, eg 3, 1, 6, 2, 5, 4. Children find the appropriate numeral cards, then place them in the correct ascending order. Repeat with a different set of numbers. Show the children some numbers, for example, 2, 5, 1, 3 and ask them to arrange these numbers in order, starting with the smallest number. *Which numbers are missing?* Extend to using sets of numbers from 0 to 10.
GROUP ACTIVITIES	**1.** Children spin a number and collect the matching numeral card. They repeat until five different numbers have been collected, then arrange the numbers in order. **2.** Children use a set of domino cards that have numerals and spots on opposite ends. They match the spots to the numerals on the opposite ends of the dominoes. **3.** Place lotto cards individually face down on the table. Children choose a grid and place it in front of them. In turn, each child turns over a lotto card and sees if they can match it to a number on their grid. The winner is the first to complete their grid. ● Provide a maths area in the classroom and introduce a range of counting games such as Snakes and Ladders and Ludo.
DIFFERENTIATION	Less able: reinforce touching and counting. Use numbers 1 to 6. More able: use numbers 0 to 10, then beyond for the **Group activities**.
PLENARY	Take feedback from the **Group activities**. Write a random set of numerals (0 to 6) on the flip chart. Ask children to order these. Extend using numbers 0 to 10.

LESSON 3 + 4

RESOURCES

Egg boxes; different-coloured beads; cubes; dominoes; dice (1–6 and 0–5); number tracks.

LEARNING OUTCOMES

ORAL AND MENTAL STARTER
● **Begin to relate addition to combining two groups of objects,** counting all the objects.
● **Begin to relate subtraction to 'taking away'** and counting how many are left.

WHOLE-CLASS TEACHING ACTIVITY
● **Begin to use the vocabulary involved in adding and subtracting.**
● **Begin to relate addition to combining two groups of objects,** counting all the objects.
● **Begin to relate subtraction to 'taking away'** and counting how many are left.

ORAL AND MENTAL STARTER

FINGER ADD AND SUBTRACT: Ask the children to add two numbers up to 5. They hold up their fingers to show answers. Repeat for 'taking away'.

VOCABULARY

Add; more; and; make; sum; total; altogether; take (away); leave; how many are left?; how many are left over?; how many have gone?; how many fewer is... than..?

WHOLE-CLASS TEACHING ACTIVITY

ADDING AND SUBTRACTING PROBLEMS: Remind the children they have been working on adding and subtracting. Explain that you will be saying some number problems involving addition and subtraction and you want them to work them out. Tell them to hold up their fingers to show the answers. Demonstrate: *2 add 3 more is 5.*

Addition
Three and 1 more?
2 add 7 makes?
The total of 2 and 3 is?
0 add 2. How many altogether?
Find the sum of 3 and 3.

Subtraction
5 take away 0 is?
10 take away 5?
9 subtract 1. How many are left?
8 take away 5. How many have gone?
3 subtract 3. How many are left over?

Addition and subtraction
0 and 6 more makes?
10 take away 10. How many are left?
1 add 4 more. What is the total?
take away 5 form 8. How many are left over?
What is the sum of 3 and 5?

GROUP ACTIVITIES

Choose from this selection for Lessons 3 and 4:
1. Investigate ways of making six using an egg box and two sets of differently-coloured beads.
2. Make towers of eight cubes using two colours.
3. Use dominoes to find how many have spots that add up to 5.
4. Throw two dice (1–6) and discover which numbers make 7.
5. Use number tracks to count back from 10. Throw a dice (1–5) to give the number of steps to be counted back each time.
6. Start with seven cubes. Throw a dice and take away that number of cubes.
7. Use cubes to find out what makes 10 by taking away some cubes.
8. Make up some addition and subtraction stories with numbers to 5.

Provide a maths area in the classroom and introduce a range of counting games such as Snakes and Ladders and Ludo.

DIFFERENTIATION

Less able: during the **Group activities**, use a range of practical counting activities such as counting on and back in twos, starting at different numbers and jumping backwards and forwards, for example start at 5, jump on 4, or start at 8, jump back 2. Limit the numbers to 10 then extend up to 20.

More able: encourage children to make up their own number stories, for example, 'I have two dogs and three cats. I have five pets altogether.' 'Flossie has six sweets and she gives Leon three. She has three sweets left.'

PLENARY

Ask the children to demonstrate some of their findings and share their investigations.

LESSON 4

Choose from the **Whole-class teaching activity** and **Group activities** in Lesson 3, above. In the **Plenary** play 'Finger add and subtract'. Then invite the children to make up some problems for a partner and the rest of the class.

LESSON 5

RESOURCES	Flip chart; marker pen; large cut-outs of coins; washing line; pegs; real coins; a couple of enlarged money pet cards. **Group activities:** items for the role-play shop; pencils; paper; blank labels; purses; money labels saying 7p, 12p, 9p, 6p, 15p, 20p; real and plastic coins; money dice (1p, 2p, 5p, 10p, 20p, 50p); Money pets (page 16).
LEARNING OUTCOMES	**ORAL AND MENTAL STARTER** ● Sort coins, including the £1 and £2 coins. **WHOLE-CLASS TEACHING ACTIVITY** ● Begin to understand and use the vocabulary related to money. Sort coins, including the £1 and £2 coins, and use them in role play to pay and give change.
ORAL AND MENTAL STARTER	ORDERING MONEY: Children peg coin cut-outs on the washing line according to value. Ask: *Is 5p more than 2p? What is the highest value coin?*
WHOLE-CLASS TEACHING ACTIVITY	FIVE CURRANT BUNS…: Sing this song with children using real money to act out the roles. Make up some money problems: *How much would three buns cost? How many buns could I buy with 10p? If I've 10p and buy six buns, how much change do I have?*
GROUP ACTIVITIES	**1.** Use the role-play area as a shop. Children make their own labels and price lists. **2.** Place the money labels in front of the purses. Children fill the purses with the correct amount of coins. **3.** Give children a copy of page 16 (Money pets). They roll the money dice and place the correct coins on the money pets. ● Provide a range of maths games in the play area.
DIFFERENTIATION	Less able: sorting activities with real coins, then make amounts to 5p using 1p coins. More able: make amounts up to 50p.
PLENARY	Discuss the **Group activities**. Draw some 'Money pets' on the flip chart. The children throw dice and cross out appropriate amounts.

LESSON 6

RESOURCES	Real and plastic coins. **Group activities:** paper; pencils; labels; money dice (1p, 2p, 5p, 10p, 20p, 50p); Money pets (page 16).
LEARNING OUTCOMES	**ORAL AND MENTAL STARTER** ● Sort coins, including the £1 and £2 coins. **WHOLE-CLASS TEACHING ACTIVITY** ● Begin to understand and use the vocabulary related to money. Sort coins, including the £1 and £2 coins, and use them in role play to pay and give change.
ORAL AND MENTAL STARTER	SHOW ME: From a selection of real and plastic coins on the table, ask children: *Can you show me a 50p coin? Show me a coin that is worth more than 10p. Show me a coin that is less than 20p. What is the total of 2p and 10p?*
WHOLE-CLASS TEACHING ACTIVITY	FIVE CURRANT BUNS IN THE BAKER'S SHOP: Sing the song but extend to 10. Invite the children to role-play with real money using 1p, 2p, 5p and 10p coins. Ask the 'shopkeeper' to give change from the coins. Repeat, giving different prices for the buns. Make up some money problems: *If I have 10p and spend 3p, how much change would I have? If I spend 3p and 5p, how much have I spent in total?*
GROUP ACTIVITIES	**1.** Change the role-play area into a 'Poundsaver' shop. Children choose items for sale, and make their own labels and price lists for items up to £1.00. **2.** Children throw money dice and collect the amount in coins. Use amounts to £1.00. **3.** Children roll money dice and place correct coins on the Money pets (page 16). ● Take a group of children to the local shops to buy items for cooking. Make a list of items required and involve the children in paying, checking the bill and counting out the change.
DIFFERENTIATION	Less able: sorting activities with real coins, then make amounts to 5p using 1p coins. More able: make amounts up to 50p.
PLENARY	Discuss the **Group activities**. Ask children to sort a selection of coins placed on the table. *Sort out 20p, 10p, 50p, £1 and £2. Put them in order, starting with the coin that has the smallest value. Find two coins that make 2p. Find coins worth £1.00.*

LESSON 7 + 8

RESOURCES

Flip chart; marker pen; *The Lighthouse Keeper's Lunch* (by Ronda and David Armitage, Puffin). **Group activities:** different types of bread, for example white, brown, granary; recipe and ingredients to make bread rolls; balances.

PREPARATION

Enlist adult support. You will need a simple bread recipe; allow time for the dough to rise and be cooked – start early!

LEARNING OUTCOMES

ORAL AND MENTAL STARTER
● Work out by counting how many more are needed to make a larger number.

WHOLE-CLASS TEACHING ACTIVITY
● Solve simple problems or puzzles in a practical context, and respond to 'What could we try next'.
● **Use developing mathematical ideas and methods to solve practical problems** involving counting and comparing in a real or role play context.

VOCABULARY

Add; more; and; make; sum; total; altogether; one more, two more, ten more; how many more to make...?; how many more is... than...?; how many fewer is... than...?; difference between; is the same as; half; halve.

ORAL AND MENTAL STARTER

DUOS: Give children two numbers and ask them to use their fingers to find out how many more are needed to make a larger number. Say: *Show me 3. How many more are needed to make a total of 10? There are five cakes, how many more are needed to make 12?*

WHOLE-CLASS TEACHING ACTIVITY

THE LIGHTHOUSE KEEPER'S LUNCH: Read the story. Ask: *Why did the lighthouse-keeper's wife have to send the lunch to the lighthouse keeper? How did his wife let him know it was time for lunch? How many children bring sandwiches for lunch?* The children count how many of them have sandwiches, how many have a school lunch and how many go home. Record the answers on the flip chart. *Do more children have sandwiches than a school lunch? Do fewer children go home than have sandwiches? How many more have a school lunch compared with those who have sandwiches?* Ask the children to name some of the fillings in the sandwiches in the story. Next, invite them to give their favourite sandwich fillings, for example cheese, chicken, jam, egg, etc. Write on the flip chart 'Our favourite sandwich fillings' and draw a chart with columns for each filling. The children put up their hands to choose their favourite. Count the number and record this on the chart. Point out the numbers for each choice. *Which is the most popular filling? Which is the least popular?*

GROUP ACTIVITIES

1. Children find how many ways a slice of bread can be cut (halves, quarters, diagonally).
2. Make a menu for a week using various sandwich fillings so that each day is different.
3. Carry out a survey of the class' sandwich fillings on one particular day of the week.
4. Plan a picnic for a group of friends. *How many sandwiches would be needed for each person to have four sandwiches with two different fillings. How many chocolate biscuits?*
5. Find out if there are the same number of slices in different loaves of bread and record.
6. Children make home-made bread rolls with adult supervision. *How many rolls are needed for each child to have four each? How many more would be needed for six each?*
7. Children weigh different slices of bread to see if some are heavier or lighter than others. They compare using their hands then weigh using balances and place in order.
8. Draw a chart of the lighthouse keeper's lunches. *What did his wife give him first, etc?*
Turn the role-play area into a sandwich bar.

DIFFERENTIATION

Less able: during the **Group activities**, support children in working out their own answers, perhaps using practical apparatus or fingers to support their counting.
More able: encourage children's problem solving by asking *What would happen if...?* and extend the ideas. Invite children to record their findings in their own ways.

PLENARY

Take feedback from the **Group activities**.

LESSON 8

Recall the problems they solved in Lesson 7 and how they found out what their favourite sandwiches were by using a chart. Solve further problems. Choose from the **Group activities** in Lesson 7, so that children have experience of at least two of the activities.

UNIT 6: Assess & Review

Choose from the following activities over the two lessons. During the group activities, some of the children can work with you on practical tasks, while others complete assessment worksheets 1a and 1b, which assess their skills in reading and writing, ordering numbers and addition. The specific assessment criteria for the assessment sheets can be found at the bottom of each sheet.

RESOURCES

Sets of numeral cards for each child (page 12); assessment photocopiables 1a and 1b; a selection of counting objects; interlocking cubes; 2-D and 3-D shapes; a selection of items for measuring; different sized and shaped containers; water; dry items such as lentils, conkers, beads; 1p, 2p, 5p, 10p, 20p, 50p £1 and £2 coins; pencils; paper.

ORAL AND MENTAL STARTER

ASSESSMENT
● Can the children: **Say and use the number names in order in familiar contexts? Count reliably up to 10 everyday objects?**
KNOWING THE NUMBERS: Sing the song 'Five little speckled frogs'.
COUNTING: The children count with you, from 0 to 10 and back, then 0 to 20 and back, then from any number to 10 and back. Who counts with confidence and who needs more practice? Allow individual children opportunities to count out objects while you observe who is doing this confidently.

GROUP ACTIVITIES

ASSESSMENT
● Can the children: **Count reliably up to 10 everyday objects? Recognise numerals 1 to 9? Use language such as more or less, greater or smaller to compare two numbers? Use language such as circle or bigger to describe the shape and size of solids and flat shapes? Use everyday words to describe position? Use language such as heavier or lighter to compare mass** by making direct comparison of two objects? **Talk about, recognise and recreate simple patterns? Use developing mathematical ideas and methods to solve practical problems? Begin to relate addition to combining two groups of objects? Begin to relate subtraction to 'taking away'?**
COUNTING OBJECTS: Children count out a given quantity of cubes. *Count out four, seven, eight and ten objects.* Check they count accurately and can tell you how many they have.
RECOGNITION OF NUMERALS 1 TO 9: Ask children to place the numeral cards on the table face up. Say a number and ask children to pick it out.
COMPARE TWO NUMBERS: Ask children to count out a given quantity of cubes (1–5). Can they say how many objects they have? Repeat using a different quantity (1–10). Ask children if there are more or less, or a greater or smaller number of objects.
SHAPE MATCHING: Ask the children to match your shape from a selection in front of them. Ask: *Is the shape the same?* Ask children to find a bigger one of the same shape.
IN POSITION: Use some of the activities given for the Whole-class teaching activity and Group activities in Lesson 3, Unit 3, Term 2 on page 85, or make up some similar ones.
COMPARING MASS: Use activities given for the Whole-class and Group activities in Lesson 2, Unit 4, page 89 or make up similar ones. Provide items for children to compare. Encourage them to guess, then use their hands to compare. Compare two, then three items. *How do you know that something is going to be heavy or light?* Include small items that are heavy and large items that are light, eg a weight, a bag of cotton-wool balls.
SIMPLE PATTERNS: Children count and clap a sequence up to 5, then 10. Make a pattern using two coloured beads. Ask: *What would come next?* Children copy a simple pattern.
SOLVING ADDITION AND SUBTRACTION PROBLEMS: Choose some problems from Lessons 3 and 4, Unit 5, Term 2, page 96, or make up similar ones. Children show and describe how they worked out their answer for each problem.

Name

Assessment 1a

Write the missing numbers:

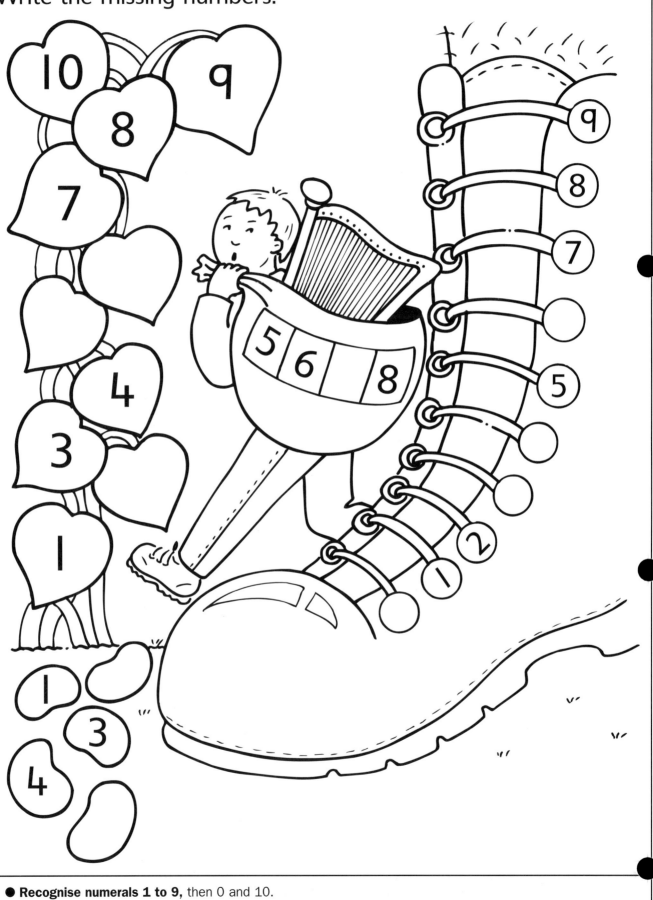

● **Recognise numerals 1 to 9,** then 0 and 10.

Name

Assessment 1b

Write the answers to these adding sums:

 add is ☐

 add is ☐

 add is ☐

Match the numbers to the objects:

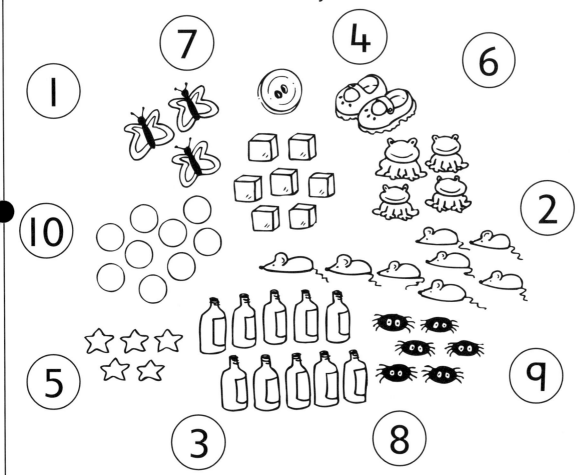

⑦ ④ ⑥ ① ⑩ ② ⑤ ⑨ ③ ⑧

● **Count reliably up to 10 everyday objects,** giving just one number name to each object.
● **Begin to relate addition to combining two groups of objects,** counting all the objects.

UNIT 7

ORGANISATION (5 LESSONS)

	LEARNING OUTCOMES	ORAL AND MENTAL STARTER	WHOLE-CLASS TEACHING ACTIVITY	PLENARY
LESSON 1	● **Recognise numerals 1 to 9,** then 0 and 10, then beyond 10. ● **Count reliably up to 10 everyday objects** (first to 5, then 10, then beyond), giving just one number name to each object.	NUMBER TRACKING: Children count numbers along a number track.	NUMBERS EVERYWHERE: Recognising numbers in the environment.	Feedback from activities. Recognising and ordering numbers.
LESSON 2	● **Recognise numerals 1 to 9,** then 0 and 10, then beyond 10. ● Order a given set of numbers: for example, the set of numbers 1 to 6 given in random order.	CARRY ON COUNTING: Children count around the class.	NUMBER TRACKING: Counting and number recognition.	COUNT ON, COUNT BACK: Children count on and back from numbers.
LESSON 3	● **Use language such as more or less, greater or smaller, to compare two numbers** and say which Is more or less, and say a number which lies between two given numbers. ● Order a given set of selected numbers: for example, the set 2, 5, 1, 8, 4.	FINGER ADD AND SUBTRACT: Children hold up their fingers to show answers to adding and subtracting problems.	TWO GIRLS, THREE BOYS: Looking at numbers greater and smaller.	Feedback from activities.
LESSON 4 + 5	● **Recognise numerals 1 to 9,** then 0 and 10, then beyond 10. ● Order a given set of numbers: for example, the set of numbers 1 to 6 given in random order	NUMBER TRACKING: Children count numbers on a number line.	NUMBER PRACTICE: Ordering numbers.	Feedback from activities. Children order numbers in the range 0–10 then 0–20.

ORAL AND MENTAL SKILLS **Recognise numerals 1 to 9,** then 0 and 10, then beyond 10. Recite the number names in order, continuing the count forwards or backwards from a given number. **Say and use the number names in order in familiar contexts** such as number rhymes, songs, stories, counting games and activities (first to five then ten, then twenty and beyond). Order a given set of numbers. **Begin to relate addition to combining two groups of objects,** counting all the objects. **Begin to relate subtraction to 'taking away'** and counting how many are left.

Lessons 1 and 3 are given in full, while Lessons 2, 4 and 5 are provided in outline.

RESOURCES

Large number track 1–20; pointer; a selection of items with numbers on, for example playing cards, birthday cards, calendar, clock face, computer keyboard, story books with numbers in the title, for example 'The Three Billy Goats Gruff'; individual sets of numeral cards (page 12); flip chart; marker pen. **Group activities:** zigzag books; 3 × 3 grids with the numbers 1–9 written on them in order; thin card; scissors; adhesive; sets of numeral cards (page 12).

PREPARATION

Display the large number track. Make the 3 × 3 grids. Cut the thin card to the same size as the 3 × 3 grids. Make the zigzag books.

LEARNING OUTCOMES

ORAL AND MENTAL STARTER
● Recite the number names in order, continuing the count forwards or backwards from a given number.
● Order a given set of numbers.

WHOLE-CLASS TEACHING ACTIVITY
● **Recognise numerals 1 to 9,** then 0 and 10, then beyond 10.
● **Count reliably up to 10 everyday objects** (first to 5, then 10, then beyond), giving just one number name to each object.

<table>
<tr><td>

VOCABULARY

Counting;
number, zero,
one, two,
three... to
twenty and
beyond; none;
how many?;
count; count
(up) to; count
on (from, to);
count back
(from, to);
count in ones;
twos... tens...,
more; less.

</td></tr>
</table>

ORAL AND MENTAL STARTER

NUMBER TRACKING: Count along the number track from 1 to 20. Ask individuals to count as you point. Ask: *What comes before 6? What comes after 17? What number comes between 12 and 14?* Count back from 20 to 0.

WHOLE-CLASS TEACHING ACTIVITY

NUMBERS EVERYWHERE: Explain that numbers are very important in our lives and we see and use them every day. Point out the number of children in the class: *How many are there? How many are away?* Discuss why we need to know how many people are having school lunches and how many are having sandwiches. Explain that some numbers are special to us, for example, our age, our telephone number, our house number, the number of people in our family. Ask individuals to tell you numbers that are special to them. Next, invite children to look around the classroom to see if they can spot any numbers. Point out items which display numbers, for example a dice, a domino, a computer keyboard, a calendar, a clock face, story books, a birthday card. Ask children to read out some of the numbers.

GROUP ACTIVITIES

1. Children fill in zigzag books for 'My special numbers'. Include house number, age, number of members in the family, my favourite number, and so on.
2. Take children on a number walk around the school.
3. Give each child a number grid and a piece of card. Children cut out the numbers and stick them in any order on to their blank piece of card to make a lotto card. Match the individual numbers to their lotto game.

 Children write numbers onto card in order from 0 to 10 to make a number line hat.

DIFFERENTIATION

Less able: work with numbers 1 to 10 then 20.
More able: extend the range of numbers to 20 then beyond.

PLENARY

Ask children to discuss their activities. Give out the numeral cards in random order and write a selection of numbers on the flip chart. *Look at the numbers one at a time. Who has the number...?* Individuals come out and show their number. Ask children to read the number sequence. *Are the numbers in order? What comes first?* Ask the children to arrange themselves in ascending order. Repeat, using another set of numbers.

RESOURCES	Large tiles with numbers painted on them; plastic hoop. **Group activities:** resources as for Lesson 1, page 102.
LEARNING OUTCOMES	**ORAL AND MENTAL STARTER** ● Recite the number names in order, continuing the count forwards or backwards from a given number. **WHOLE-CLASS TEACHING ACTIVITY** ● **Recognise numerals 1 to 9,** then 0 and 10, then beyond 10. ● Order a given set of numbers.
ORAL AND MENTAL STARTER	CARRY ON COUNTING: Count around the class from 1 to 10, then 0 to 10, then to 20 and beyond.
WHOLE-CLASS TEACHING ACTIVITY	NUMBER TRACKING: Show children the pile of number tiles. Explain that you are going to make a special number track. Ask: *What number is needed to start?* Invite individuals to arrange the number tiles in order. Place the hoop on a tile. Count and jump along the track until you reach the hoop. Repeat with children placing the hoop, then jumping and counting.
GROUP ACTIVITIES	Choose from the **Group activities** in Lesson 1, page 103.
DIFFERENTIATION	Less able: work with numbers 1 to 10, then up to 20. More able: extend the range of numbers to 20 and beyond.
PLENARY	COUNT ON, COUNT BACK. Change the starting number and count on to 10 then 20. Repeat by counting back to 0.

RESOURCES

Cubes; flip chart; marker pen. **Group activities:** counters; (1–10) spinners; labels; cubes; beads; threading lace; dice (1–6); paper; pencils.

PREPARATION

Make labels saying 'greater' and 'smaller'. Prepare some items for the children to continue, for example, make some towers of cubes, thread some beads on to a lace, stick some coloured stars onto a sheet of paper.

LEARNING OUTCOMES

ORAL AND MENTAL STARTER
● **Begin to relate addition to combining two groups of objects,** counting all the objects.
● **Begin to relate subtraction to 'taking away'** and counting how many are left.

WHOLE-CLASS TEACHING ACTIVITY
● **Use language such as more or less, greater or smaller, to compare two numbers** and say which is more or less, and say a number which lies between two given numbers.
● Order a given set of selected numbers: for example, the set 2, 5, 1, 8, 4.

ORAL AND MENTAL STARTER

FINGER ADD AND SUBTRACT: Ask the children to add two numbers and hold up their fingers to show the answers. Repeat for 'taking away'.

WHOLE-CLASS TEACHING ACTIVITY

TWO GIRLS, THREE BOYS: Ask two girls to come out to the front of the class, then ask three boys. Count the girls and say: *Two girls.* Count the boys and say: *Three boys. Are there more boys or more girls? How can we make the number of girls greater than the number of boys?* Make a tower of five cubes, then another one of seven cubes. Ask children to count out the cubes in the first tower then the second. *Which tower has the smaller number of cubes?* Invite children to come out and make towers that are greater and smaller than your towers. Write a pair of numbers on the flip chart, for example, 7, 2. *Which is the greater number? Which number is the smaller?* Write a number on the flip chart. *Give me a number that is smaller. Show me a number that is greater.* Write two numbers, for example 12 and 9. *Which number is greater? Tell me a number that comes in between 9 and 12.*

VOCABULARY

Add; more; and; make; sum; total; altogether; one more; two more; how many more to make…?; how many is… than…?; take (away); leave; how many are left/left over?; how many have gone?; one less; two less; how many fewer is… than…?.

GROUP ACTIVITIES

1. Give children counters, a 1–10 spinner, and the 'greater' and 'smaller' labels. In pairs, they take turns to spin the spinner and take that number of counters. The children place the labels to show which number of counters is greater and smaller.

2. Give each child one of the sets you have prepared, for example the tower of cubes. Children count out the number of items then make or draw a 'greater' or 'smaller' set themselves.

3. In pairs, children take turns to roll a dice. They record the numbers they have thrown and find a number which is in between these two.

 Provide number and counting games such as Ludo or Snakes and Ladders.

DIFFERENTIATION

Less able: limit the range of numbers to 10.
More able: use numbers to 20 and beyond.

PLENARY

Take feedback from the **Group activities**.

RESOURCES	Large number tracks (1–20); individual sets of numeral cards (page 12); flip chart; pointer; marker pen; numeral cards 0 to 20; plastic container; Post-it notes. **Group activities:** selection of counting objects; lotto cards; spinners; domino cards showing numerals and spots; 3 × 3 grids with the numbers 1–9 written on them in order; thin card; scissors; adhesive; sets of numeral cards (page 12); large dice; programmable toy.
LEARNING OUTCOMES	**ORAL AND MENTAL STARTER** ● **Recognise numerals 1 to 9,** then 0 and 10, then beyond 10. ● **Say and use the number names in order in familiar contexts** such as number rhymes, songs, stories, counting games and activities (first to five then ten, then twenty and beyond). **WHOLE-CLASS TEACHING ACTIVITY** ● **Recognise numerals 1 to 9,** then 0 and 10, then beyond 10. ● Order a given set of numbers: for example, the set of numbers 1 to 6 given in random order.
ORAL AND MENTAL STARTER	NUMBER TRACKING: Ask the children to count as you point to numbers on a number track, first to 10, then 20. Ask individuals to read out numbers.
WHOLE-CLASS TEACHING ACTIVITY	NUMBER PRACTICE: Choose from these activities over the two lessons: Children hold up numeral cards or count out objects for a given number. They then arrange a selection of numeral cards given out in order from 1–6, then a random set of numeral cards from 1–6. Extend using 0–10. Draw a 3 × 4 grid on the flip chart. Ask the children to choose some numbers from 0 to 20. Write the numbers inside the grid. Put the numeral cards (0–20) in a container and let individuals pick out a card and say the number. If the number is on the grid, cover it with a Post-it note. Repeat until all the numbers are covered.
GROUP ACTIVITIES	**1.** Children spin a number, collect a numeral card and count out that number of objects. **2.** Children match the numerals and spots on the domino cards. **3.** Children play Number Lotto as in Lesson 1, Group activity 3, page 103. Place numeral cards face down. In turn, children select one and try to match it with a number on their Lotto card. ● In groups of two or three, children throw a large dice and make a programmable toy move that number of 'steps'.
DIFFERENTIATION	Less able: reinforce touching and counting. Use numbers 1 to 6. More able: use numbers 0 to 10, then beyond.
PLENARY	Take feedback from the **Group activities**. Write a random set of numerals (0–6) on the flip chart. Ask the children to order these. Extend using numbers 0–10.

UNIT 8

ORGANISATION (5 LESSONS)

	LEARNING OUTCOMES	ORAL AND MENTAL STARTER	WHOLE-CLASS TEACHING ACTIVITY	PLENARY
LESSON 1	● Count in twos.	NUMBER PROBLEMS: Addition and subtraction problems.	TWO-BY-TWO: Recognising odd and even numbers.	Odd and even number recognition.
LESSON 2	● **Begin to use the vocabulary involved in adding.** ● Begin to relate addition to counting on.	COUNT IN TWOS: Children count in twos up to and back from 20.	COUNTING ON: Counting on from a given number	Class completes photocopiable sheet.
LESSON 3	● **Begin to use the vocabulary involved in subtracting.** ● Remove a smaller number from a larger and find out how many arc lcft by counting back from the larger number.	COUNT IN TWOS: Children count in twos up to and back from 20.	TEN LITTLE TEDDY BEARS: Subtraction activities.	Feedback from activities. Class completes photocopiable sheet.
LESSON 4	● **Begin to use the vocabulary involved in adding and subtracting.** ● Begin to find out how many have been removed from a larger group of objects by counting up from a number.	COUNT IN TWOS: Children count in twos up to 20 and beyond.+	COUNT DOWN: Number problems involving subtraction.	Feedback from activities.
LESSON 5	● **Begin to use the vocabulary involved in adding and subtracting.** ● **Begin to relate addition to combining two groups of objects.** ● Begin to relate addition to counting on.	ADDITION AND SUBTRACTION FACTS: Children respond to quick-fire questions.	ADDITION AND SUBTRACTION PROBLEMS: Problem-solving using addition and subtraction.	Children recite the rhyme 'Ten fat sausages'.

ORAL AND MENTAL SKILLS Recite the number names in order, continuing the count forwards or backwards from a given number. Begin to recognise 'none' and 'zero' in stories, rhymes and when counting. Order a given set of numbers: for example, the set of numbers 1 to 6 given in random order. Count in twos. Count reliably in other contexts, such as clapping sounds or hopping movements. **Find one more or one less than a number from 1 to 10. Begin to use the vocabulary involved in adding and subtracting.**

Lessons 2 and 3 are given in full, while the rest of the unit is provided as grids.

RESOURCES	Rhymes 'Two, four, six, eight' and 'Ten little teddy bears'; flip chart; marker pen; number track (1–20). **Group activities:** selection of paired items such as socks, gloves, shoe laces (all jumbled up); copies of photocopiable page 111; 0–10 number tracks (page 13); counters; pencils.
LEARNING OUTCOMES	**ORAL AND MENTAL STARTER** ● **Find one more or one less than a number from 1 to 10.** ● **Begin to use the vocabulary involved in adding.** **WHOLE-CLASS TEACHING ACTIVITY** ● Count in twos.
ORAL AND MENTAL STARTER	NUMBER PROBLEMS: Ask children to say one more or one less than a given number. Then ask: *What is 3 take away 3? 5 add 5 makes? How many are left if I take 9 away from 12?*
WHOLE-CLASS TEACHING ACTIVITY	TWO-BY-TWO: Recite the rhyme 'Two, four, six, eight'. Write these numbers on the flip chart: *What is special about these numbers?* Point to the number track as the children count in twos to 10, then 20. Explain that these numbers are called 'even numbers': *What is the even number that comes before 10? ...after 2? ...between 4 and 8?* Explain that the other numbers are called 'odd numbers'. Ask the children to count in ones, whispering every other number. Count to 20 with you saying the odd numbers and the children saying the even numbers. Explain 'a pair' and ask children to suggest 'pairs' such as shoes, gloves, etc. Explain a pair of trousers (ie trouser legs), a pair of tights, a pair of spectacles.
GROUP ACTIVITIES	**1.** Children sort items to see if there is a pair, for example, socks: *Can you find two that match? How many pairs of [socks] are there?* **2.** Give each child a copy of photocopiable page 111. The children draw lines to match the pairs of items. **3.** Give each child a 0–10 number track (page 13). Ask them to count in twos, covering every even number with a counter. ● Make 'Our book of pairs'. Children look for pairs of objects in the environment.
DIFFERENTIATION	Less able: provide number tracks for children to refer to. Work with numbers to 10, then extend to 20. More able: work with numbers to 20 then beyond.
PLENARY	Recite the rhyme: 'Ten Little Teddy Bears'. Write a set of random numbers on the flip chart. Decide whether they are odd or even numbers. Count in 2s to 20 then beyond.

RESOURCES

Two large foam dice; flip chart; marker pen; cubes; box; copies of photocopiable page 112 (Adders). **Group activities:** dice (1–6 and 0–5); individual 0–10 number tracks (page 13); numeral and vocabulary cards.

PREPARATION

Make bingo cards, individual numeral cards and vocabulary cards using the computer. Mount on to card and cover with adhesive film. Make the required number of copies of photocopiable page 112, enough for one for each pair plus an enlarged copy. Draw two bingo cards on the flip chart.

LEARNING OUTCOMES

ORAL AND MENTAL STARTER
● Recite the number names in order, continuing the count forwards or backwards from a given number.
● Begin to recognise 'none' and 'zero' in stories, rhymes and when counting.

WHOLE-CLASS TEACHING ACTIVITY
● **Begin to use the vocabulary involved in adding.**
● Begin to relate addition to counting on.

ORAL AND MENTAL STARTER

COUNT IN TWOS: Count together in twos to 10, then 20, then back from 10 to 0, and back from 20 to 0.

VOCABULARY
Add; more; and; make; sum; total; altogether; score; one more; two more; ten more...; how many more to make...?; how many more is... than...?

WHOLE-CLASS TEACHING ACTIVITY

COUNTING ON: Ask the children to carry on a count that starts from different numbers: *Starting at 3, count in ones to 17.* Explain that you want the children to count on from a given number. Ask them to show three fingers on one hand. *Keep this number in your head. Now show me four fingers on the other hand. How many altogether?* Count out loud: *3 – 4, 5, 6, 7. 3 add 4 is 7.* Repeat several times using different numbers. Explain that you are going to throw the large dice to get the starting number. Throw the dice again to find the amount to add. (Remind children to keep the first number in their head.) Say: *6 count on 2. How many altogether? 6 – 7, 8. 6 count on 2 makes 8.* Write the numbers on the flip chart. Ask individuals to come and place two cubes in a box: *How many are in the box? Count out three more and put them into the box. What is the total number?*

Show the children your enlarged copy of photocopiable page 112 (Adders). Explain that you will play with one snake and the children will play with the other. Say: *I am going to throw two dice. If the total of the dice is on my snake, I can cross out the number. If the total is not there, I cannot cross out a number.* Select children to come out and roll the dice. Ask the whole class and individuals to add the two numbers together by counting on. The first person to cross out all the numbers on their snake wins.

GROUP ACTIVITIES

1. In pairs, children throw a dice (1–6) and move to that number on the number track. They throw the dice again and count on, eg, '6 count on 4 makes 10'. Children use numeral cards and vocabulary cards (count on, add, make) to 'record' their working.
2. Using photocopiable page 112 (Adders), pairs play as in the **Whole-class teaching activity** above.
3. In pairs, children use cubes to add by counting on. The first child throws a dice (0–5) and takes that number of cubes. The second child then throws the dice and takes the appropriate number of cubes. Both children count on from the first number to the second and 'record' using individual numeral and vocabulary cards (count on, add, makes, altogether).

 Number bingo – each child has a bingo card with numbers to 10. They throw the dice to find the first number, then throw again and count on to find the total. If the number is on their card, they cover it with a counter. First to complete the bingo card wins.

DIFFERENTIATION

Less able: use adult support to check that they are counting on and reinforce vocabulary. More able: encourage children to 'record' their own number sentences using numeral and vocabulary cards or by making their own markings. Extend numbers to 20.

PLENARY

Repeat the **Whole-class teaching activity** game of 'Adders'.

RESOURCES

Large tiles with numbers on them; dice (1–6 and 7–12); flip chart; marker pen; rhyme 'Ten little teddy bears'. **Group activities:** copies of photocopiable page 113 (Ladders); dice (1–6); money bags; money dice (0p, 1p, 2p, 3p, 4p, 5p); labels for money bags.

PREPARATION

Make the required copies of photocopiable page 113, plus an enlarged copy. Fill five bags with different amounts of money. Put a label showing money values on each money bag, eg 10p, 8p, 5p, 6p, 9p.

LEARNING OUTCOMES

ORAL AND MENTAL STARTER

● Count in twos.
● Order a given set of numbers: for example, the set of numbers 1 to 6 given in random order.
● Count reliably in other contexts, such as clapping sounds or hopping movements.

WHOLE-CLASS TEACHING ACTIVITY

● **Begin to use the vocabulary involved in subtracting.**
● Remove a smaller number from a larger and find how many are left by counting back from the larger number.

VOCABULARY

Take (away); leave; how many are left/ left over?; how many have gone?; one less; two less...; ten less...; how many fewer is... than...?; difference between; is the same as.

ORAL AND MENTAL STARTER

COUNT IN TWOS: From 0 to 20, then beyond. Then count back in twos, from 20 to 0, and extend beyond 20. Ask a group of children to make a number track from 10 to 0 using the large number tiles. *Which number will come first? Which will come last?* Throw the dice (7–12) and say the number thrown, for example: *Stand on 9.* Throw the other dice (1–6) and say this number. Tell the children that you are going to jump back that number of tiles. Jump back 4. Say: *9 count back 4. 9 – 8, 7, 6, 5. 9 count back 4 is 5.* Write this number sentence on the flip chart.

WHOLE-CLASS TEACHING ACTIVITY

TEN LITTLE TEDDY BEARS: Recite this rhyme. Ask the children to fold down their fingers as they count back. Explain that we can subtract by counting back. Ask the children to show ten fingers then count back 5: *How many fingers are left?*

GROUP ACTIVITIES

1. Number tracking: Repeat from **Group activity** 1, Lesson 2, page 108.
2. Give each child a copy of photocopiable page 113 (Ladders). Children place counters at the top of the ladders. In pairs, they take turns to throw the dice (1–6), then count back that number. The first child to get to the bottom of the ladder wins.
3. Children throw a money dice and take away that amount from a prepared money bag until all the money has gone.
Encourage children to give change in the role-play shop or café.

DIFFERENTIATION

Less able: use adult support to focus on the activity. Reinforce vocabulary and understanding by careful questioning.
More able: encourage them to check partners' calculations.

PLENARY

Take feedback from the **Group activities**, reinforcing the vocabulary. Play a whole-class game of 'Ladders' using the enlarged copy.

UNIT 8

LESSON 4

RESOURCES	Rhymes 'Five currant buns' and 'Ten fat sausages'; flip chart; marker pen; egg boxes; chocolate eggs. **Group activities:** paper; pencils; dice (5–10 and 0–5); sets of individual 0–10 numeral cards (page 12); number bingo cards.
LEARNING OUTCOMES	**ORAL AND MENTAL STARTER** ● Count in twos. ● Recite the number names in order, continuing the count forwards and backwards from a given number. **WHOLE-CLASS TEACHING ACTIVITY** ● **Begin to use the vocabulary involved in adding and subtracting.** ● Begin to find out how many have been removed from a larger group of objects by counting up from a number.
ORAL AND MENTAL STARTER	COUNT IN TWOS: Count to 20 and beyond. Ask the class to count together, then count around the class in ones, then twos. Count in ones to 20, with the class whispering every other number.
WHOLE-CLASS TEACHING ACTIVITY	COUNT DOWN: Recite 'Five currant buns'. *If there were five currant buns and two have been sold, how many are left?* Count up from 2 to 5. *3. 3 add 2 is 5, 5 take away 3 is 2.* Show the egg box with six eggs. Take out four eggs. *How many are in the box?* Count up from 4. *2. 4 add 2 is 6, 6 take away 2 is 4.* Write the number sentences on the flip chart. Repeat, using different numbers. Recite 'Ten fat sausages'. Ask children to show fingers as they count down in twos. *How many in the pan?* Count up from 2. *2 – 4, 6, 8, 10. 2 add 8 makes 10, 10 subtract 8 is 2.*
GROUP ACTIVITIES	**1.** In pairs, children remove chocolate eggs from an egg box to create their own calculations. They record these pictorially. **2.** In pairs, children choose two numeral cards and subtract the smaller number from the larger. Record their answer on paper. **3.** In pairs, children play number bingo. They throw two dice (5–10 and 0–5) and subtract the smallest number from the largest. If the answer appears on the bingo card it is crossed out. ● Set up Snakes and Ladders for the children to play.
DIFFERENTIATION	Less able: use adult support to focus on the **Group activities**. More able: extend using numbers to 20. Encourage simple recording.
PLENARY	Feedback from the **Group activities**.

LESSON 5

RESOURCES	Appropriate resources from Lessons 2, 3 and 4.
LEARNING OUTCOMES	**ORAL AND MENTAL STARTER** ● **Begin to use the vocabulary involved in adding and subtracting.** **WHOLE-CLASS TEACHING ACTIVITY** ● **Begin to use the vocabulary involved in adding and subtracting.** ● **Begin to relate addition to combining two groups of objects.** ● Begin to relate addition to counting on.
ORAL AND MENTAL STARTER	ADDITION AND SUBTRACTION FACTS: Ask quick-fire questions such as: *5 more than 2? 6 add 1? 1 less than 9? 2 take away 0? What is the total of 6 add 3? 10 subtract 5? 7 take away 6, how many left?*
WHOLE-CLASS TEACHING ACTIVITY	ADDITION AND SUBTRACTION PROBLEMS: Recite 'Ten fat sausages'. Children show fingers and count down in twos. Working individually, children show numeral cards or use fingers to answer addition and subtraction problems. Use a range of number problems and reinforce the vocabulary for addition and subtraction. Say: *There are six people on a bus, three get off. How many are there now? Three children are playing in the sand, one more comes to play. How many altogether? Seven baby birds, two fly away. How many are left?*
GROUP ACTIVITIES	Choose from the activities suggested for Lessons 2, 3 and 4 in this unit.
DIFFERENTIATION	Less able: target questions carefully. Use number facts to 10. More able: extend numbers to 20.
PLENARY	Repeat the rhyme 'Ten fat sausages' using role-play.

Pairs

Match the pairs:

Name

Adders

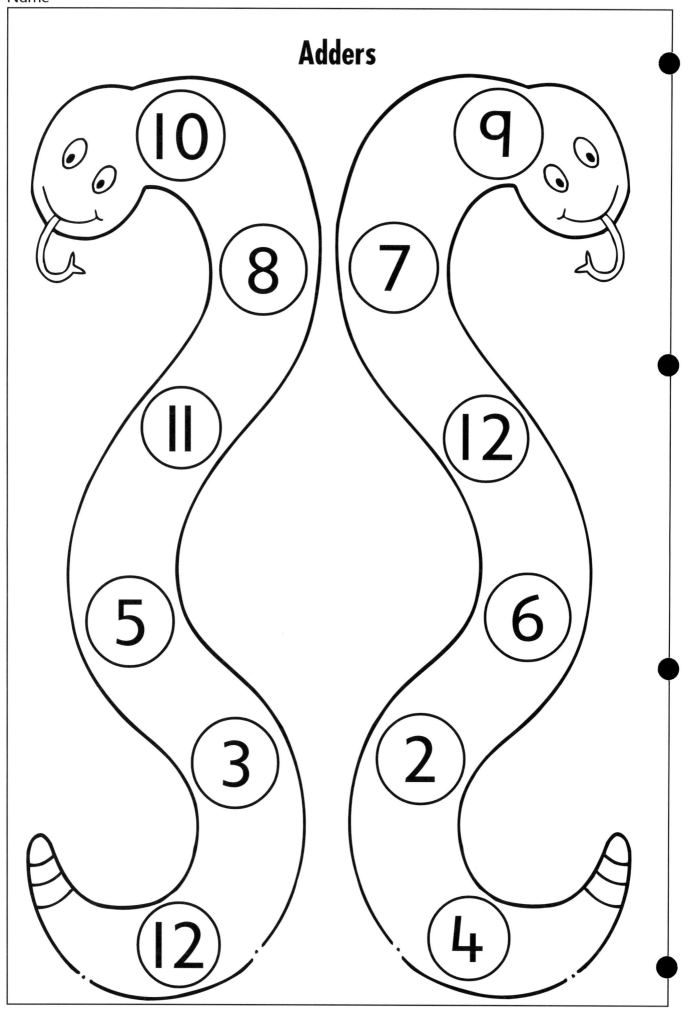

Name

Ladders

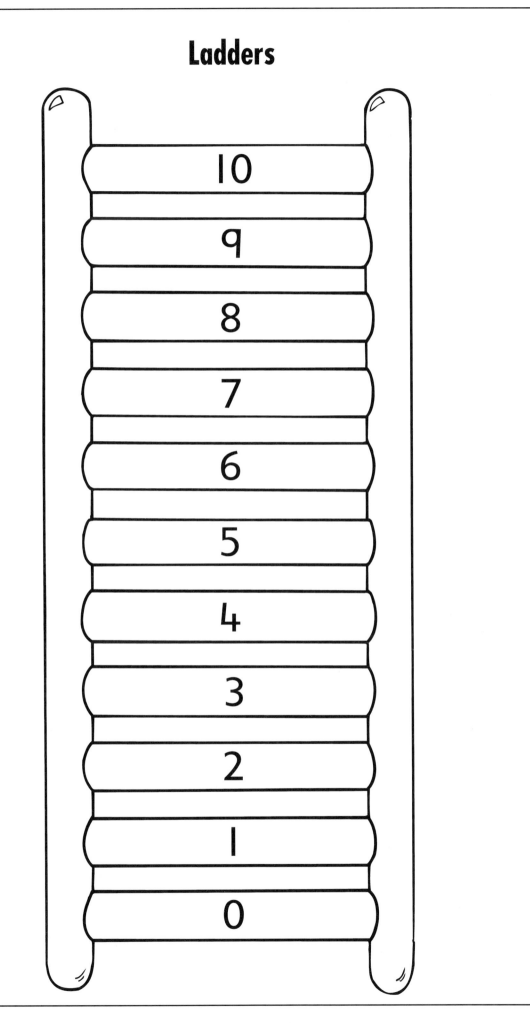

10

9

8

7

6

5

4

3

2

1

0

UNIT 9

ORGANISATION (5 LESSONS)

	LEARNING OUTCOMES	ORAL AND MENTAL STARTER	WHOLE-CLASS TEACHING ACTIVITY	PLENARY
LESSON 1	● Put sets of objects in order of size.	FINGER COUNT: Children show a given number.	ORDERING SIZE: Ordering items by comparing and using associated language.	Feedback from activities.
LESSON 2	● **Use language such as circle or bigger to describe the shape and size of solids and flat shapes.** ● Put sets of objects in order of size.	NUMBER FLASH: Children identify a number without counting it.	IN THE FAMILY: Matching 2-D and 3-D shapes according to shape and size.	Feedback from activities.
LESSON 3	● **Use everyday words to describe position.**	COUNT AND SHOW: Children match a card to a given number.	PILE THEM HIGH: Children use positional language to place items.	Feedback from activities. Positional game.
LESSON 4	● Talk about, recognise and recreate patterns: for example simple repeating patterns in the environment.	COUNT AND CLAP: Children clap and count around the class.	PATTERNS: Children make patterns using three properties.	Feedback from activities.
LESSON 5	● Sort and match objects, pictures or children themselves, justifying the decisions made.	COUNT AND CLAP: Children clap and count around the class.	SORT IT AND MATCH IT: Sorting and matching activities.	Feedback from activities.

ORAL AND MENTAL SKILLS **Use language such as more or less, greater or smaller, to compare two numbers** and say which is more or less, and say a number which lies between two given numbers. Recognise small numbers without counting. **Recognise numerals 1 to 9,** then 0 and 10, then beyond 10. **Count reliably up to 10 everyday objects** (first to 5, then 10, then beyond), giving just one number name to each object. Count reliably in other contexts, such as clapping sounds or hopping movements.

Lesson 3 only is given in full in this unit. Lessons 1, 2, 4 and 5 are provided as grids and revisit previously taught content.

LESSON 1

RESOURCES	*Jasper's Beanstalk* by Mick Inkpen and Nick Butterworth (Hodder); five different-sized plants. **Group activities:** spring flowers; garden sticks; a selection of containers.
LEARNING OUTCOMES	**ORAL AND MENTAL STARTER** ● **Use language such as more or less, greater or smaller, to compare two numbers** and say which is more or less, and say a number which lies between two given numbers. **WHOLE-CLASS TEACHING ACTIVITY** ● Put sets of objects in order of size.
ORAL AND MENTAL STARTER	FINGER COUNT: Children use fingers to show a number that is more or less, greater or smaller than a given number. Repeat with children finding a number between two numbers, for example a number between 5 and 7.
WHOLE-CLASS TEACHING ACTIVITY	ORDERING SIZE: Read *Jasper's Beanstalk*. Ask: *What happens when we plant a seed? Does it grow taller or shorter?* Explain that the lesson is about size. Introduce the plants in the pots one at a time in any order: *Is this plant tall or small?* Introduce the second plant: *Is this plant tall or small?* Encourage the children to compare the plants. *Which is the tallest/smallest?* Repeat with the third, then fourth plant. Invite individuals to order the plants according to size from tallest to smallest then vice versa. Introduce another plant. *Where does this plant fit in the order?* Muddle up the plants and invite children to arrange them in order.
GROUP ACTIVITIES	**1.** Children order a selection of spring flowers from smallest to tallest then vice versa. **2.** Children match and order the plants, plant pots and garden sticks. **3.** Give each child a spring flower. They arrange the flowers in ascending order of size, then order a selection of containers in descending order of size. ● Show the children how to grow sunflowers or broad bean seeds. Compare and record the sizes of the plants.
DIFFERENTIATION	Less able: work with three, then four objects. Extend to five, if appropriate. More able: work with three, four, five items and extend.
PLENARY	Feedback on the **Group activities**.

LESSON 2

RESOURCES	Individual set of numeral cards (page 12); selection of counting objects; large selection of different-sized 2-D and 3-D shapes, feely bag or box. **Group activities:** sorting rings; pattern blocks.
LEARNING OUTCOMES	**ORAL AND MENTAL STARTER** ● Recite the number names in order, continuing the count forwards or backwards from a given number. ● Recognise small numbers without counting. **WHOLE-CLASS TEACHING ACTIVITY** ● **Use language such as circle or bigger to describe the shape and size of solids and flat shapes.** ● Put sets of objects in order of size.
ORAL AND MENTAL STARTER	NUMBER FLASH: Count in ones from 0 to 10, then to 20. Count back from 10 to 0, then 20 to 0. Ask the class to look at the number of fingers or objects you hold up, they then hold up a numeral card to show how many there are without counting each object. Repeat, asking individuals to answer.
WHOLE-CLASS TEACHING ACTIVITY	IN THE FAMILY: Display a selection of 2-D and 3-D shapes of different sizes. Place a selection of 2-D shapes into a feely bag or box. Explain the game: You will choose a shape and describe it. The children have to guess the shape. Remind children they can look at the set of shapes displayed to help them. Say: *My shape belongs to the 2-D family. It is a flat shape. It has three sides. All the sides are straight. It has three corners. Guess my shape.* Repeat with other 2-D and 3-D shapes.
GROUP ACTIVITIES	**1.** Children sort a collection of different-sized and coloured 2-D shapes into trays. Encourage them to explain how they have sorted the objects. **2.** Children make shape people and animals using pattern blocks. They count the number of shapes they have used altogether. *How many squares? How many rectangles? How many circles?* **3.** Children sort a collection of different-sized 3-D shapes into rings. They explain how they have sorted the objects, then name and describe the shapes. ● Children make a selection of shape biscuits, with adult supervision.
DIFFERENTIATION	Less able: use a limited number of shapes and sizes. More able: extend the range and size of shapes.
PLENARY	Feedback from the **Group activities**. Repeat 'Guess My Shape'.

UNIT 9

LESSON 3

RESOURCES
Packets and cartons of everyday items found in a shop; shopping bag; wooden blocks or shelves; sets of cards showing either spots, objects or numbers to 10. **Group activities:** recipe and ingredients for shape biscuits.

PREPARATION
Collect packets and cartons of items, for example, a packet of cereal, a box of chocolates, a tin of beans, a bottle of pop. Place a few items in a shopping bag. Set up the blocks and planks to look like shelves. Arrange the items on a shelf. Leave enough space for children to add items.

LEARNING OUTCOMES

ORAL AND MENTAL STARTER
● **Recognise numerals 1 to 9**, then 0 and 10, then beyond 10.
● **Count reliably up to 10 everyday objects** (first to 5, then 10, then beyond), giving just one number name to each object.

WHOLE-CLASS TEACHING ACTIVITY
● **Use everyday words to describe position,** direction and movement: for example, follow and give instructions about positions, directions and movements in PE and other activities.

<table>
<tr><td>VOCABULARY</td></tr>
<tr><td>Position; over; under; above; below; top; bottom; side; next to; between; middle.</td></tr>
</table>

ORAL AND MENTAL STARTER
COUNT AND SHOW: Give each pair a set of mixed cards. When you say a number they have to hold up a card showing that number of spots, items or number.

WHOLE-CLASS TEACHING ACTIVITY
PILE THEM HIGH: Explain that today's lesson is about position. Point out the items on the shelves: *How many of you have shopped at a small shop? There isn't as much space as in a supermarket so all the food has to be arranged on the shelves. What can you see on the top shelf? How many items are on the bottom shelf?* Ask individuals to name items that are in particular places, for example: *What is between the tin of beans and the packet of biscuits? What is next to the bottle of pop?* Ask individuals to come out and add the rest of the items to the display. Ask children to describe the position of the items as they do so. *Are the teabags next to the sugar? Where is the rice? What is above the... What is on the top shelf? What is below the...*

GROUP ACTIVITIES
1. Give instructions for children to arrange three to five items on a set of shelves: *How can these be arranged differently?*
2. Make a selection of shape biscuits. Decorate each shape with a different topping, for example coloured sweets, currants or cherries. Children place their biscuits on a plate and describe their shape, position and decoration.
3. Children investigate the role-play area and describe the position of the objects.
Ask children to set up the role-play area as a small shop.

DIFFERENTIATION
Less able: limit the number of items and language used.
More able: extend the use of language and number of items involved.

PLENARY
Feedback from the **Group activities**. Ask five children to stand in front of the class. Ask the rest of the class to look carefully at the position of the children. Tell the class to close their eyes and invite the group to rearrange themselves. *Has anything changed? Who has changed position? Where were they before?* Encourage the children to use the appropriate language.

LESSON 4

RESOURCES	Cubes; 2-D shapes, the rhyme 'Patterns' in *Seven Dizzy Dragons and Other Maths Rhymes* (Sue Atkinson et al, Cambridge University Press); artefacts and pictures showing patterns in other cultures. **Group activities:** beads; threading lace; paper; crayons.
LEARNING OUTCOMES	**ORAL AND MENTAL STARTER** ● Count reliably in other contexts such as clapping sounds or hopping movements. **WHOLE-CLASS TEACHING ACTIVITY** ● Talk about, recognise and recreate patterns: for example simple repeating patterns patterns in the environment.
ORAL AND MENTAL STARTER	COUNT AND CLAP: Count up to 5, 10, then 20 and beyond. Use a count then clap sequence.
WHOLE-CLASS TEACHING ACTIVITY	Repeat the rhyme 'Patterns' as in Unit 3, Lesson 4, page 86. Ask the children to pick out patterns in the classroom. Show the children the artefacts and pictures showing patterns from different cultures. Arrange a pattern with three cubes (red, blue, green). *What comes next in the pattern?* Make a pattern using three 2-D shapes (square, circle, rectangle). *What comes next in the pattern?* Individuals continue the pattern. Ask children to look for patterns at home.
GROUP ACTIVITIES	**1.** Children thread beads using three then four colours. **2.** Children copy patterns found in different cultures using different media. **3.** Children use three 2-D shapes to copy and continue a pattern. They extend to include size as well as shape. ● Children collect items with different patterns for a display.
DIFFERENTIATION	Less able: copy a pattern using two properties, eg colour and shape. More able: make and describe patterns using three criteria, eg large red triangle.
PLENARY	Feedback from the **Group activities**. Repeat the rhyme 'Patterns'.

LESSON 5

RESOURCES	Flip chart; marker pen; pictures of transport; selection of different clothes; sorting rings. **Group activities:** selection of objects; trays; selection of different clothes.
LEARNING OUTCOMES	**ORAL AND MENTAL STARTER** ● Count reliably in other contexts such as clapping sounds or hopping movements. **WHOLE-CLASS TEACHING ACTIVITY** ● Sort and match objects, pictures or children themselves, justifying the decisions made.
ORAL AND MENTAL STARTER	COUNT AND CLAP: Repeat the activity from Lesson 4, above. Carry on the count around the class.
WHOLE-CLASS TEACHING ACTIVITY	SORT IT AND MATCH IT: Explain that the lesson is about sorting and matching. Sort the children in different ways, eg hair colour, pets, ways of travelling to school, birthday months, shoe fastenings. Encourage them to think of other ways. Repeat sorting using a Venn diagram as described in Lesson 5, Unit 3. Show the children the transport pictures. *How can these be sorted? Can they be sorted in another way?*
GROUP ACTIVITIES	**1.** Children sort a selection of objects into trays, then explain how they have sorted the objects. **2.** Children sort the transport pictures using a Venn diagram. **3.** Children sort a selection of clothes in different ways, eg by material, fastenings pattern, etc. ● Encourage children to sort the apparatus when tidying away.
DIFFERENTIATION	Less able: encourage children to think about other ways of sorting the same item. More able: choose own criteria and explain reasons. Find and describe different ways of sorting a group of objects.
PLENARY	Take feedback from the **Group activities**.

UNIT 10

ORGANISATION (5 LESSONS)

LEARNING OUTCOMES		ORAL AND MENTAL STARTER	WHOLE-CLASS TEACHING ACTIVITY	PLENARY
LESSON 1	● **Use language such as heavier or lighter to compare two quantities,** then more than two by making direct comparisons of masses.	FINGER ADD: Children use fingers to find total by counting on.	HEAVIER AND LIGHTER: Comparison of mass: estimating, comparing with hands, checking with balance.	Feedback from activities. Children guess, compare and balance two items.
LESSON 2	● **Use language such as full or empty to compare two quantities,** then more than two by making direct comparisons of capacity.	DUOS: Children show two numeral cards that add to a given number.	WHAT FITS IN HERE? Comparing the amount of various items that will fill a container.	Class listens to story then fills a large box.
LESSON 3	● **Use language such as full or empty to compare two quantities,** then more than two by making direct comparisons of capacity.	SHOW ME: Children use fingers to 'take away' and count how many are left.	POUR IT IN: Comparison of capacity by estimating and counting.	Children compare the capacity of different containers.
LESSON 4	● **Use language such as taller or shorter to compare two quantities,** then more than two by making direct comparisons of lengths.	LONG WASHING: Children arrange strips of card in order of length.	WHICH IS TALLER?: Comparing length by estimating and checking.	Reinforcing tallest and smallest.
LESSON 5	● Begin to understand and use the vocabulary of time. ● Begin to read o'clock time.	WEEK DAYS: Children recite the days of the week. Put days in order.	HICKORY, DICKORY, DOCK: Telling the time; introducing o'clock.	Story-reading.

ORAL AND MENTAL SKILLS Put sets of objects in order of size. Begin to understand and use ordinal numbers in different contexts. **Begin to use the vocabulary involved in adding.** Find a total by counting on when one group of objects is hidden. **Begin to relate addition to combining two groups of objects. Begin to relate subtraction to 'taking away'** and counting how many are left. Begin to know the days of the week in order.

Lessons 1, 3 and 5 are provided in full, with Lessons 2 and 4 as grids, following on from previously taught concepts.

RESOURCES

Flip chart; marker pen; selection of different items, for example a potato, large shell, carrot, cotton wool balls, tin of beans, shoe, bead, cube, ruler, pencil, book; parcels of different sizes and shapes; small wooden plank; building blocks; labels; balances.
Group activities: labels; paper; crayons; items for the role-play post office.

PREPARATION

Make labels saying 'is lighter than', 'is heavier than', 'these are heavier than', 'these are lighter than'.

LEARNING OUTCOMES

ORAL AND MENTAL STARTER
● **Begin to use the vocabulary involved in adding.**
● Find a total by counting on when one group of objects is hidden.

WHOLE-CLASS TEACHING ACTIVITY

● **Use language such as heavier or lighter to compare two quantities,** then more than two, by making direct comparisons of masses.

VOCABULARY

Weigh; weighs; balances; heavy/light; heavier/ lighter; heaviest/ lightest.

ORAL AND MENTAL STARTER

FINGER ADD: Children use their fingers to count on from a given number to find the total. Number facts to 5.

WHOLE-CLASS TEACHING ACTIVITY

HEAVIER AND LIGHTER: Ask: *Can you remember how to tell if something is heavy or light?* Ask individuals to name items that are heavy or light. Show children two items, for example a large potato and a carrot. *Which one is heavier? Can you guess by looking at the items?* Invite individuals to compare the items by holding them. Explain that we need to compare things to find out if they are heavier or lighter than each other. Repeat with two different items. Next, introduce the parcels, making sure there is a small, heavy one and a large, light one. *Which parcel is heavier?* Choose individuals to compare using hands. *Is this what you expected? Why?* Encourage children to discuss their reasons.

Ask: *Why do we need to weigh things? How are items weighed?* Introduce the balance. Remind children of the nursery rhyme 'See-saw Margary Daw'. Demonstrate the see-saw action using a small plank and a building block. *What happens when teddy is placed on one end with nothing at the other?* Explain that the heavier end goes down and the lighter end goes up. If two things are placed on the see-saw and they have the same mass, they balance. Choose two parcels and ask: *Which is the lighter?* Ask individuals to compare using hands, then check using the balance. Show the labels 'is lighter than' and 'is heavier than'. Say: *The red parcel is heavier than the blue parcel.* Place the labels appropriately.

GROUP ACTIVITIES

1. Children find things in a collection that are heavier than a large potato. How many items can they find? They place labels 'these are heavier than' to show what they have found, then draw the items.
2. Find things in a collection that are lighter than a large shell. How many items can they find? Place labels 'these are lighter than' to show what they have found. Draw the items.
3. Children order a set of three objects ranging from heaviest to lightest. They guess first then compare using hands. Use the balance to check. Extend to four then five objects.
Set up a post office and include parcels and letters of different sizes.

DIFFERENTIATION

Less able: limit to two or three items.
More able: extend to five items. Encourage children to rearrange the order.

PLENARY

Draw a table on the flip chart with three columns: 'Our guess', 'Comparing with hands' and 'Checking with the balance'. Choose two items and invite children to guess, compare and check using a balance. Record their findings.

LESSON 2

RESOURCES	Flip chart; marker pen; lunch box filled with some items suitable for a packed lunch, eg crisps, apple, carton of drink, biscuits, sandwiches, plus some additional lunch items; different sized and shaped containers; labels saying 'This holds the most', 'This holds the least'; *My Cat Likes To Hide In Boxes* by Eve Sutton (Puffin); cardboard box. **Group activities:** some 'everyday' items such as a spoon, a shoe, a toy, a teddy; cubes; water tray; sand tray; wet and dry sand; pencils.
LEARNING OUTCOMES	**ORAL AND MENTAL STARTER** ● **Begin to use the vocabulary involved in adding.** ● **Begin to relate addition to combining two groups of objects.** **WHOLE-CLASS TEACHING ACTIVITY** ● **Use language such as full, empty, half full, nearly full to compare two quantities,** then more than two, by making direct comparisons of capacity.
ORAL AND MENTAL STARTER	DUOS: Children find and show two numeral cards that add to a given total, first to 5, then to 10.
WHOLE-CLASS TEACHING ACTIVITY	WHAT FITS IN HERE?: Hold up the lunch box and ask the children to look at it. *Is it full or empty? How do we know?* Ask who brings sandwiches for lunch. Make a mark for each child on the flip chart and ask the class to count the number of marks. Show the children the contents of the lunch box. Remove some items: *Is it empty or full?* Empty out the rest of the contents: *What is it now?* Count how many items were inside and write this number on the flip chart. Show the children the additional lunch items: *Will the lunch box hold these as well?* Invite children to fill the lunch box by choosing from the items. Count how many items it contains. Write the number on the chart. *Is it more or less than the first number?* Repeat. Choose three containers. Ask the children to find out how many cubes each one holds. Order them to show which holds most and least. Label them 'This holds the most' and 'This holds the least'.
GROUP ACTIVITIES	**1.** Children choose three containers and fill each one with a selection of objects. They count the number of items each time. Which holds the most/least? **2.** Children use the sand tray with wet and dry sand. They choose three containers and fill them using a smaller container. Count the number it takes to fill each one. Which holds the most/least? **3.** Use the water tray. Choose three containers and fill with a smaller container. Count the number it takes to fill each one. Which holds the most/least? ● In pairs, children see who can fit most items in a lunch box, then draw the items.
DIFFERENTIATION	Less able: make comparisons using two or three containers. Reinforce vocabulary. More able: extend to make comparisons between three then up to five containers. Include those which hold the same amount.
PLENARY	Read *My Cat Likes To Hide In Boxes*. Use a large cardboard box and find items that will and will not fit inside.

LESSON 3

RESOURCES

Containers; sticky labels; egg cup; yoghurt pot; beaker; flip chart; marker pen. **Group activities:** sand and water trays; shells, cubes, beads, etc, photocopiable page 92 (Fill it).

PREPARATION

Collect a selection of containers of different sizes and shapes and include some that contain the same amount. Cut out templates to represent the containers and attach a sticky label, say animals, to about five containers to assist identification. Place Blu-Tack on the back of each one. Choose three containers, eg egg cup, yoghurt pot, beaker, that can be used to fill the others. On the flip chart, set out a chart with three columns saying 'Our container', 'Our guess', 'It holds'.

VOCABULARY

Full; half full; empty; holds; container; more; less; arrange; rearrange; count; check; in order; guess; enough; not enough; too much; too little.

LEARNING OUTCOMES

ORAL AND MENTAL STARTER
● **Begin to relate subtraction to 'taking away'** and counting how many are left.

WHOLE-CLASS TEACHING ACTIVITY
● **Use language such as full, empty, half full, nearly full to compare two quantities,** then more than two, by making direct comparisons of capacity.

ORAL AND MENTAL STARTER
SHOW ME: Ask children to show ten fingers then 'take away' eight: *How many are left?* Repeat, using different numbers 0 to 10.

WHOLE-CLASS TEACHING ACTIVITY

POUR IT IN: Remind children that capacity is about how much something holds. Show them the different containers: *Can you arrange them in order of size, starting with the one that holds the most?* Explain that you are going to fill the bottle using the egg cup. Display the appropriate bottle template in the first column of the chart and ask individuals to guess how many egg cups of water it will take to fill the bottle. Note the amount on the flip chart. At various times ask: *Is it full? Nearly full? Half full?* Count the number of egg cups it takes to fill the bottle and record the number on the chart. Let children fill the containers and count the number of egg cups it takes to fill it to the top. Select two different containers. *What will happen when we fill the smaller container using the larger one?*

GROUP ACTIVITIES

1. Water tray activity: children use a range of containers to find out which container holds more than/less than/the same as other containers.
2. Sorting and ordering: children order other containers according to capacity using labels 'holds more than' 'less than' 'the same as'.
3. Children guess how many items fill a container, then fill it with beads, cubes, pasta etc. to check. They record using photocopiable page 92 (Fill it).

 Use a range of containers with wet and dry sand to find out which container holds more than/less than/the same as other containers.

DIFFERENTIATION

Less able: ensure children understand vocabulary. Limit number of items to 10, then 20.
More able: encourage comparison of three to five containers. Include containers that hold same amount but are different shapes.

PLENARY

Choose three containers that are the same size, eg beakers. Fill one to the top, half fill the other and leave the last one empty: *How much does each container hold?* Encourage children to compare using the words 'more', 'less', 'half full', 'full' and 'empty'. Ask the children to arrange the containers in order. *Can we rearrange these in a different order?* Ask individuals to pour water into the beakers to change the amount each holds.

LESSON 4

RESOURCES	Six strips of card (different lengths, widths and colours); washing line; pegs; paintbrush; pencil; garden cane; flashcards saying 'tallest', 'shortest'; zigzag books. **Group activities:** paper; crayons; labels saying 'are taller than', 'are shorter than'.
LEARNING OUTCOMES	**ORAL AND MENTAL STARTER** ● Put sets of objects in order of size. ● Begin to understand and use ordinal numbers in different contexts. **WHOLE-CLASS TEACHING ACTIVITY** ● **Use language such as longer or shorter to compare two quantities,** then more than two by making direct comparisons of lengths.
ORAL AND MENTAL STARTER	LONG WASHING: Hold up the six strips of card. Explain that they are different sizes. Discuss the differences. Children peg the strips of card on the washing line in order of length. *Which colour is first? Which colour comes between the third and fifth strip?*
WHOLE-CLASS TEACHING ACTIVITY	WHICH IS TALLER?: Hold up a paintbrush and a pencil: *Which is taller?* Add a garden cane. *Which is tallest?* Show the flashcards. Invite two children out: *How can we find out who is the tallest?* Stand the children back to back. *Emily is taller than Navraj.* Ask another child to join and get the children to estimate. *Is John taller or shorter than Emily?* Compare with Navraj. Ask the children to stand in descending order then ascending order. *Navraj is shorter than Emily but taller than John.* Repeat using five children.
GROUP ACTIVITIES	**1.** Children find things that are taller than a chosen item. Record by drawing. **2.** Compare items that are taller/shorter than a given item. Use the labels to record. **3.** Compare and sort items into longest/shortest/same as. Use the labels to record. ● Children complete zigzag books after comparing heights of others in the group. They draw pictures of children shorter and taller than themselves.
DIFFERENTIATION	Less able: compare using two items then extend to three. More able: compare using up to five items.
PLENARY	Sing 'Two fat gentlemen met in the lane'. Children show their tallest/smallest fingers.

RESOURCES

Flip chart; marker pen; flashcards giving days of the week; selection of clocks, including 'play' clocks; *The Bad-tempered Ladybird* by Eric Carle (Puffin); dice showing clock faces.
Group activities: paper plates; felt tipped pens; clock stamps; zigzag books; 3 × 3 grids; individual clock cards showing o'clock times; mouse templates.

PREPARATION

Make six sets of clock bingo cards using the 3 × 3 grids and the clock stamps. Make cards to match the clock cards.

LEARNING OUTCOMES

ORAL AND MENTAL STARTER
● Begin to know the days of the week in order.

WHOLE-CLASS TEACHING ACTIVITY
● Begin to understand and use the vocabulary of time.
● Begin to read o'clock time.

VOCABULARY

Days of the week; Monday; day; week; morning; afternoon; evening; night; bedtime; dinnertime; playtime; today; yesterday; tomorrow; before; after; next; last; hour; o'clock; clock; hands.

ORAL AND MENTAL STARTER

WEEK DAYS: Recite the days of the week. Put the day cards in order: *Which day comes before Tuesday? ...after Friday? ...in between Sunday and Tuesday?* Discuss familiar activities that happen on different days of the week.

WHOLE-CLASS TEACHING ACTIVITY

HICKORY, DICKORY, DOCK: Explain that the lesson is about telling the time. Discuss different ways of telling the time, for example listening to the radio, setting the alarm, listening to chimes, looking at a clock or watch, setting a timer. Hold up a large clock and ask the children to look at the clock face. *What is special about the numbers?* Count around the clock. Point out the difference between the hands and demonstrate how the longer hand moves quickly around the face (telling the minutes), while the shorter hand moves slowly (telling the hours). Show 9 o'clock and point out that when the long hand is pointing to the 12 it always says 'o'clock' and the short hand tells the hour. Ask what time it says. Discuss special times in the school day. Point them out on the clock. Invite children to demonstrate o'clock times on the clock. Write special times on the flip chart. Recite the rhyme 'Hickory Dickory Dock': *What happened at 1 o'clock?*

GROUP ACTIVITIES

1. Children make individual clocks using paper plates.
2. Make zigzag books showing special times in the school day.
3. Clock bingo: Children match individual o'clock cards to a base board.

 Throw a dice showing o'clock times. Every time a child gets 1 o'clock he or she collects a cardboard mouse. The first person to collect three mice wins.

DIFFERENTIATION

Less able: allow plenty of practical activity to reinforce position of hands on the clock for o'clock.
More able: challenge them to think of their own special times.

PLENARY

Read *The Bad-tempered Ladybird*.

UNIT 11

ORGANISATION (5 LESSONS)

LEARNING OUTCOMES		ORAL AND MENTAL STARTER	WHOLE-CLASS TEACHING ACTIVITY	PLENARY
LESSON 1	● Recite the number names in order, continuing the count forwards or backwards from a given number. ● Count in tens.	COUNT ON: Children count on several numbers from a given number.	TENS: Activities involving numbers 10 to 100.	Feedback from activities. Counting in tens.
LESSON 2 +3	**● Begin to use the vocabulary involved in adding and subtracting.** **● Begin to relate addition to combining two groups of objects,** counting all the objects. ● Begin to relate addition to counting on. ● Find a total by counting on when one group of objects is hidden. ● Separate (partition) a given number of objects into two groups. ● Select two groups of objects to make a given total. **● Begin to relate subtraction to 'taking away'** and counting how many are left. ● Remove a smaller number from a larger and find how many are left by counting back from the larger number. ● Work out by counting how many more are needed to make a larger number.	FINGER ADD AND SUBTRACT: Children count on in twos and tens.	ADDING AND SUBTRACTING ACTIVITIES: Problem-solving using addition and subtraction	Feedback from activities.
LESSON 4 +5	**● Use developing mathematical ideas and methods to solve practical problems** involving counting and comparing in a real or role play context. **● Begin to use the vocabulary involved in adding and subtracting.** ● Begin to understand and use the vocabulary related to money. Sort coins, including the £1 and £2 coins, and use them in role play to pay and give change.	FINGER ADD AND SUBTRACT: Children count on in twos and tens.	WHAT'S IN MY PURSE?: Problem-solving activities using money contexts.	Feedback from activities.

ORAL AND MENTAL SKILLS Recite the number names in order, continuing the count forwards or backwards from a given number. Count in twos. Count in tens. **Begin to relate addition to combining two groups of objects,** counting all the objects. **Begin to relate subtraction to 'taking away'** and counting how many are left.

Lesson 1 is provided in a grid. Lessons 2 and 4 are shown in detail. Lessons 3 and 5 are continuations of what have been taught and follow on sequentially.

LESSON 1

RESOURCES	Large class 'tens' number track (0–100); pointer; 100 square. **Group activities:** individual 100 grids; crayons; copies of photocopiable page 127 (Mixed up tens); scissors; adhesive; card; number tracks (10–100); (10–100) spinners.
LEARNING OUTCOMES	**ORAL AND MENTAL STARTER** ● Recite the number names in order, continuing the count forwards or backwards from a given number. **WHOLE-CLASS TEACHING ACTIVITY** ● Recite the number names in order, continuing the count forwards or backwards from a given number. ● Count in tens.
ORAL AND MENTAL STARTER	COUNT ON: Ask children to count on several numbers from a given number. Say: *Start at 5 count on 4. 5 – 6, 7, 8, 9. 5 count on 4 is 9.* Repeat, using different starting and counting on numbers.
WHOLE-CLASS TEACHING ACTIVITY	TENS: Look together at the tens 0–100 number track. Ask the class to count in tens to 50 as you point to the number track. Repeat to 100. Ask groups, pairs and individuals to count in tens. Say: *Counting in tens, which number comes before 30? Which number comes after 60? Which number comes in the middle of 40 and 60?* Show the children a 100 grid. Colour in every tenth square to 50. Ask: *Can you see a pattern?*
GROUP ACTIVITIES	**1.** Give each child a 100 grid and crayons. Children colour in every tenth square. **2.** Give each child a copy of photocopiable page 127 (Mixed-up tens). They cut out the numbers and arrange them to make a 10–100 number track. Check to see if they are in the correct order then mount on card. **3.** Give pairs a number track (10–100) each and a spinner (10–100). Children take it in turns to spin the spinner and colour in that number on their track. The first child to colour all their numbers wins. ● The children can play dot-to-dot activities in tens to 100.
DIFFERENTIATION	Less able: count in tens to 50. More able: count to 100 and back.
PLENARY	Feedback from the **Group activities**. Count in tens to 50 then 100.

LESSON 2 + 3

RESOURCES

Flip chart; marker pen; conkers; containers. **Group activities:** skittles; ball; paper; pencils; plates; packet of biscuits; bucket; bean bags; dice (1–6); individual number tracks (0–10) (page 13).

PREPARATION

Photocopy the number tracks. Set up the skittles, bean bags and bucket in an open space.

LEARNING OUTCOMES

ORAL AND MENTAL STARTER
● Count in twos.
● Count in tens.
● **Begin to relate addition to combining two groups of objects,** counting all the objects.
● **Begin to relate subtraction to 'taking away'** and counting how many are left.

WHOLE-CLASS TEACHING ACTIVITY
● **Begin to use the vocabulary involved in adding and subtracting.**
● **Begin to relate addition to combining two groups of objects,** counting all the objects.
● Begin to relate addition to counting on.
● Find a total by counting on when one group of objects is hidden.
● Separate (partition) a given number of objects into two groups.
● Select two groups of objects to make a given total.
● **Begin to relate subtraction to 'taking away'** and counting how many are left.
● Remove a smaller number from a larger and find how many are left by counting back from the larger number.
● Work out by counting how many more are needed to make a larger number.

VOCABULARY

Adding; subtracting; add; more; and; make; sum; total; altogether; score; double; one more; how many more to make...?; how many more is... than...?; take (away); leave; how many are left/left over?; how many have gone?

ORAL AND MENTAL STARTER

FINGER ADD AND SUBTRACT: Warm-up, and revisit the previous lesson's work, by counting in twos, then tens. Set the scene for the **Whole-class teaching activity** by asking children to add two numbers and hold up fingers to show answers. Repeat for 'taking away'.

WHOLE-CLASS TEACHING ACTIVITY

ADDING AND SUBTRACTING ACTIVITIES: In these activities lots of skills practice is suggested. Your choice of group work could focus this on a narrower range of strategies. Remind the children they have been working on adding and subtracting. Explain that in the next two lessons they are going to work on different adding and subtracting activities and outline the activities provided for the groups. Display the 0–10 number track. Explain that you want the children to make two jumps to make 10. Say: *How shall we do that?* Invite and show suggestions from the children. Use the number track to demonstrate by jumping on to a number then counting the number of jumps it takes to reach ten. Say: *Jump on to 4, then count each jump to 10. 4 add 6 makes 10. The total of 4 add 6 is 10.* Record the number sentences on the flip chart. Repeat using other numbers.

Count out eight conkers into a container. *How many conkers?* Take out two. *How many conkers are there now? Count back from 8. 7, 6. There are six conkers left. 8 subtract 2 is 6.*

GROUP ACTIVITIES

Choose from this selection for Lessons 2 and 3:
1. Set up the skittles. Ask the children to take turns to throw the ball. Children record how many are left standing and how many fall over.
2. Ask children to work in pairs. Give each pair two plates. Each pair counts out ten biscuits. Ask the children to find as many ways as they can of putting the ten biscuits into two plates. Children record their answers (numerals or pictorially).
3. Place a bucket in an open space and mark out a starting point. Place five bean bags close by. Children take turns to throw the bean bags into the bucket. Children record on the flip chart, with support from an adult helper, how many bean bags go into the bucket and how many stay outside each time.
4. Working in pairs, children have two dice. Each child takes a turn to throw the dice. Children record the pairs of numbers that have a total of six.
5. Ask children to count out eight conkers into a container. In pairs, one child removes a number of conkers from the container. Their partner works out how many conkers are left in the container by counting back from 8.
6. Each child has a number track (0–10) and finds ways they can make two jumps that make 10, as demonstrated in the **Whole-class teaching activity**.

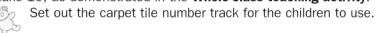 Set out the carpet tile number track for the children to use.

DIFFERENTIATION

Less able: ask a classroom assistant to support them.
More able: extend the activities to make them more challenging, such as find three jumps that make 10.

PLENARY

Take feedback from the **Group activities**.

RESOURCES

Purses; assorted coins; flip chart; marker pen. **Group activities:** copies of photocopiable pages 128 (Making money) and 129 (The garden centre); coin stamps; selection of coins; assorted everyday items such as a beaker, doll, book, pencil; money dice (1p, 2p, 5p, 10p, 20p, £1); items for a role-play garden centre.

PREPARATION

Place a selection of coins in each purse. Write out the price labels and attach one to each item.

LESSON 4 + 5

LEARNING OUTCOMES

ORAL AND MENTAL STARTER
● Count in twos.
● Count in tens.
● **Begin to relate addition to combining two groups of objects,** counting all the objects.
● **Begin to relate subtraction to 'taking away'** and counting how many are left.

WHOLE-CLASS TEACHING ACTIVITY
● **Use developing mathematical ideas and methods to solve practical problems** involving counting and comparing in a real or role play context.
● **Begin to use the vocabulary involved in adding and subtracting.**
● Begin to understand and use the vocabulary related to money. Sort coins, including the £1 and £2 coins, and use them in role play to pay and give change.

VOCABULARY
Add; more; and; make; sum; total; altogether; take (away); leave; how many are left/ left over?; how many have gone?; how many fewer is... than..?; compare; count out; left; left over; money; coin; penny; pence; pound; price; cost; buy; sell; spend; spent; pay; change; dear; costs more; cheap; costs less; cheaper; costs the same as; how much...?; how many...?; total

ORAL AND MENTAL STARTER

FINGER ADD AND SUBTRACT: As for Lessons 2 and 3, page 125.

WHOLE-CLASS TEACHING ACTIVITY

WHAT'S IN MY PURSE?: Empty out the contents of a purse. Ask children to come out and identify the coins as you record them on the chart. *Are there any 2p coins? How many are there?* Write the amount of each coin in the appropriate column, such as 2p, 2p, 2p in the 2p column. Repeat with all the coins. Ask the children to look at the chart. *Are there more 2p coins than 5p coins? How many more 10p coins are there than 1p coins? Is 50p more than £1.00? How could we find out how much we have in 2p coins?* Add up the amount and record the total: *The total amount of 2p coins is 12p. 2p add 2p add 2p add 2p add 2p add 2p. Six 2p coins make 12p altogether.* Repeat using other coins. Ask: *How many coins are there altogether? Shall we find out how much money is in the purse altogether?* Support the children to find the total amount.

Give out a purse containing coins to each pair of children. Explain that you want them to work in pairs to make 5p using their coins. Ask pairs of children to explain which coins they have used to make 5p. Record these on the flip chart. Say: *Are there any other ways?*

GROUP ACTIVITIES

Choose from this selection for Lessons 4 and 5:
1. Give each child a copy of photocopiable page 128 (Making money). Children find different ways of making the different amounts. They can record on their sheet by placing money, using money stamps or drawing around each coin.
2. Place a selection of items with price labels on the table. In pairs, children choose an item, then match the coins to the price label.
3. Give children a money dice. Ask them to roll the dice and collect coins to make amounts, for example 5p in 1p coins, 10p in 2p coins, £6.00 in £1.00 coins.
4. Give each child a copy of photocopiable page 129 (The garden centre). Children make up the amounts for the various items using the price list.

Set up a garden centre in the role-play area.

DIFFERENTIATION

Less able: limit the range of coins to 10p, then 20p and beyond.
More able: challenge the children to make amounts using larger values.

PLENARY

Ask the children to share their findings with the whole class.

Mixed-up tens

100	60	100
40	80	50
20	30	80
80	70	10
50	50	60
70	10	30
30	100	20
90	40	90
60	90	40
10	20	70

UNIT 11

Making money

Make the purses hold the total amount given.
Draw the coins inside the purses.

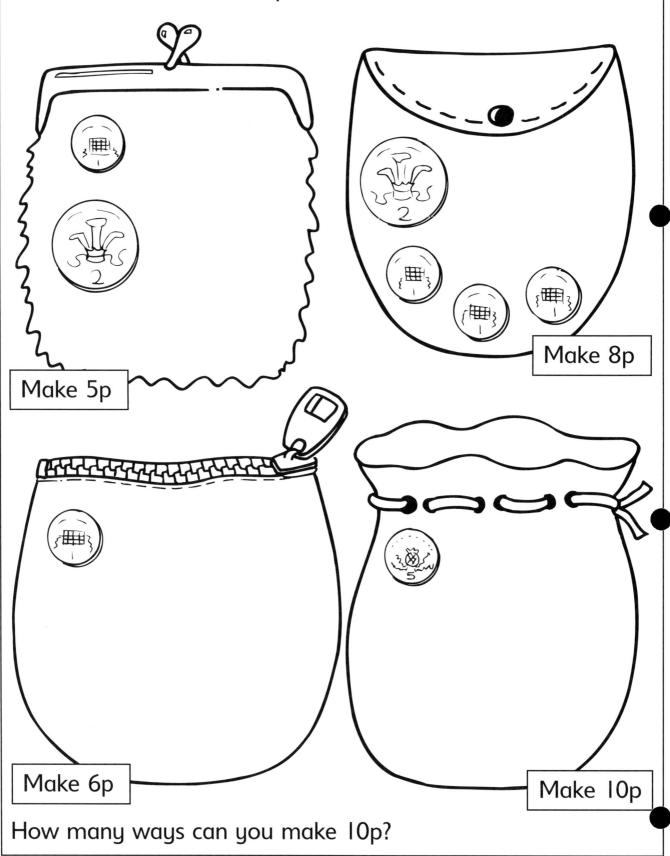

Make 5p

Make 8p

Make 6p

Make 10p

How many ways can you make 10p?

Name

The garden centre

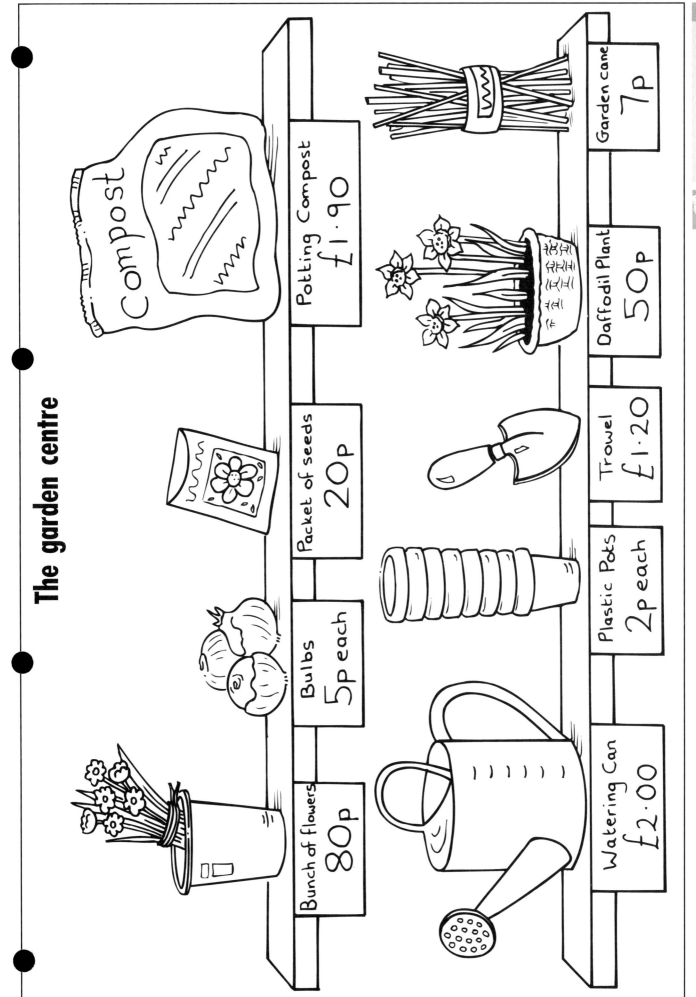

Compost

Potting Compost £1·90

Garden cane 7p

Daffodil Plant 50p

Packet of seeds 20p

Trowel £1·20

Bulbs 5p each

Plastic Pots 2p each

Bunch of flowers 80p

Watering Can £2·00

UNIT 12: Assess & review

Choose from the following activities over the two lessons. During the group activities some of the children can work with you on practical tasks, while others complete assessment worksheets 2a and 2b which assess their skills in counting, reading and writing, and ordering numbers and addition. The specific assessment criteria for the assessment sheets can be found at the bottom of each sheet.

RESOURCES

Large number track; individual number tracks (page 13); large set of numeral cards; individual sets of numeral cards for each child; assessment photocopiables 2A and 2B; a selection of objects for counting; interlocking cubes, sets of 2-D and 3-D shapes; a selection of items for measuring; different sizes and masses of parcels; items such as shells, fir cones, shoe, book, cotton reels; beads; 1p, 2p, 5p, 10p, 20p, 50p £1.00 and £2.00 coins; pencils and paper for recording.

ORAL AND MENTAL STARTER

ASSESSMENT

● Can the children: **Recognise numerals 1 to 9? Begin to use the vocabulary involved in adding and subtracting?**
NUMBERS TO 9: Ask children to count with you using the number track. Point to different numerals. Ask the class and individuals to read out the numeral.
ADDING AND SUBTRACTING: Explain that you are going to say two numbers. You want the children to hold the first number in their heads. Say that you will give another number. You want the children to add that number to the first. Then they show you the total by holding up a numeral card. Start with numbers that total 5, then 10, then beyond. Observe and record who adds with confidence and who needs more practice. Allow individual children opportunities to add using their fingers. Observe who is doing this confidently and who needs more practice. Repeat the activity using subtraction.

GROUP ACTIVITIES

ASSESSMENT

● Can the children: **Recognise numerals 1 to 9? Use language such as circle or bigger to describe the shape and size of solids and flat shapes?** Compare mass by direct comparison of two objects? **Use developing mathematical ideas and methods to solve practical problems** using adding and subtraction?
RECOGNITION OF NUMERALS 1 TO 9: Ask children to point out the numerals on a number track as you say them. Then point to a numeral and ask children to say which it is.
SHAPE AND SPACE: Place a selection of 2-D and 3-D shapes in a feely bag. Ask children to feel a shape and say what it is. Ask children how they could tell it was that shape. Provide a set of the same shapes for children to match. Observe who is doing this confidently without the support of the shapes and who needs more practice.
COMPARING MASS: Place two objects on the table. Ask children to guess which is the heavier. Then ask them to handle the objects, then use the balance to check if they were correct. Repeat the activity with different objects. Check children can understand and use the vocabulary of mass.
SOLVING PROBLEMS: Either choose some problems from Unit 11, Lessons 4 and 5 or make up some similar ones. Provide counting resources such as cubes, everyday items and coins. Encourage children to show and describe how they worked out their answer for each problem.

Assessment 2a

Read the numbers. Draw the correct number of objects.
Count carefully.

| 5 | 3 | 7 | 10 | 1 |

| 4 | 8 | 2 | 9 | 6 |

Find how much:

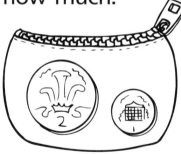 add   makes [ ] p

 add   makes [ ] p

● **Recognise numerals to 1 to 9,** then 0 and 10.
● **Count reliably up to 10 everyday objects.**
● **Begin to relate addition to combining two groups of objects.**

Assessment 2b

Count the monsters and match to the numbers.

Read these numbers. Fill in the missing numbers.

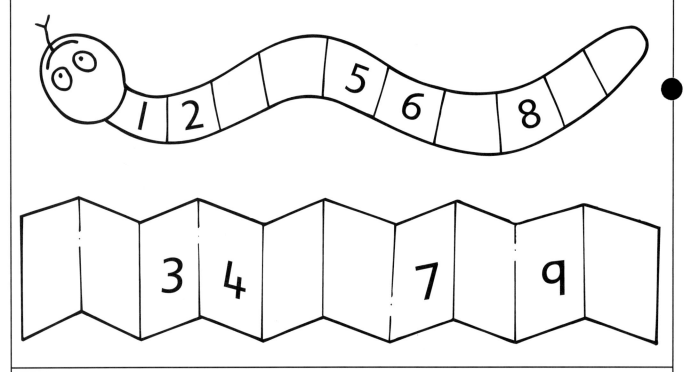

- **Recognise numerals 1 to 9,** then 0 and 10.
- **Count reliably up to 10 everyday objects,** giving just one number name to each object.
- Begin to record numbers.

TERM 3

During the summer term children consolidate their knowledge and understanding of number. Different vocabulary and methods are used for addition and subtraction, including counting on and back, doubling and partitioning. Children recognise, read and write numbers and ordinal numbers are introduced. They develop mathematical ideas and methods through problem-solving and 'real life' contexts.

In 'Shape and space' children continue to consolidate concepts of 2-D and 3-D shape. Position and direction are developed further and symmetrical patterns are introduced.

In 'Measures' children's abilities to compare more quantities in capacity, mass and length are extended and they begin to use non-standard units and balances to compare objects and carry out simple recording.

ENLARGE THIS SHEET TO A3 AND USE IT AS YOUR LONG TERM PLANNING GRID.

ORAL AND MENTAL SKILLS: Say and use the number names in order in familiar contexts such as number rhymes, songs, stories, counting games and activities (first to five, then ten, then twenty and beyond). Recite the number names in order, continuing the count forwards or backwards from a given number. **Use language such as more or less, greater or smaller, to compare two numbers** and say which is more or less, and say a number which lies between two given numbers. **Recognise numerals 1 to 9**, then 0 and 10, then beyond 10. Count in tens. Count in twos. **Use language such as circle or bigger to describe the shape and size of solids and flat shapes.** Begin to name solids such as a cube, cone, sphere... and flat shapes such as a circle, triangle, square, rectangle. **Begin to relate addition to combining two groups of objects,** counting all the objects; extend to three groups of objects. Begin to relate addition to counting on. **Begin to relate subtraction to 'taking away'** and counting how many are left. Begin to find out how many have been removed from a larger group of objects by counting up from a number. Begin to understand and use the vocabulary related to money. Sort coins, including the £1 and £2 coins, and use them in role play to pay and give change.

Unit	Topic	Objectives: children will be taught to...
1	Counting, reading and writing numbers Comparing and ordering numbers	● Estimate a number in the range that can be counted reliably, then check by counting. ● **Recognise numerals 1 to 9,** then 0 and 10, then beyond 10. ● **Use language such as more or less, greater or smaller, to compare two numbers** and say which is more or less, and say a number which lies between two given numbers. ● Order a given set of numbers: for example, the set of numbers 1 to 6 given in random order. ● Order a given set of selected numbers: for example, the set 2, 5, 1, 8, 4. ● Begin to record numbers, initially by making marks, progressing to simple tallying and writing numbers.
2	Counting, reading and writing numbers Adding and subtracting	● **Begin to use the vocabulary involved in adding and subtracting.** ● Begin to relate addition to counting on. ● Separate (partition) a given number of objects into two groups. ● Count in twos. ● Begin to find out how many have been removed from a larger group of objects by counting up from a number.
3	Shape and space Reasoning	● Begin to name solids such as a cube, cone, sphere... ● **Use language such as circle or bigger to describe the shape and size of flat shapes.** ● Begin to name flat shapes such as a circle, triangle, square, rectangle... ● **Use everyday words to describe position,** direction and movement: for example, follow and give instructions about positions, directions and movements in PE and other activities. ● Talk about, recognise and recreate patterns: for example simple repeating patterns in the environment.
4	Counting, reading and writing numbers Measures	● **Recognise numerals 1 to 9,** then 0 and 10, then beyond 10. ● Begin to record numbers, initially by making marks, progressing to simple tallying and writing numerals. ● **Use language such as longer or shorter, heavier or lighter, more or less to compare two quantities,** then more than two, by making direct comparisons of lengths, masses. ● Begin to record numbers, initially by making marks, progressing to simple tallying and writing numerals.
5	Counting, reading and writing numbers Adding and subtracting Money and 'real life' problems	● **Use developing mathematical ideas and methods to solve practical problems** involving counting and comparing in a real or role play context. ● Begin to understand and use the vocabulary related to money. Sort coins, including the £1 and £2 coins, and use them in role play to pay and give change.
6	Assess and review	

ORAL AND MENTAL SKILLS: Recognise numerals 1 to 9, then 0 and 10, then beyond 10. **Say and use the number names in order in familiar contexts. Begin to relate addition to combining two groups of objects,** counting all the objects. Begin to relate addition to counting on. Find the total by counting on when one group of objects is hidden. **Begin to relate subtraction to 'taking away'** and counting how many are left. **Use language such as more or less, greater or smaller, to compare two numbers** and say which is more or less, and say a number which lies between two given numbers. **Say and use the number names in order in familiar contexts.** Count in twos. Order a given set of numbers given in random order. Order a given set of selected numbers. Begin to understand and use ordinal numbers in different contexts. Recite the number names in order, continuing the count forwards or backwards from a given number. **Count reliably up to 10 everyday objects. Find one more or one less than a number from 1 to 10. Begin to use the vocabulary involved in adding and subtracting.**

7	Counting, reading and writing numbers Comparing and ordering numbers	● **Recognise numerals 1 to 9,** then 0 and 10, then beyond 10. ● Begin to record numbers, initially by making marks, progressing to simple tallying and writing numerals ● **Count reliably in other contexts** such as sounds. ● Begin to understand and use ordinal numbers in different contexts. ● **Use language such as more or less, greater or smaller, to compare two numbers** and say which is more or less, and say a number which lies between two given numbers. ● Order a given set of numbers: for example, the set of numbers 1 to 6 given in random order. ● Order a given set of selected numbers: for example, the set of 2, 5, 1, 8, 4
8	Counting, reading and writing numbers Adding and subtracting	● **Begin to relate addition to combining two groups of objects,** counting all the objects. ● Separate (partition) a given number of objects into two groups. ● Select two groups of objects to make a given total ● **Begin to relate subtraction to 'taking away'** and counting how many are left. ● Remove a smaller number from a larger and find how many are left by counting back from the larger number. ● Begin to use the vocabulary involved in adding and subtracting
9	Shape and space Reasoning	● Use everyday words to describe position. ● Put sets of objects in order of size. ● **Use everyday words to describe position,** direction and movement. ● Talk about, recognise and recreate patterns: for example, simple repeating or symmetrical patterns in the environment.
10	Counting, reading and writing numbers Measures, including time	● Begin to understand and use the vocabulary of time. Sequence familiar events. ● Begin to read o'clock time. ● **Use language such as more or less, longer or shorter, heavier or lighter ... to compare two quantities,** then more than two, by making direct comparisons of lengths or masses, and by filling and emptying containers.
11	Counting, reading and writing numbers Adding and subtracting Money and 'real life' problems	● **Use developing mathematical ideas and methods to solve practical problems** involving counting and comparing in a real or role-play context. ● Begin to understand and use the vocabulary related to money. Sort coins, including the £1 and £2 coins, and use them in role play to pay and give change
12	Assess and review	

UNIT 1

ORGANISATION (5 LESSONS)

LEARNING OUTCOMES	ORAL AND MENTAL STARTER	WHOLE-CLASS TEACHING ACTIVITY	PLENARY
LESSON 1 ● Estimate a number in the range that can be counted reliably, then check by counting.	ONE MAN WENT TO MOW: Children recite the rhyme, counting up to 10.	GUESSTIMATE: Estimating and counting activities.	Children estimate items or people around the school.
LESSON 2 ● **Recognise numerals 1 to 9,** then 0 and 10, then beyond 10. ● **Use language such as more or less, greater or smaller, to compare two numbers** and say which is more or less, and say a number which lies between two given numbers.	FIND ME: Children identify given numbers.	NEXT-DOOR NUMBERS: Identifying what comes before or after a given number, or in between two numbers.	Reinforcing number order.
LESSON 3 ● **Recognise numerals 1 to 9,** then 0 and 10, then beyond 10. ● **Use language such as more or less, greater or smaller, to compare two numbers** and say which is more or less, and say a number which lies between two given numbers. ● Order a given set of numbers: for example, the set of numbers 1 to 6 given in random order. ● Order a given set of selected numbers: for example, the set 2, 5, 1, 8, 4.	CARRY ON COUNTING: Children count on from a given number, stopping at another.	ORDER, ORDER: Ordering activities using objects, dot patterns and numerals.	CHANGE OVER: Children identify aspects of a sequence that have been misplaced.
LESSON 4 ● **Recognise numerals 1 to 9,** then 0 and 10, then beyond 10. ● **Use language such as more or less, greater or smaller, to compare two numbers** and say which is more or less, and say a number which lies between two given numbers. ● Order a given set of numbers: for example, the set of numbers 1 to 6 given in random order. ● Order a given set of selected numbers: for example, the set 2, 5, 1, 8, 4.	COUNT ON: children count on several numbers starting at a given number.	GET IN LINE: Children order a set of numbers.	Reinforcing descending and ascending order.
LESSON 5 ● **Use language such as more or less, greater or smaller, to compare two numbers** and say which is more or less, and say a number which lies between two given numbers. ● Begin to record numbers, initially by marks, progressing to simple tallying and writing numbers.	COUNT BACK: Children count back several numbers starting from a given number.	NUMBERS EVERYWHERE: Recognising, reading and writing numbers.	Feedback from activities.

ORAL AND MENTAL SKILLS **Say and use the number names in order in familiar contexts** such as number rhymes, songs, stories, counting games and activities (first to five, then ten, then twenty and beyond). Recite the number names in order, continuing the count forwards or backwards from a given number. **Use language such as more or less, greater or smaller, to compare two numbers** and say which is more or less, and say a number which lies between two given numbers. **Recognise numerals 1 to 9,** then 0 and 10, then beyond 10.

Lessons 2 and 3 are given in full, with Lesson 4 extending what has been introduced in Lesson 3. Lessons 1 and 5 are provided in grid form.

LESSON 1

RESOURCES	Counting items such as cubes or beads; small, clear plastic bags; flip chart; marker pen. **Group activities:** small containers such as egg cups, Smartie tubes, yoghurt pots, matchboxes, lidded tubs; paper; pencils.
LEARNING OUTCOMES	**ORAL AND MENTAL STARTER** ● **Say and use the number names in order in familiar contexts** such as number rhymes, songs, stories, counting games and activities (first to five, then ten, then twenty and beyond). **WHOLE-CLASS TEACHING ACTIVITY** ● Estimate a number in the range that can be counted reliably, then check by counting.
ORAL AND MENTAL STARTER	ONE MAN WENT TO MOW: Sing this song. Aim to count up to 10.
WHOLE-CLASS TEACHING ACTIVITY	GUESSTIMATE: Place a number of cubes in a plastic bag. Ask: *How many cubes are there in the bag?* Get individuals to estimate the number and write each guess on the flip chart. Ask children to count cubes. *Did anybody guess the right number? Which guess is nearest? Which guesses are too few? Which guesses are more than the right number?* Repeat by placing beads in another bag. *How many beads are in this bag? Are there more or less beads than cubes?* Count and check as before.
GROUP ACTIVITIES	**1.** Children work in pairs. Place a number of items in a bag. Each child estimates the number, writes it down on a piece of paper and places it face down on the table. Count out and record the actual number of items. Pairs turn over the estimates to find who is nearest. **2.** Provide several small, closed containers, each with a number of items inside, for example two beads in a matchbox. Each child estimates the number of items inside and records their estimate. Check by counting. **3.** Children guess how many items are in a selection of containers, for example an egg cup, a yoghurt pot, a matchbox, a Smartie tube. They record their answers using pictures and markings. ● Children estimate and count throughout the day: *Are there more boys present than girls? More children having sandwiches than school lunches? More children who are four than five?*
DIFFERENTIATION	Less able: limit the number of items to 10. Give support for writing numbers. More able: extend numbers to 20 and beyond.
PLENARY	Ask children to estimate how many boys there are in class, then girls. *Are there more or less boys than girls?* Repeat using different items, eg children who walk to school, chairs and tables, etc.

LESSON 2

RESOURCES

Flip chart; marker pen; individual sets of 0–9 numeral cards (page 12); enlarged 0–20 numeral cards. **Group activities:** dice; (1–10) spinners; outdoor number tracks (0–10, 0–20) or large number tiles for indoor tracks; paper; pencils.

LEARNING OUTCOMES

ORAL AND MENTAL STARTER AND WHOLE-CLASS TEACHING ACTIVITY
● **Recognise numerals 1 to 9,** then 0 and 10, then beyond 10.
● **Use language such as more or less, greater or smaller, to compare two numbers** and say which is more or less, and say a number which lies between two given numbers.

<table>
<tr><td>

VOCABULARY

Number; zero, one, two, three… to twenty and beyond; more; larger; bigger; greater; less; fewer; smaller; next; between; before; after; order.

</td></tr>
</table>

ORAL AND MENTAL STARTER

FIND ME: Give each child a set of 0–9 numeral cards. Ask the children to find and hold up a given number.

WHOLE-CLASS TEACHING ACTIVITY

NEXT-DOOR NUMBERS: Explain that the lesson is about 'next-door numbers'. Write the number 6 on the flip chart. *Which numbers live next door to 6? What comes after 6? What number comes before 6?* Shuffle the large numeral cards (0–20) and ask a child to pick one. *What number is it?* Write the number on the flip chart. Get children to write the number in the air. *Which numbers are its neighbours? Which number comes before? Which comes after?* Return the card to the set and repeat the activity.

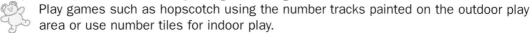

GROUP ACTIVITIES

1. In pairs, children take turns to throw a dice. They record the number and then write down the 'before' and 'after' numbers.

2. Scatter a set of individual numeral cards face down on the table. In turn, children turn one card over, then another. If the cards are neighbours the player keeps them. Otherwise they are turned back over.

3. Each child chooses a number and writes it on a piece of paper. Children take it in turns to spin the spinner to see if they can get the neighbour number.

Play games such as hopscotch using the number tracks painted on the outdoor play area or use number tiles for indoor play.

DIFFERENTIATION

Less able: work with numbers to 10, then extend to 20.
More able: extend beyond 20.

PLENARY

Take feedback from the **Group activities**. Repeat 'Find me'. Highlight the fact that children need to know the numbers next to, in front, before and after, in order to count and order/ sequence numbers. Reinforce positional language.

RESOURCES

Counting items such as buttons, pasta, beads, cubes, conkers; plastic containers; number tracks (see **Preparation**); Post-it notes; enlarged and individual dotty number cards (page 18). **Group activities:** individual numeral cards (page 12); items with numbers on such as raffle tickets, birthday cards, playing cards; washing line; pegs.

PREPARATION

Make enlarged photocopies of the dotty number cards. Place sets of the counting items into containers for ordering, one in the first, two in the second, and so on. Make a selection of number tracks with two, three and four numbers in the wrong order.

LEARNING OUTCOMES

ORAL AND MENTAL STARTER

● Recite the number names in order, continuing the count forwards or backwards from a given number.

WHOLE-CLASS TEACHING ACTIVITY

● **Recognise numerals 1 to 9,** then 0 and 10, then beyond 10.
● **Use language such as more or less, greater or smaller, to compare two numbers** and say which is more or less, and say a number which lies between two given numbers.
● Order a given set of numbers: for example, the set of numbers 1 to 6 given in random order.
● Order a given set of selected numbers: for example, the set 2, 5, 1, 8, 4.

VOCABULARY
Number; zero, one, two, three… to twenty and beyond; more; less; larger; bigger; greater; fewer; fewest; smaller; less; next; between; before; after; order.

ORAL AND MENTAL STARTER

CARRY ON COUNTING: Ask the class to start counting from a given number and to stop at another number, for example: *Start at 5. Hold 5 in your head and count on to 13.* Repeat with other examples for the whole class, groups, pairs and individuals.

WHOLE-CLASS TEACHING ACTIVITY

ORDER, ORDER: Show the children the plastic containers with the items inside. Ask: *If I want to put these in order what do I need to do?* Invite the children to count the objects in each container. *Which number is the smallest? Does this come before/after this? Which number comes in between these two numbers?* Write the number of items in each container on a Post-it note and place on the container as the correct number is given. Now, hand out a set of the large dotty cards randomly to individuals. Ask the children which dotty numbers they have. *Who has the largest number? Who has the smallest?* Children come out to the front of the class and order the cards from largest to smallest. *Does Laura's number come before or after Harry's? Is Hannah's number smaller or larger than Alex's? How can we change the order from smallest to largest?* Finally, show the children the prepared number tracks and ask: *Which two numbers have changed over on the number track?* Repeat using different examples with two, three and four numbers changed over.

GROUP ACTIVITIES

1. Place the numeral cards face down on the table. Children (in pairs or small groups) each take a card and place them side-by-side to make a number track. When five cards have been collected, they order the numbers from smallest to largest then vice versa.
2. In pairs, children place dotty cards in order from smallest to largest, then vice versa.
3. Children put in order sets of items (buttons, cubes, conkers, pasta, beads, etc) in containers from smallest to largest then vice versa.
4. Put up the washing line. Give out a random number of numeral cards to individuals. They peg them on the line in order from smallest to largest then vice versa.
5. Children work in small groups to arrange some shuffled numeral cards in order. They then find which numbers are missing from the sequence.
6. Put a set of items on the table that have numbers, for example birthday cards, playing cards, raffle tickets. Children then place these in order.
 Encourage children to order coins in the role-play shop or café.

DIFFERENTIATION

Less able: provide plenty of opportunity for ordering with objects. Limit the numbers to 10.
More able: encourage children to devise their own ordering activities to share with others.

PLENARY

CHANGE OVER: Randomly peg a set of dotty cards on the washing line. Ask the children to identify the numbers which have been misplaced in the sequence. Repeat using numeral cards. Attach the altered number tracks to the flip chart. *Which numbers have changed over?*

RESOURCES

See Lesson 3, page 137.

PREPARATION

See Lesson 3, page 137.

LEARNING OUTCOMES

ORAL AND MENTAL STARTER
● Recite the number names in order, continuing the count forwards or backwards from a given number.

WHOLE-CLASS TEACHING ACTIVITY
● **Recognise numerals 1 to 9,** then 0 and 10, then beyond 10.
● **Use language such as more or less, greater or smaller, to compare two numbers** and say which is more or less, and say a number which lies between two given numbers.
● Order a given set of numbers: for example, the set of numbers 1 to 6 given in random order.
● Order a given set of selected numbers: for example, the set 2, 5, 1, 8, 4.

ORAL AND MENTAL STARTER

COUNT ON: Ask the class to count on several numbers starting from a given number, for example: *Count on five numbers starting from 2.*

WHOLE-CLASS TEACHING ACTIVITY

GET IN LINE: Give out a selection of 0–9 numeral cards to individuals. Ask children to come out and arrange themselves in order to make a number line (smallest to largest). *Which number is the greatest? Which number is more than 6? Which numbers are less than 10?* Ask the class to read out the numbers. *Which numbers are missing? How could we arrange the numbers in a different order?* Repeat the activity with a set of numbers to 20.

GROUP ACTIVITIES

Choose from the **Group activities** in Lesson 3, page 138.

DIFFERENTIATION

Less able: concentrate on ordering smallest to largest then reverse the order. More able: encourage children to look for the missing numbers in a sequence.

PLENARY

Feedback from the **Group activities**. Make sure the children can put numbers in ascending/descending order. Reinforce the language greater/smaller etc.

RESOURCES	Feely bag; plastic or wooden numeral templates. **Group activities:** paper; pencils; crayons; a variety of papers and fabric; adhesive; coloured art paper; numeral, dotty and written word cards (pages 12 and 18); prepared blank 4 × 4 grids; counters.
LEARNING OUTCOMES	**ORAL AND MENTAL STARTER** ● Recite the number names in order, continuing the count forwards or backwards from a given number. **WHOLE-CLASS TEACHING ACTIVITY** ● **Use language such as more or less, greater or smaller, to compare two numbers** and say which is more or less, and say a number which lies between two given numbers. ● Begin to record numbers, initially by marks, progressing to simple tallying and writing numbers.
ORAL AND MENTAL STARTER	COUNT BACK: Children count back several numbers starting from a given number: *Start from 13. Hold 13 in your head. Count back to 5.*
WHOLE-CLASS TEACHING ACTIVITY	NUMBERS EVERYWHERE: Explain that numbers are everywhere and it is important to be able to count, read, write and recognise numbers. Talk about some numbers that you encounter in everyday life. Ask children to think of other special numbers, for example their house and telephone numbers, bus numbers, calendar dates, pages in a book. Draw a number in the air: *What number is it? How can you tell?* Ask individuals to come and draw numbers in the air for others to guess. Show the children the feely bag. Secretly place a number template inside. Ask a child to come and guess the number by feeling the shape.
GROUP ACTIVITIES	**1.** Provide different materials and get the children to make their own feely numbers. **2.** Give the children the 4 × 4 grids and ask them to write a number in each square to make their own number bingo cards. An adult helper calls out the numbers. Children cover their numbers with counters. **3.** Children play 'Kim's game' and find the matching numeral, dotty card and written word card. ● Provide writing and marking materials in the role-play area, for example shop, post office.
DIFFERENTIATION	Less able: give support for number formation. More able: encourage children to be 'callers' in the number bingo.
PLENARY	Take feedback from the **Group activities**. Repeat the 'Numbers everywhere' activities from the **Whole-class teaching activity.**

LESSON 5

UNIT 2

ORGANISATION (5 LESSONS)

	LEARNING OUTCOMES	ORAL AND MENTAL STARTER	WHOLE-CLASS TEACHING ACTIVITY	PLENARY
LESSON 1	● **Begin to use the vocabulary involved in adding and subtracting.** ● Begin to relate addition to counting on.	COUNT IN TENS: children count in tens from 0 to 50 then beyond.	ADD ON: Children use the throws of a dice to count on.	Feedback from activities.
LESSON 2	● **Begin to use the vocabulary involved in adding and subtracting.** ● Separate (partition) a given number of objects into two groups.	COUNT IN TWOS: Children count in twos to 10, then 20 and beyond.	SEPARATE US: Partitioning groups of children.	DUOS: Children hold up two numeral cards to show a given total.
LESSON 3	● Count in twos. ● **Begin to use the vocabulary involved in adding and subtracting.** ● Begin to relate the addition of doubles to counting on.	CARRY ON COUNTING IN TWOS: Children count around the class in twos.	DOUBLES: Doubling activities.	Feedback from activities. Children repeat doubling work.
LESSON 5	● **Begin to use the vocabulary involved in adding and subtracting.** ● Begin to find out how many have been removed from a larger group of objects by counting up from a number.	ODDS AND EVENS: Children count in twos, whispering and shouting alternate numbers.	ADD AND TAKE AWAY: Subtraction activities.	Feedback from activities. Children solve number problems.
ORAL AND MENTAL SKILLS Recognise numerals **1 to 9,** then 0 to 10, then beyond 10. Say a number which lies between two given numbers. Recite the number names in order, continuing the count forwards or backwards from a given number. Count in tens. Count in twos.				

Lessons 1, 2 and 5 are provided as grids. Lesson 3 is given in full, together with extension ideas for Lesson 4.

LESSON 1

RESOURCES	Number track (0–100); numeral cards (0–100); flip chart; marker pen; large foam dice with numerals 1–6 and 0–5; large and small cubes. **Group activities:** dotty cards (page 18); ladybird templates (page 15); small dice; counters.
LEARNING OUTCOMES	**ORAL AND MENTAL STARTER** ● Count in tens. ● **Recognise numerals 1 to 9,** then 0 and 10, then beyond 10. **WHOLE-CLASS TEACHING ACTIVITY** ● **Begin to use the vocabulary involved in adding and subtracting.** ● Begin to relate addition to counting on.
ORAL AND MENTAL STARTER	COUNT IN TENS: Count in tens to 50, then 100. Next, think of a total, say 5, and ask the children to hold up two numeral cards to show this, for example: 3 and 2 give 5.
WHOLE-CLASS TEACHING ACTIVITY	ADD ON: Ask the children to read the numbers on each side of the 1–6 dice (in a random order). Throw the dice and tell them the number. Starting with this number, the children count on to 10, using their fingers to help. Demonstrate: *5... 6, 7, 8, 9, 10. 5 add 5 makes 10.* Write this on the flip chart. Throw the dice again and repeat. Ask individuals to read the sum. Using the large cubes, make a series of steps from 0 to 5. Throw the dice and use the number to add together cubes to make 5. Throw the dice (0–5). Say: *3... Where can I put my three cubes to make 5?* Read out the number: *3 add 2 makes 5.*
GROUP ACTIVITIES	**1.** Each child makes a staircase of cubes (0 to 5). They take turns to throw the dice (0 to 5) and add to their cubes so that each set adds up to 5. **2.** Give each child a ladybird template (page 15). Children place counters on each wing to make a total of five spots. **3.** Arrange dotty cards face up on the table. Children choose a card, then find another to make 5. The child with the most sets totalling 5 is the winner. ● Ask children: *How many more?* are allowed in different activities throughout the day. For example, four children are allowed in the role-play shop. Two children are playing: *How many more can go and play?*
DIFFERENTIATION	Less able: work with numbers to 5, then extend to 10. More able: work with numbers to 10 and record.
PLENARY	Feedback from the **Group activities**. Ask the children to describe the activity they have been doing.

LESSON 2

RESOURCES	Flip chart; marker pen. **Group activities:** cubes; small counting items; sets of dominoes; sorting rings; paper; pencils; sugar paper.
LEARNING OUTCOMES	**ORAL AND MENTAL STARTER** ● Count in twos. **WHOLE-CLASS TEACHING ACTIVITY** ● **Begin to use the vocabulary involved in adding and subtracting.** ● Separate (partition) a given number of objects into two groups.
ORAL AND MENTAL STARTER	COUNT IN TWOS: Recite the rhyme 'Two, four, six, eight...'. Children count in twos to 10, then 20 and beyond.
WHOLE-CLASS TEACHING ACTIVITY	SEPARATE US: Ask five children to come to the front of the class. Ask: *How many ways can we separate this group of five?* Arrange the children into 2 and 3: *2 add 3 makes 5.* Write this on the flip chart. Invite children to find other ways and to record these on the chart. Remind children to include 0 and 5. Show them how to write their sums in order to see whether any have been repeated. *How many ways did we find? What happens if we use six children?*
GROUP ACTIVITIES	**1.** In pairs, children separate a number of cubes (up to 5 then beyond) and record (by placing numeral cards or writing) what makes the given number. **2.** Children partition a sorting ring of ten objects to find what makes 10. **3.** Give children a set of dominoes and ask them to find the six dominoes that have a total of five spots. They can record their findings on sheets of sugar paper. ● Children sort equipment that they pack away into different sets.
DIFFERENTIATION	Less able: partition numbers to 5 using practical activities before extending to 10. More able: encourage children to investigate numbers to 10 then beyond, and record in their own way.
PLENARY	DUOS: Children hold up two numeral cards to show a given number.

RESOURCES

Flip chart; marker pen; dice (large and small); number track to 50; individual numeral cards (page 12). **Group activities:** cubes; dominoes; 'doubles' sheet; number carpet tiles; plastic drink bottles; plastic ball; paper; pencils; chalk or tape; number tracks to 10; dice (0–5); wrapping paper.

PREPARATION

Cover the plastic drink bottles with wrapping paper. Make numeral cards saying 1, 2, 3, 4, 5 (values 1–5). Attach a numeral card to each skittle and arrange them in a large space. Draw a starting line on the floor. On a large sheet of paper draw a three column grid saying 'Number', 'Double', 'Total'. In the 'Number' column write the numbers 3, 2, 5, 4, 1.

LEARNING OUTCOMES

ORAL AND MENTAL STARTER

● Count in twos.

Number	Double	Total
3		
2		
5		
4		
1		

WHOLE-CLASS TEACHING ACTIVITY

● Count in twos.
● **Begin to use the vocabulary involved in adding and subtracting.**
● Begin to relate the addition of doubles to counting on.

VOCABULARY

Number,; zero, one, two, three... to twenty and beyond; zero, ten, twenty... one hundred; none; how many...?; count; count (up) to; count on (from, to); count back (from, to); count in twos...; odd; even; every other; add; more; and; make; sum; total; altogether; score; double; two more.

ORAL AND MENTAL STARTER

CARRY ON COUNTING IN TWOS: Explain to the children that, going around the class, you want them to carry on counting individually in twos to 20. When 20 is reached, the next person starts at 0 again.

WHOLE-CLASS TEACHING ACTIVITY

DOUBLES: Sing the song 'The animals went in two by two': *If two giraffes and two elephants went into the ark, how many were there altogether? If three tigers and three cats went in, how many altogether? If there were four mice and four bears, what is the total?* Explain that this lesson is about doubles. Point to the number track: *If we make two jumps, each the same, where do we land?* Demonstrate by starting on 0: *Jump on two, then another two. Where do we land?* Repeat using different numbers. Stress that the two jumps are always the same size. Tell children that you are going to throw the dice to get a starting number. *Start with 4, then jump four more. Where do we land?* (8) *4 add 4 makes 8.* Repeat using different starting numbers. Record the answers on the flip chart.

GROUP ACTIVITIES

1. Give each child a number track (0–10) and a counter. Each child throws a dice for the starting number and covers this with their counter. The child then makes a second jump, counting on the same number.
2. Place a set of dominoes face up on the table. Children work in pairs to find the doubles, then record the total, eg 4 add 4 makes 8.
3. Give each pair the 'doubles' sheet you have prepared. Children work in pairs to find the double and then the total number.
4. Give each child some cubes. They add on the same number. *How many altogether?*
5. Children put beads into each row of an egg box (6, then 12), record how many in each row and how many altogether.
6. Set up the skittles (numbered 1–5) in a large space. Allow each child three throws to knock down the skittles. Each child 'doubles' their final score. So if a child knocks down 1, 3, 5 = 9, the total score is 18. The winner is the child with the highest score.

Children use large floor number tiles to jump in doubles.

DIFFERENTIATION

Less able: work with numbers to 10 and provide adult support and counting apparatus.
More able: encourage children to make their own doubles with numbers to 20 and beyond.

PLENARY

Feedback from the **Group activities**. Write a number (to 5, then 10 and beyond) on the flip chart. Ask children to give the double.

LESSON 4

Repeat Lesson 3, but in the **Oral and mental starter**, count back as a class in twos from 20 to 0, then extend beyond 20. Ask children to start at a given number and count in twos up to a given number. Say: *Start at 4 and count on in twos up to 14; Start at 1 and count on in twos to 9.* Remind the children of the previous doubles **Whole-class teaching activity**. Ask them to look at the number track: *What is double 4? 4 add 4 is 8. What is double 7? 7 add 7 makes 14.* Ask children to use their numeral cards and show you the answer to some doubles. Say: *The total of 5 add 5 is...? What is double 10?* Then choose from the **Group activities** given in Lesson 3. Take feedback from the activities in the **Plenary**. Present the children with some doubling problems. Choose from the following:
● How many wheels on two buses?
● How many eggs in two boxes?
● If I have 8p and 8p in my purse, how much do I have altogether?
● How many fingers on two hands?
● Is 14 the total of double 7?
● What is the sum of 9 add 9?

LESSON 5

RESOURCES	Flip chart; marker pen; cubes. **Group activities:** plastic coins; purses; counters; empty boxes; counting objects; (0–10) spinners; paper bags; paper; pencils; numeral cards (page 12); vocabulary cards (add, take away, makes).
LEARNING OUTCOMES	**ORAL AND MENTAL STARTER** ● Say a number which lies between two given numbers. ● Recite the number names in order, continuing the count forwards or backwards from a given number. **WHOLE-CLASS TEACHING ACTIVITY** ● Begin to use the vocabulary involved in adding and subtracting. ● Begin to find out how many have been removed from a larger group of objects by counting up from a number.
ORAL AND MENTAL STARTER	ODDS AND EVENS: Explain that you want the children to count in ones from 0 to 20, shouting every other number. Repeat starting from 1 to 20. Say: *Tell me an odd number between 1 and 8. Say the even numbers between 6 and 18.*
WHOLE-CLASS TEACHING ACTIVITY	ADD AND TAKE AWAY: Recite 'Ten fat sausages frying in a pan'. The children hold up their fingers as sausages. During the rhyme, ask: *How many sausages have gone?* Count up from 4: *5, 6, 7, 8, 9, 10* and say: *6. 4 add 6 is 10.* Explain that we can use adding and subtraction. *10 take away 6 is 4.* Count out five cubes. Put some in each hand. Hold out one hand: *If there are three cubes in here, how many are there in my other hand?* Ask the children to count out loud from 3: *4, 5. There are two in the other hand. 3 add 2 is 5, 5 take away 2 is 3.* Write both methods on the flip chart. Ask children to find the missing number by counting up. For example: *Eight cats were sitting on the wall. There are only three now. How many have left? 5. 3 add 5 is 8, 8 take away 5 is 3.* Write both methods on the flip chart.
GROUP ACTIVITIES	**1.** Give each pair an empty box and some counting objects. They place ten items inside. One child removes a number of items and places them on the table. The other child finds the number in the box. **2.** Give children a set of counters and a paper bag. They place ten counters in the bag and with their eyes shut remove some counters. They find how many are left in the bag and record their answers using the numeral and vocabulary cards or by marking. **3.** Children work in pairs. Each pair has a purse and a selection of coins. One child places 10 × 1p coins in the purse. The other child then spins the spinner, removes that number of coins from the purse and places them on the table. The second child counts on to find the number of coins left in the purse, eg if 5 are taken out, they count on 6, 7, 8, 9, 10: *There are 5 × 1p coins left in the purse.* ● Children can count up to give change in the role-play shop or café.
DIFFERENTIATION	Less able: provide adult support. Reinforce counting on with numbers to 5, then 10. More able: encourage children to record by marking and make their own 'number problems' to share with a partner.
PLENARY	Take feedback from the **Group activities**. Make up a range of number problems and ask individuals to count on to find the missing numbers. Record the addition and subtraction methods on the flip chart. Ask both the whole-class and individuals to read out the number sentences.

UNIT 3

ORGANISATION (5 LESSONS)

LEARNING OUTCOMES	ORAL AND MENTAL STARTER	WHOLE-CLASS TEACHING ACTIVITY	PLENARY
LESSON 1 ● **Use language such as circle or bigger to describe the shape and size of solids.** ● Begin to name solids such as a cube, cone, sphere...	COUNT ON AND COUNT BACK: Children count from 0 to 20 then beyond, then in tens to 100.	THE 3-D SHAPE FAMILY: 3-D shape recognition activities.	Feedback from activities. Children answer questions about shapes.
LESSON 2 ● **Use language such as circle or bigger to describe the shape and size of flat shapes.** ● Begin to name flat shapes such as a circle, triangle, square, rectangle...	CARRY ON COUNTING: Children count in ones from 0 to 20 then beyond. Count in twos to 20 and beyond.	THE 2-D SHAPE FAMILY: 2-D shape recognition activities	Feedback from activities. Children answer questions about shapes.
LESSON 3 ● **Use everyday words to describe position,** direction and movement: for example, follow and give instructions about positions, directions and movements in PE and other activities.	GUESS MY NAME: Children try to guess which 2-D or 3-D shape is being described.	WHERE DOES IT GO?: Positional activities.	Children play 'Simon says'.
LESSON 4 ● Begin to name flat shapes such as a circle, triangle, square, rectangle... ● **Use everyday words to describe position,** direction and movement: for example, follow and give instructions about positions, directions and movements in PE and other activities.	FORWARDS AND BACKWARDS: Children count to 20 and beyond in twos.	WASHING LINE: Shape and position activities.	Feedback from activities.
LESSON 5 ● Talk about, recognise and recreate patterns: for example simple repeating patterns in the environment.	TENS AND TWOS: Children count in twos to 20 and beyond, then count in tens.	MAKING PATTERNS: Recognising and continuing patterns	Children play 'Guess my pattern' game.

> **ORAL AND MENTAL SKILLS** **Use language such as circle or bigger to describe the shape and size of solids and flat shapes.** Begin to name solids such as a cube, cone, sphere... and flat shapes such as a circle, triangle, square, rectangle. Recite the number names in order, continuing the count forwards or backwards from a given number. Count in tens. Count in twos.

Lessons 1, 2 and 5 are given in full, with Lessons 3 and 4 provided as grids.

RESOURCES

Wrapping paper or tin foil; reclaimed materials such as packets, rolls, containers, boxes, tins etc; different size 3-D shapes such as spheres, cubes, cuboids, cylinders, cones, pyramids; a small table or cupboard top; a large 0–100 number line; pointer.
Group activities: building bricks.

PREPARATION

Wrap a range of 3-D shapes in wrapping paper or tin foil. Make labels saying 'cylinders', 'spheres', 'cubes', 'cuboids', 'pyramids', 'not cylinders', 'not spheres', 'not cubes', 'not cuboids', 'not pyramids'. Display the shapes on a table or cupboard top. Place a range of unwrapped shapes in the middle of each table. Display the 0–100 number line in a prominent place.

LEARNING OUTCOMES

ORAL AND MENTAL STARTER
● Recite the number names in order, continuing the count forwards or backwards from a given number.
● Count in tens.

WHOLE-CLASS TEACHING ACTIVITY
● **Use language such as circle or bigger to describe the shape and size of solids.**
● Begin to name solids such as a cube, cone, sphere...

VOCABULARY

What could we try next?; count; sort; group; set; match; shape; pattern; flat; curved; straight; round; hollow; solid; corner; face; side; edge; end; sort; make; build; draw; cube; pyramid; sphere; cone; circle; triangle; square; rectangle; star; size; bigger; larger; smaller.

ORAL AND MENTAL STARTER

COUNT ON AND COUNT BACK: Ask children to count from 0 to 20 then back. Show the children the 0–100 number line. Ask them to count beyond 20 as you point out the numbers. Repeat counting in tens to 100.

WHOLE-CLASS TEACHING ACTIVITY

THE 3-D SHAPE FAMILY: Remind children of the 3-D shape family from Term 1, Unit 3, Lesson 1, page 33. Hold up each shape and ask the children to tell you the names of them. Show children the labels and read them out, picking up an appropriate shape each time. Ask the children to sort all the cuboids. Explain that all the other shapes are not cuboids. Repeat with the other shapes. Remind children of the various properties of the shapes, for example, number of faces, straight or curved sides, hollow or solid shapes. Ask children to work in pairs. Explain that when you say the name or describe a shape you want the children to find it and hold it up. *Find me a shape that has straight sides. Find me a shape that has curved sides and is hollow.* Show the children the wrapped shapes but do not say what they are. Ask individuals to find a shape that matches one of the wrapped shapes. Encourage children to name the shapes.

GROUP ACTIVITIES

1. Children sort 3-D shapes according to different criteria, for example shape, number of sides, hollow, curved and straight sides.
2. Prepare a simple 3-D model. The children then copy it using matching shapes.
3. In pairs, children investigate which solid shapes roll and do not roll, slide and do not slide. Model making. Children describe the 3-D shapes they have used in their building.

DIFFERENTIATION

Less able: limit the shapes to sphere, cube, cuboid and cylinder. Emphasise the vocabulary used.
More able: extend the range of 3-D shapes. Encourage children to use their own criteria for sorting and to make their own models for others to copy.

PLENARY

Take feedback from the **Group activities**. Play 'Tell me': Hold up individual shapes and ask individuals to answer questions about each shape: *How many sides? How many corners? Does it slide? Does it roll? What is it called?* Say: *Show me something that is the same shape but smaller than mine, ...is the same shape but larger than mine.*

RESOURCES

Wrapping paper or tin foil; range of 2-D shapes of different sizes and materials.
Group activities: pencils; crayons; paper.

PREPARATION

Wrap a range of 2-D shapes in wrapping paper or tin foil. Make labels saying 'squares', 'circles', 'triangles', 'rectangles', 'hexagons', 'not squares', 'not circles', 'not triangles', 'not rectangles', 'not hexagons'. Display the shapes on a table or cupboard top. Place a range of unwrapped shapes in the middle of each table.

LESSON 2

LEARNING OUTCOMES

ORAL AND MENTAL STARTER
● Recite the number names in order, continuing the count forwards or backwards from a given number.
● Count in twos.

WHOLE-CLASS TEACHING ACTIVITY
● **Use language such as circle or bigger to describe the shape and size of flat shapes.**
● Begin to name flat shapes such as a circle, triangle, square, rectangle...

VOCABULARY

What could we try next?; count; sort; group; set; match; shape; pattern; flat; curved; straight; corner; face; side; edge; make; build; draw; circle; triangle; square; rectangle; star; size; bigger; larger; smaller.

ORAL AND MENTAL STARTER

CARRY ON COUNTING: Carry on a count around the class starting and finishing at a given number. Recite the rhyme: 'Two, four, six, eight'. Count in twos to twenty and then beyond.

WHOLE-CLASS TEACHING ACTIVITY

THE 2-D SHAPE FAMILY: Remind children of the 2-D shape family from Term 1, Unit 3, Lesson 1, page 33. Hold up each shape and ask the children to tell you the names of them. Show children the labels and read them out, picking up an appropriate shape each time. Invite children to sort all the circles. Explain that the other shapes are not circles. Repeat with other shapes. Remind children of the various properties of the shapes, for example number of edges, straight or curved sides, number of corners. Ask children to work in pairs. Explain that when you say the name or describe a shape you want the children to find it and hold it up. *Find me a shape that has straight sides. Find me a shape that has curved sides. Find me a shape with four straight sides.* Show the children the wrapped shapes but do not say what they are. Ask individuals to find a shape that matches the wrapped shape. Encourage children to describe and name the shapes.

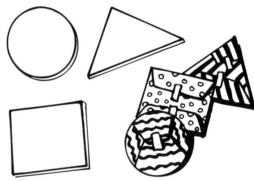

GROUP ACTIVITIES

1. Children sort 2-D shapes according to different criteria, for example shape, number of sides, corners, edges, etc.
2. Prepare a simple 2-D picture. The children then copy it using matching shapes.
3. Children trace around different 2-D shapes and draw them.
Use programmable toys or a simple computer game to make and match simple 2-D shapes.

DIFFERENTIATION

Less able: make sure children understand and use the words face, edge, corner, side, straight and curved.
More able: extend the range of 2-D shapes. Encourage children to use their own criteria for sorting and to describe the attributes of each shape.

PLENARY

Take feedback from the **Group activities**. Hold up various shapes and ask individuals to answer questions: *How many sides? How many corners? How many edges? What is it called?* Say: *Show me something that is the same shape but smaller than mine; ...is the same shape but larger than mine.*

RESOURCES	Feely bag; an assortment of 2-D and 3-D shapes; a large 3 × 3 grid drawn on the flip chart; cut-outs of objects mounted on card; Blu-Tack; simple instructions written on card, eg *Place a bird in the middle of the paper. Put a black cloud above it*. **Group activities:** individual 3 × 3 grids; selection of everyday objects, items or pictures of objects that can be found above, below, or on the ground such as a carrot, flower, worm, mole, aeroplane, tree, car, cloud; paper; drawing materials; pencils.
LEARNING OUTCOMES	**ORAL AND MENTAL STARTER** ● **Use language such as circle or bigger to describe the shape and size of solids and flat shapes.** ● Begin to name solids such as a cube, cone, sphere... and flat shapes such as a circle, triangle, square, rectangle. **WHOLE-CLASS TEACHING ACTIVITY** ● **Use everyday words to describe position,** direction and movement: for example, follow and give instructions about positions, directions and movements in PE and other activities.
ORAL AND MENTAL STARTER	GUESS MY NAME: Give clues about the 2-D and 3-D shapes hidden in a feely bag. Children try to guess the shape.
WHOLE-CLASS TEACHING ACTIVITY	WHERE DOES IT GO?: Play 'Simon says'. Ask children to carry out activities that use positional and directional language. Show children the 3 × 3 grid. Ask them to tell you where to place the picture cards on the grid. Demonstrate using three items: *Is the tree under the bird? Is the flower above the tree?* The children instruct you where to place the other items. Ask children to close their eyes. Remove some items from the grid. Children open their eyes and identify what is missing and where it should go.
GROUP ACTIVITIES	**1.** In pairs, children take it in turns to give instructions as to where to place everyday items onto their individual 3 × 3 grids. **2.** Children sort pictures to show those found above, below or on the ground. They draw and label each set of pictures. **3.** Ask children to listen to and follow a set of simple instructions given by an adult helper, eg: *Place a yellow flower in the vase. Put it in the middle of the table.* ● Set up the role-play area to be a shop. Children sort and position items.
DIFFERENTIATION	Less able: encourage children to describe positions. More able: use directional as well as positional vocabulary.
PLENARY	Repeat the game 'Simon says'.

RESOURCES	Washing line; pegs; large cut-outs of different sizes and colours of 2-D shapes - circles, squares, rectangles, triangles. **Group activities:** individual 3 × 3 and 3 × 2 grids; shape cards; taped instructions; tape recorder; sets of shapes.
LEARNING OUTCOMES	**ORAL AND MENTAL STARTER** ● Count in twos. ● Recite the number names in order, continuing the count forwards or backwards from a given number. **WHOLE-CLASS TEACHING ACTIVITY** ● Begin to name flat shapes such as a circle, triangle, square, rectangle... ● **Use everyday words to describe position,** direction and movement: for example, follow and give instructions about positions, directions and movements in PE and other activities.
ORAL AND MENTAL STARTER	FORWARDS AND BACKWARDS: Count in twos to 20, then beyond. Count forwards and backwards in ones, starting and finishing at different numbers. Extend using numbers beyond 20.
WHOLE-CLASS TEACHING ACTIVITY	WASHING LINE: Ask children to peg cut-out shapes on the line: *Peg the small orange circle in the middle.* Give instructions to individuals to complete a line of 2-D shapes. Children describe the position of a shape, or describe the size, colour and shape.
GROUP ACTIVITIES	**1.** Give each child a 3 × 3 grid showing different coloured 2-D shapes. Place the shape cards face down on the table. Children take turns to pick up a shape card and see whether it matches one on their grid. Winner is first to cover all shapes on their grid. **2.** In pairs, one child chooses some 2-D shapes and places them on a 3 × 2 grid without showing his/her partner. The other child has a blank grid. The first child describes each shape and gives instructions where to place it. Both children check to see whether their grids match. **3.** Children have a set of shapes. They follow simple taped instructions using colour, size and 2-D shapes, eg: *Put the large triangle in the yellow square.* ● Children make marks in the sand tray using 2-D shapes and sizes.
DIFFERENTIATION	Less able: limit to shape and position. More able: extend using shape, size and colour.
PLENARY	Take feedback from the **Group activities**.

RESOURCES

Flip chart; marker pen; collection of items with a clear pattern such as fabric, wallpaper, wrapping paper, clothes, cubes, beads, laces; 2-D shapes; display area; table or cupboard top. **Group activities:** squared paper; crayons; paints; rubber stamps; paper.

PREPARATION

Collect a variety of objects that have a pattern and create a wall display above a cupboard or table top. Make a large caption saying 'Patterns everywhere'. Make some 6 × 2 grids. Assemble rubber stamps or other materials for printing.

LEARNING OUTCOMES

ORAL AND MENTAL STARTER

● Recite the number names in order, continuing the count forwards or backwards from a given number.
● Count in twos.
● Count in tens.

WHOLE-CLASS TEACHING ACTIVITY

● Talk about, recognise and recreate patterns: for example simple repeating patterns in the environment.

VOCABULARY

Pattern; what could we try next?; how did you work it out?; count; set; match; shape; flat; curved; straight; round; corner; face; side; edge; end; make; build; draw; circle; triangle; square; rectangle; star; size; bigger; larger; smaller; repeating pattern.

ORAL AND MENTAL STARTER

TENS AND TWOS: Whole class say the rhyme 'Ten fat sausages sizzling in the pan'. Count up to ten and back in twos. Repeat, counting up to 20 and back. Explain that the children can count in tens and you will write the count on the flip chart. Write the numbers 0 to 100 (in tens). Repeat the count and point to the numbers as the children count.

WHOLE-CLASS TEACHING ACTIVITY

MAKING PATTERNS: Gather the children around the pattern display: *Who can see a pattern?* Encourage individuals to describe the patterns. Ask: *What is a pattern?* Place two different-coloured cubes on the table: *Is this a pattern? What do I need to do to make it a pattern?* Add two more cubes to make a pattern: *If I want to make the pattern grow, what would come next?* Show the children how to record this on squared paper. Repeat using one 2-D shape with two colours. Individuals can extend the pattern.

GROUP ACTIVITIES

1. Place different-coloured cubes on the table with crayons and squared paper. Children choose two colours and make a repeating pattern. They record this on squared paper. Repeat using three colours.
2. Give children paints, printing materials or rubber stamps and a 6 × 2 grid. Individuals choose two items and print a pattern. Reverse the pattern for the next row of the grid.
3. Children work in pairs to make patterns using 2-D shapes. Children choose the same shape with two different colours. Extend to using the same colour with different shapes.

 Ask the children to add to the display by becoming 'pattern detectives'. Encourage them to look for patterns around school and home. Include these on the display and record in a 'patterns everywhere' book.

DIFFERENTIATION

Less able: make sure children can create patterns using two colours or shapes. Support them in recording their patterns on paper.
More able: extend pattern making using size, shape and colour.

PLENARY

GUESS MY PATTERN: Make different patterns using shape, colour and size. Use objects and draw your patterns on the flip chart. Children work out the patterns.

UNIT 4

ORGANISATION (8 LESSONS)

	LEARNING OUTCOMES	ORAL AND MENTAL STARTER	WHOLE-CLASS TEACHING ACTIVITY	PLENARY
LESSON 1	● **Recognise numerals 1 to 9,** then 0 and 10, then beyond 10. ● Begin to record numbers, initially by making marks, progressing to simple tallying and writing numerals.	FINGER ADD: Children add numbers to 10 and beyond, using their fingers to give the answers.	TRACE ME: Recognising and writing numerals.	Children trace, copy and write numbers.
LESSON 2	● **Recognise numerals 1 to 9,** then 0 and 10, then beyond 10. ● Begin to record numbers, initially by making marks, progressing to simple tallying and writing numerals.	FINGER SUBTRACT: Children take away numbers to 10 and beyond, using their fingers to give the answers.	WHAT'S THE NUMBER?: Recognising random numbers in a grid.	Feedback from activities.
LESSON 3	● **Use language such as longer or shorter to compare two quantities,** then more than two, by making direct comparisons of lengths. ● Begin to record numbers, initially by making marks, progressing to simple tallying and writing numerals.	FINGER ADD AND SUBTRACT: Children add and subtract two sets of numbers.	LONGER AND SHORTER: Comparing and recording length.	Reinforcing long and short.
LESSON 4	● **Use language such as longer or shorter to compare two quantities,** then more than two, by making direct comparisons of lengths. ● Begin to record numbers, initially by making marks, progressing to simple tallying and writing numerals.	FINGER ADD: Adding two and three groups of numbers.	TALLER AND SMALLER: Comparing length and height.	Feedback from activities.
LESSON 5	● **Use language such as heavier or lighter to compare two quantities,** then more than two, by making direct comparisons of masses. ● Begin to record numbers, initially by making marks, progressing to simple tallying and writing numerals.	SHOW ME SUBTRACT: Children solve subtraction problems.	HEAVY AND LIGHT: Comparing the mass of items.	Awareness of items in the environment that are weighed.
LESSON 6	● **Use language such as heavier or lighter to compare two quantities,** then more than two, by making direct comparisons of masses. ● Begin to record numbers, initially by making marks, progressing to simple tallying and writing numerals.	FINGER ADD: Children combine numbers using their fingers.	WEIGH ME: Comparing parcels by handling and balancing.	Children estimate the weight of various bags.
LESSON 7	● **Use language such as more or less to compare two quantities,** then more than two, by filling and emptying containers. ● Begin to record numbers, initially by making marks, progressing to simple tallying and writing numerals.	COUNT ON: Children count on from one number to another.	FIT INSIDE: Children estimate how many items will fill another object.	Filling and comparing activities.
LESSON 8	● **Use language such as more or less to compare two quantities,** then more than two, by filling and emptying containers. ● Begin to record numbers, initially by making marks, progressing to simple tallying and writing numerals.	COUNT UP: Children subtract using counting up.	CAPACITY: Children compare the masses of various items.	Feedback from activities.

LESSON 1

> **ORAL AND MENTAL SKILLS Begin to relate addition to combining two groups of objects,** counting all the objects; extend to three groups of objects. Begin to relate addition to counting on. **Begin to relate subtraction to 'taking away'** and counting how many are left. Begin to find out how many have been removed from a larger group of objects by counting up from a number.

Lessons 1, 3, 6 and 7 are given in full, while Lessons 2, 4, 5 and 8 extend the content to other measures and basic recording, and are presented as grids.

RESOURCES

Flip chart; marker pen; a selection of small items for counting; numeral cards (0–10) (page 12); washing line; pegs; cut-out numeral clothes or cards (0–20); plastic numbers; scraps of material such as felt, suede, woollen, velvet, cord, tin foil; strong adhesive; spreader; thick card; drawing pins; cork tiles; different-coloured paper and card; small pieces of card. **Group activities:** dotty cards (page 18); object cards; crayons; pencils.

PREPARATION

Cut out numerals from different materials and stick them on to the thick card. Tap drawing pins into cork tiles to form numerals. Cut large number shapes out of different-coloured paper and card.

LEARNING OUTCOMES

ORAL AND MENTAL STARTER
- **Begin to relate addition to combining two groups of objects,** counting all the objects.
- Begin to relate addition to counting on.

WHOLE-CLASS TEACHING ACTIVITY
- **Recognise numerals 1 to 9,** then 0 and 10, then beyond 10.
- Begin to record numbers, initially by making marks, progressing to simple tallying and writing numerals.

VOCABULARY
Number; zero, one, two, three ...to twenty and beyond; zero, ten, twenty... one hundred; none; how many...?; count; count (up) to; count on (from, to); count back (from, to); count in ones, twos... tens...; more; less; guess; estimate; nearly; close to; about the same as.

ORAL AND MENTAL STARTER

FINGER ADD: Ask the children to add numbers to 10 then beyond, eg 3 + 4, 8 + 2. They hold up their fingers to show the answers. Ask: *Is 20 more than 10? Give me a number less than 15. Show me a number between 5 and 10. What is 0 add 0?*

Say: *Count on from the number in your head to the other number. 2 (keep it in your head) add 2. 1 and 2, 3, 4. 2 count on 2 is 4.*

WHOLE-CLASS TEACHING ACTIVITY

TRACE ME: Put up the washing line and peg up the cut-out clothes (0–20). Ask the children to read the numbers as you point from 0 to 20. Pick out individual numbers. *What number is this?* Trace numerals in the air, for example 7, and say: *Across and down.* Start with numerals that go from top to bottom: 1, 3, 7, then follow with instructions for others.

Show the children the cut-out numerals made from different materials. Trace the numerals, repeating the instructions for correct number formation. Ask children to work in pairs. *Draw a number on your friend's back. What number did he/she draw? Was that correct?*

GROUP ACTIVITIES

1. Children write and place number labels to go with sets of objects.
2. Children choose cut-out numbers and trace them with their fingers. They then copy the numbers on to large number shapes cut out of paper and card.
3. Place sets of numeral, object and dotty cards face down on a table. Children turn over two cards in turn and see whether they match by having the same number – either numeral, spots or objects.

 Label large play toys (such as cars, bikes) or small play toys with numbers. Make numbered 'parking places' for the toys.

DIFFERENTIATION

Less able: provide plenty of opportunities for tactile activities so that the children can trace numbers.

More able: encourage children to make marks and write numerals. Ask them to give instructions to you or a friend to write the numbers using the correct formation.

PLENARY

Give instructions to the children to trace numerals in the air. Ask individuals to come out and copy or write numbers on the flip chart. Draw a set of objects. Ask children to write the number of objects. Repeat by drawing numbers and asking children to pick out or draw that number of objects.

RESOURCES	Copies of randomly placed numbers on 4 × 4 grids; dice (1-6); Post-it notes. **Group activities:** sets of dominoes with ends showing numbers and spots; blank 4 × 4 grids; thick card; a range of objects: toy car, small teddy, paintbrush, ball, shell; sand tray; cardboard box filled with polystyrene chips; paper; pencils; crayons.
LEARNING OUTCOMES	**ORAL AND MENTAL STARTER** ● **Begin to relate subtraction to 'taking away'** and counting how many are left. **WHOLE-CLASS TEACHING ACTIVITY** ● **Recognise numerals 1 to 9,** then 0 and 10, then beyond 10. ● Begin to record numbers, initially by making marks, progressing to simple tallying and writing numerals.
ORAL AND MENTAL STARTER	FINGER SUBTRACT: Ask children to 'take away' numbers from 10, then beyond. Hold up fingers to show answers. Say: *10 take away 10 makes? 12 subtract 5? What is 11 take away 0?*
WHOLE-CLASS TEACHING ACTIVITY	WHAT'S THE NUMBER?: Show children the number grids and ask them to read out the numbers from left to right. Explain that they are going to play a number game. Throw a dice (1–6). *What is the number? Is it on the grid?* Cover with a Post-it note if it is. Repeat several times. *Which numbers are left? Which is the smallest? Which is the largest? Tell me a number bigger than...* Ask children to trace numbers in the air.
GROUP ACTIVITIES	**1.** Children work in small groups. Place dominoes on the table face down. Each child picks one domino, then takes turns to choose another and see if it matches either end of their one. The winner is the child with the most dominoes that match. **2.** Each child has a 4 × 4 grid. Give each child thick pieces of card with a line drawn down the centre. The child cuts up the grid and sticks one set of domino shapes on one side of the card and writes numbers into these. The remaining domino shapes are stuck onto the other side of the card. The children draw objects or stick shapes onto this to make their own set of dominoes. **3.** Bury several objects in the sand and the box of polystyrene chips. Children search for the treasure. They record what they find on paper. ● Make menus with price lists for the role-play café.
DIFFERENTIATION	Less able: children will need adult support for activities (1) and (2). More able: children can choose their own numbers for the game.
PLENARY	Feedback from the **Group activities**. Play 'Guess my number'. Ask children to guess the number you are tracing in the air. Invite individuals to come out to the front of the class and 'draw' on their backs. Ask children to repeat this with a partner.

RESOURCES

Flip chart; marker pen; range of longer and shorter items such as scarves, socks, ribbons, paintbrushes, crayons, towers of cubes, garden canes, necklaces, learning links. **Group activities:** small plastic bags; lengths of ribbon, wool, string, paper, rope, lace; copies of photocopiable page 157 (Compare me); thick card; scissors; sticky tape; strips of paper cut to different lengths.

PREPARATION

Using the thick card, cut out different-sized mouse templates. Cut string, rope, ribbon, wool, paper, and lace into different lengths. Place these in separate plastic bags. Cut strips of paper into different lengths. Assemble the other resources on a table or cupboard top. Draw a four column table on the flip chart with the headings 'Item', 'Longer', 'Shorter', 'About the same as'.

LEARNING OUTCOMES

ORAL AND MENTAL STARTER

● **Begin to relate addition to combining two groups of objects**, counting all the objects; extend to three groups of objects.
● **Begin to relate subtraction to 'taking away'** and counting how many are left.

WHOLE-CLASS TEACHING ACTIVITY

● **Use language such as longer or shorter to compare two quantities,** then more than two, by making direct comparisons of lengths.
● Begin to record numbers, initially by making marks, progressing to simple tallying and writing numerals.

VOCABULARY

Measure; size; compare; guess; estimate; nearly; close to; about the same as; just over; just under; length; width; long; short; wide; narrow; longer; shorter; longest; shortest; near; close.

ORAL AND MENTAL STARTER

FINGER ADD AND SUBTRACT: Ask children to add and subtract two sets of numbers with total to 10: *Add 3 and 4. 8 take away 7. 6 add 3.* Hold up fingers to show the answers.

WHOLE-CLASS TEACHING ACTIVITY

LONGER AND SHORTER: Show the children the families of items, for example the scarves. *Which is long? Which is short?* Say: *The red scarf is longer than the blue scarf.* Include a third item. *Which is the longest/shortest?* Ask children to put them in order from longest to shortest, shortest to longest. *The blue scarf is shorter than the red scarf but longer than the green scarf.* Show the children the table on the flip chart. Choose one item, for example a sock. Draw a picture of it in the first column. Point out the columns for 'Longer', 'Shorter' and 'About the same as'. Ask individuals to find an item that is longer than the sock. Repeat with 'shorter' and 'about the same length as'. Say: *The ribbon is longer than the sock. The crayon is shorter than the sock. The tower of cubes is about the same length as the sock.* Add pictures to the appropriate column on the flip chart.

GROUP ACTIVITIES

1. Place a set of assorted objects on the table. Give each child a copy of photocopiable page 157 (Compare me). In pairs, children compare different items with one chosen item and record on their sheet items that are longer, shorter and about the same length.
2. Children make a family of mice (between three and five) and add tails of different lengths.
3. Children sort a set of objects (up to five) in order (shortest to longest, then vice versa), then find objects that are the same size as one other.

 As part of a science or story focus (eg 'Jack and the Beanstalk') help the children to plant seeds (eg beans, peas, cress, sunflowers) and measure their growth.

DIFFERENTIATION

Less able: make sure children can compare two objects before moving to three, then five. More able: extend to five, then more. Encourage children to describe their comparisons and think about what would happen if another item was added.

PLENARY

Feedback from the **Group activities**. Ask the class to form a line. Say: *Is it long or short? Make a line of boys and a line of girls. What can you tell me about the line? Make three lines that are different lengths.* Repeat using four and five lines.

LESSON 4

RESOURCES	Individual sets of numeral cards (page 12); *Mr Tall* by Roger Hargreaves (World International); flip chart; marker pen. **Group activities:** camera; large sheets of sugar paper; items for comparison: sets of Russian dolls, teddy bears, bottles, vases, cardboard tubes; copies of photocopiable page 158 (Tall and short); cubes; beads; Duplo; LEGO. On the flip chart draw a table with the headings 'taller' and 'smaller'.
LEARNING OUTCOMES	**ORAL AND MENTAL STARTER** ● **Begin to relate addition to combining two groups of objects,** counting all the objects; extend to three groups of objects. **WHOLE-CLASS TEACHING ACTIVITY** ● **Use language such as longer or shorter to compare two quantities,** then more than two, by making direct comparisons of lengths. ● Begin to record numbers, initially by making marks, progressing to simple tallying and writing numerals.
ORAL AND MENTAL STARTER	FINGER ADD: Ask children to use fingers to add two, then three groups of numbers together. Children hold up numeral cards to show answers.
WHOLE-CLASS TEACHING ACTIVITY	TALLER AND SMALLER: Read *Mr Tall*. *What sort of things would Mr Tall like?* (Giraffes, cranes, blocks of flats, ladders.) Ask five children to come out to the front. *How can we find out who is the tallest? Is Ella smaller than Jo? Is Harry taller than Nassau? Who is about the same height as Peter?* Show children the 'taller' and 'smaller' table. Demonstrate with a chosen item and record. Repeat using another item.
GROUP ACTIVITIES	**1.** Take a small group of children on a 'tall and short trail'. Photograph tall and small objects in the environment. **2.** Place various items on each table. Children compare three, then five items against a chosen item. They record their work on photocopiable page 158 (Tall and short). **3.** In pairs, children build and make items for Mr Tall, eg a house, table, chair. ● I spy with my little eye something that's taller/shorter than...
DIFFERENTIATION	Less able: reinforce tall/short. Get them to point out tall and short objects in the classroom. More able: extend comparisons to five then beyond. Encourage them to describe how they compared and to record.
PLENARY	Feedback from activities. Recite 'Two fat gentlemen met in the lane' using finger play.

LESSON 5

RESOURCES	Individual numeral cards (page 12); story of 'The Enormous Turnip', vegetables: potatoes, carrot, tomato, swede. turnip, marrow; labels saying 'is heavier than', 'is lighter than'. **Group activities:** sets of different sizes and types of vegetables; pencils; items for comparison; balances.
LEARNING OUTCOMES	**ORAL AND MENTAL STARTER** ● **Begin to relate subtraction to 'taking away'** and counting how many are left. **WHOLE-CLASS TEACHING ACTIVITY** ● **Use language such as heavier or lighter to compare two quantities,** then more than two, by making direct comparisons of masses. ● Begin to record numbers, initially by making marks, progressing to simple tallying and writing numerals.
ORAL AND MENTAL STARTER	SHOW ME SUBTRACT: Give out the sets of numeral cards. Children work out how many are left when some are taken away: *10 take away 5.* Demonstrate using fingers. *10 take away 5 leaves 5.* Repeat several times. Children hold up numeral cards to show the answer.
WHOLE-CLASS TEACHING ACTIVITY	HEAVIER AND LIGHTER: Read 'The Enormous Turnip'. *What happened to the turnip? Do you think it was heavy or light when it was enormous?* Show children the vegetables. Ask individuals to pick out something that is light/heavy. Ask children to compare two vegetables: *Is the carrot heavier than the marrow?* Children compare by holding them in their hands. Place and read the labels 'is heavier than' and 'is lighter than'. Say: *The tomato is lighter than the potato.* Repeat using five vegetables.
GROUP ACTIVITIES	**1.** Give each child a set of vegetables. Ask them to choose a vegetable and then match it with one that is heavier or lighter than it. **2.** In small groups, children find three things that are heavier and three things that are lighter than a given item. **3.** In pairs, children estimate then check by using balances whether items are heavier or lighter than a given set of objects. ● Make vegetable soup with the children.
DIFFERENTIATION	Less able: reinforce vocabulary. Limit to three items, then compare with five. More able: include items that 'are the same as'. Use simple recording.
PLENARY	Ask children to think of things that are weighed, for example, fruit, vegetables, meat, babies, ourselves. Encourage children to describe where they have seen people using weighing scales. Explain why and how things are weighed.

RESOURCES

Five boxes of different sizes and shapes; wrapping paper; silver foil; labels; balances.
Group activities: variety of containers; items for weighing such as beads, cubes, conkers, shells, pasta, dried beans, feathers, polystyrene chips; sticky tape; small plastic bags.

PREPARATION

Cover the boxes with wrapping paper and silver foil to make parcels. Write labels saying 'heavier than', 'lighter than', 'weighs about the same as', 'balances'. Fill the plastic bags with different items, for example feathers, shells, polystyrene chips, pasta. Make some of the bags equal in weight and secure with tape. Make up a set of bags with different items all weighing the same amount, eg 25g.

LEARNING OUTCOMES

ORAL AND MENTAL STARTER
● **Begin to relate addition to combining two groups of objects**, counting all the objects; extend to three groups of objects.

WHOLE-CLASS TEACHING ACTIVITY
● **Use language such as heavier or lighter to compare two quantities,** then more than two, by making direct comparisons of masses.
● Begin to record numbers, initially by making marks, progressing to simple tallying and writing numerals.

VOCABULARY
Measure; size; compare; guess; estimate; enough; not enough; too much; too little; too many; too few; nearly; close to; about the same as; mass; weigh; weighs; balances; heavy/light; heavier/lighter; heaviest/ lightest; weight; balance; scales.

ORAL AND MENTAL STARTER

FINGER ADD: Ask the children to combine two numbers by counting on their fingers. They show the answer by holding their fingers in the air. Say: *4 add 3*. Demonstrate on fingers: *4 add 3 makes 7. Show me seven fingers.* Repeat using numbers to 10. Direct questions at individuals.

WHOLE-CLASS TEACHING ACTIVITY

WEIGH ME: Show the children three of the parcels. Ask: *Which parcel is the heaviest? How can we find out?* Ask children to come and compare the parcels. Place them in order. Read the labels 'is heavier than', 'is lighter than' and say: *If this parcel is the heaviest it must be heavier than both the other parcels.* Ask: *Which is the lightest parcel?* Place the labels. Say: *We can check by using the balance.* Remind children how to use the balance. Ask individuals to come up and place two of the parcels on the balance. *Which parcel is the heavier? How can we tell?* Repeat until all three parcels have been checked. *Were we correct with our order?* Introduce the two other parcels. Ask individuals to come and hold them to guess where they should go in the order.

GROUP ACTIVITIES

1. Children use the balances to weigh one of the parcels against different items and record their weighing by placing items in order.
2. In pairs, children make parcels that are heavier/lighter/the same as a given parcel, using their hands to estimate the weight.
3. Children pick up the plastic bags and compare the weight of the items. They place them in order and check their findings using the balance.

 Investigate what happens to heavy and light objects in the water tray.

DIFFERENTIATION

Less able: concentrate on comparison of two then three items.
More able: encourage children to record their findings pictorially or by labelling. Introduce items that weigh the same amount.

PLENARY

Discuss the findings from the plastic bag activity. Show the children the 'special set' of bags. Hold up two bags, for example, pasta and feathers, and ask: *Which bag is the heaviest? Why do you think that bag is heavier than the other?* Ask individuals to come out and compare the two bags by holding them in their hands. Invite two others to use the balance. Explain that both the bags weigh the same amount.

RESOURCES

A selection of ladies', gents', children's and babies' shoes; play-people; flip chart; marker pen. **Group activities:** Various items of footwear such as a slipper, wellington boot, ballet shoes etc; teapot; flowerpot; egg cup; soft toys; water tray; food colouring; plastic containers; paper; pencils.

PREPARATION

Assemble a collection of containers and 'filling' objects. Make labels saying 'holds more than', 'holds less than', 'holds the same amount'. Fill the water tray and add food colouring.

LEARNING OUTCOMES

ORAL AND MENTAL STARTER

● Begin to relate addition to counting on.

WHOLE-CLASS TEACHING ACTIVITY

● **Use language such as more or less to compare two quantities,** then more than two, by filling and emptying containers.
● Begin to record numbers, initially by making marks, progressing to simple tallying and writing numerals.

ORAL AND MENTAL STARTER

COUNT ON: Explain that you are going to say a number. The children must keep it in their heads. Then you give another number. Say: *Count on from the number in your head to the other number. 5 (Keep it in your head!) add 4.* Count out loud: *5 – 6, 7, 8, 9. 5 count on 4 is 9.* Repeat using different numbers to 20.

WHOLE-CLASS TEACHING ACTIVITY

FIT INSIDE: Say the rhyme 'There was an old woman who lived in a shoe'. Repeat with the whole class joining in. Ask: *How many children did the old woman have? How many people would fit inside a shoe?* Show the children the woman's shoe. *How many people would fit in here?* Hold up the play-people. *If we used the play-people, I wonder if we could estimate/ guess how many would fit in the shoe?* Invite individuals to estimate and write these on the flip chart with their names. Ask a child to fill the shoe with play-people. Tell the children that they can count as they are placed in the shoe and you will make a mark on the flip chart to represent each play-person that goes in the shoe. Ask: *Is the shoe full? Will any more people fit inside? How many did you count?* Write the number on the flip chart. Ask children to count up the number of marks. *Is it the same number?* Look at the estimates. *Did anyone make a correct estimate/guess?* Look how many estimates were more than and less than the answer. Introduce a child's shoe. *Is this larger or smaller than the other shoe? Will it hold the same number as the other shoe? Will it hold more or less play-people?* Children estimate, then check how many play-people fit inside the child's shoe. Make a tally on the flip chart as children count. Repeat the activity using the man's shoe.

VOCABULARY

Measure; size; compare; guess; estimate; enough; not enough; too much; too little; too many; too few; nearly; close to; about the same as; just over; just under; full; half full; empty; holds; container.

GROUP ACTIVITIES

1. Children fit play-people and soft toys into a selection of shoes – wellingtons, slippers, trainers, football boots, ballet shoes. They record their answers by simple marking.
2. Children investigate how many items fit inside different containers – teapot, egg cup, jelly mould, flower pot.
3. Using the water tray, children use different containers to fill others. They order the containers to show which holds most/least.

 Provide a range of containers such as buckets, spoons, measures, basins, and reclaimed materials like yoghurt pots, jelly moulds for children to use in the sand tray.

DIFFERENTIATION

Less able: make comparisons with three containers then extend to five.
More able: extend the number of containers. Encourage estimating and recording.

PLENARY

Feedback from activities. Ask children to discuss the objects they used to fill the containers and how many it took to fill them. Draw a table with three columns on the flip chart. Label these: 'container' 'filling objects' 'total number'. Ask children to choose three or four containers, eg teapot, egg cup, jelly mould. Draw the container in the first column. Ask: *What should we use to fill it? Which items would be best?* Get the children to count out the total number of items used to fill the container. Record the answer on the flip chart. Repeat the activity using the same container but different filling items. Compare the results.

RESOURCES	Flip chart; marker pen; *My Cat Likes To Hide In Boxes* by Eve Sutton (Puffin), a box wrapped in silver foil; beads; pasta; dried beans; cubes; learning links. **Group activities:** small boxes of Smarties; an assortment of boxes (different sizes and shapes); pencils; paper.
LEARNING OUTCOMES	**ORAL AND MENTAL STARTER** ● Begin to find out how many have been removed from a larger group of objects by counting up from a number. **WHOLE-CLASS TEACHING ACTIVITY** ● **Use language such as more or less to compare two quantities,** then more than two, by filling and emptying containers. ● Begin to record numbers, initially by making marks, progressing to simple tallying and writing numerals.
ORAL AND MENTAL STARTER	COUNT UP: Explain that you want the class to subtract by counting up. Say: *10 subtract 6.* Start with 6, and count up using fingers to 10. *6 – 7, 8, 9, 10. 10 subtract 6 is 4.* Write the number sentence on the flip chart. Repeat using other examples. Ask the class or individuals to count up together and hold up their fingers to show the answer. Extend to 20.
WHOLE-CLASS TEACHING ACTIVITY	CAPACITY: Read *My Cat Likes To Hide In Boxes.* Select the silver box. Ask children to estimate how many cubes will fill it. Write the estimates on the flip chart. Fill the box. Ask children to count out the number of cubes. Look at the estimates: *Did anybody give a correct estimate? Who gave the nearest guess?* Write '20 cubes fill the silver box'. Choose another 'filling' object. *Will it take more or less beads than cubes to fill the box?* Children estimate then count. Compare the amounts.
GROUP ACTIVITIES	**1.** In pairs, children count and record how many Smarties are in their box. Then fill the box with another 'filling' item. **2.** Give children a selection of boxes. They choose a 'filling' item and find which box holds the most/least/same amount as it. Ask them to record their findings on paper. **3.** Children have a variety of boxes. They arrange the boxes in order, estimating which holds the most/least amount. Then check using 'filling objects. ● Collect a variety of boxes and packets for junk modelling.
DIFFERENTIATION	Less able: help children to choose their 'filling' items so that the total number is within their counting range, otherwise give support for counting. More able: encourage children to estimate, count and record.
PLENARY	Take feedback from the **Group activities**.

Name

Compare me

I chose:			
I found these:			
longer		shorter	about the same

Name

Tall and short

I chose:

I found these:

taller	shorter

UNIT 5

ORGANISATION (5 LESSONS)

	LEARNING OUTCOMES	ORAL AND MENTAL STARTER	WHOLE-CLASS TEACHING ACTIVITY	PLENARY
LESSON 1	● **Use developing mathematical ideas and methods to solve practical problems** involving counting and comparing in a real or role play context. ● Begin to understand and use the vocabulary related to money. Sort coins, including the £1 and £2 coins, and use them in role play to pay and give change.	BUNS: Children work out the combined cost of various items.	WHAT'S IN MY PURSE?: Children sort coins of different value.	Children turn the role-play area into a shop.
LESSON 2	● **Use developing mathematical ideas and methods to solve practical problems** involving counting and comparing in a real or role play context. ● Begin to understand and use the vocabulary related to money. Sort coins, including the £1 and £2 coins, and use them in role play to pay and give change.	ODDS AND EVENS: Reinforcing odd and even numbers.	BAKER'S SHOP: Understanding the use of money and the cost of items.	Feedback from activities. Making amounts.
LESSON 3 + 4	● **Use developing mathematical ideas and methods to solve practical problems** involving counting and comparing in a real or role play context. ● Begin to understand and use the vocabulary related to money. Sort coins, including the £1 and £2 coins, and use them in role play to pay and give change.	ODDS AND EVENS: Reinforcing odd and even numbers.	WHAT'S IN MY PURSE?: Problem-solving activities using money.	Feedback from activities. Making amounts.
LESSON 5	● **Use developing mathematical ideas and methods to solve practical problems** involving counting and comparing in a real or role play context. ● Begin to understand and use the vocabulary related to money. Sort coins, including the £1 and £2 coins, and use them in role play to pay and give change.	SHOW ME ADD: Children solve addition problems.	SORT THE COINS: Problem-solving activities using money.	Feedback from activities.

ORAL AND MENTAL SKILLS   **Say and use the number names in order in familiar contexts.** Begin to understand and use the vocabulary related to money. Sort coins including the £1 and £2 coins, and use them in role play to pay and give change. Recite the number names in order, continuing the count forwards and backwards from a given number. **Order a given set of selected numbers**. Count in twos. Count in tens. **Begin to relate addition to combining two objects,** counting all the objects; extend to three groups of objects.

Lessons 1 and 3 are given in full. Lesson 4 develops Lesson 3. Lessons 2 and 5 are provided as grids to suggest follow on work to Lessons 1 and 3.

RESOURCES

Selection of different money including foreign currency: coins, notes, cheque, bank card, real and plastic coins; purses; flip chart; marker pen. **Group activities:** money dice (1p–6p); small boxes or containers; ingredients for simple biscuits and cakes.

PREPARATION

Make labels for the small boxes or containers showing a number of coins for each one, for example, 5 × 2p coins, 3 × 10p coins, 2 × 20p coins and attach these to the lids. Place a variety of coins in the purse. Make labels for the purses for the **Group activities** showing amounts that require a number of coins, for example, 7p, 12p, 6p, 4p with amounts to 20p. Make a label saying 'Banker'.

LEARNING OUTCOMES

ORAL AND MENTAL STARTER
● **Say and use the number names in order in familiar contexts** such as number rhymes.
● Begin to understand and use the vocabulary related to money. Sort coins, including the £1 and £2 coins, and use them in role play to pay and give change.

WHOLE-CLASS TEACHING ACTIVITY
● **Use developing mathematical ideas and methods to solve practical problems** involving counting and comparing in a real or role play context.
● Begin to understand and use the vocabulary related to money. Sort coins, including the £1 and £2 coins, and use them in role play to pay and give change.

ORAL AND MENTAL STARTER

BUNS: Sing the rhyme 'Five currant buns'. Ask: *How many buns can I buy with 5p? How much would three buns cost? I have 5p and I spend 3p. How much change would I have? If jam doughnuts cost 2p each in the baker's shop, how many can I buy for 4p? I have 10p and I buy three jam doughnuts, how much change do I have?* Repeat the rhyme but change to 'jam doughnuts'.

WHOLE-CLASS TEACHING ACTIVITY

WHAT'S IN MY PURSE?: Ask the children to tell you places where money is used such as shops, cafés, markets, school, car boot sales, banks, holidays. Ask: *How do we pay for things? Coins, notes, cheques, credit cards, foreign coins.* Show the children some examples of different money, then show them a selection of coins, 1p, 2p, 5p, 10p, 20p, 50p, £1, £2. *Which is worth the most? Which has the least value?*

Show the children the contents of the purse. Say: *Name the coins. How many coins are there? How many different coins? How many of each coin?* Say: *2 × 5p coins, 3 × 10p coins.* Record the amount of money on the flip chart. Point out the 'p' to show that this numeral represents money. Order the coins from smallest to largest value. Add the value of coins in the purse.

GROUP ACTIVITIES

1. In pairs, children sort money into labelled containers, for example 5 × 2p coins, 3 × 10p coins, 2 × 20p coins.
2. In groups, children place the correct value coins in purses labelled with amounts, eg 7p, 12, 6p, 4p.
3. Children throw a dice (1p, 2p, 3p, 4p, 5p, 6p) and collect that amount of money from the banker (an adult). First child to collect 10p wins. Extend to different amounts to win.
Make salt/flour dough cakes, biscuits, rolls etc. for the 'Baker's shop'.

DIFFERENTIATION

Less able: allow plenty of sorting and ordering activities.
More able: extend to use amounts to 20p and beyond.

PLENARY

Feedback from the **Group activities**. Sing 'Five currant buns' with role-play. Suggest that the role-play area be turned into a baker's shop. Invite the children to think of items that might be sold in the shop such as cakes, biscuits, buns, sausage rolls, sandwiches, pies, pasties, bread, bread rolls.

VOCABULARY

Compare; count out; share out; left; left over; list; money; coin; penny; pence; pound; price; cost; buy; sell; spend; spent; pay; change; costs more; costs less; cheaper; costs the same as; how much...?; how many...?; total.

RESOURCES	Flip chart; marker pen; items for role-play baker's shop such as play bread, sandwiches, sausage rolls, cakes, buns, biscuits; bags; plastic coins; play till; large sign saying 'Baker's shop'; examples of till receipts; price list for the Baker's shop. **Group activities:** small plastic bags; real coins; individual sets of 'money' cards (some sets should show written amounts, the other sets coins); Post-it notes; photocopiable page 164 (The Baker's).
LEARNING OUTCOMES	**ORAL AND MENTAL STARTER** ● Recite the number names in order, continuing the count forwards and backwards from a given number. **WHOLE-CLASS TEACHING ACTIVITY** ● **Use developing mathematical ideas and methods to solve practical problems** involving counting and comparing in a real or role play context. ● Begin to understand and use the vocabulary related to money. Sort coins, including the £1 and £2 coins, and use them in role play to pay and give change.
ORAL AND MENTAL STARTER	ODDS AND EVENS: Ask the children to count up to 20 then beyond. You start the count and say the odd numbers while the children say the even numbers. Repeat with boys saying even and girls odd, or clapping odd then even. Write all the odd then even numbers on the flip chart.
WHOLE-CLASS TEACHING ACTIVITY	BAKER'S SHOP: Show children the items and sign for the 'Baker's shop'. Explain that they are going to set up the shop. Ask them what happens when you buy items in a shop. Show the example till receipts and point out the list of items, the cost per item, total, change. Write an example on the flip chart. Show the price list and ask children to read out the prices: *How much is a sausage roll? If I buy a cake and a bread roll, how much would that cost?*
GROUP ACTIVITIES	**1.** Give each child photocopiable page 164 (The baker's) and a selection of coins. They have to place on the sheet the coins that they would use to buy each item. **2.** Place money cards face down on the table. Children turn over two cards and see whether they match. **3.** Children choose a money card and then select coins to make the amount (up to 10p) for a money bag. They write the amount and label their money bag. ● The children can make labels, price lists, posters, bakery items, and so on for the role-play shop.
DIFFERENTIATION	Less able: limit amounts to 5p, then extend to 10p. More able: extend amounts to 20p, then beyond.
PLENARY	Feedback from the **Group activities**. Write an amount on the flip chart: Ask: *What could I use to make this amount?* Repeat using different examples.

RESOURCES

Flip chart; marker pen; purse; coins; price list for the baker's shop. **Group activities:** copies of photocopiable page 164 (The Baker's); pencils; sets of money cards; domino cards showing money amounts; labelled containers; selection of different purses; dice; items for the baker's shop; Post-it notes.

PREPARATION

Label the containers saying 5 × 2p coins, 3 × 10p coins, 2 × 20p coins. Place a variety of coins in the purse. Make labels for the purses for group activities showing amounts that require a number of coins, for example 7p, 12p, 6p, 4p with amounts to 20p.

LEARNING OUTCOMES

ORAL AND MENTAL STARTER
● Count in twos.
● Count in tens.
● Order a given set of selected numbers.

WHOLE-CLASS TEACHING ACTIVITY
● **Use developing mathematical ideas and methods to solve practical problems** involving counting and comparing in a real or role play context.
● Begin to understand and use the vocabulary related to money. Sort coins, including the £1 and £2 coins, and use them in role play to pay and give change.

VOCABULARY

Compare; count out; share out; left; left over; money; coin; penny; pence; pound; price; cost; buy; sell; spend; spent; pay; change; dear; costs more; costs less; cheaper; costs the same as; how much...?; how many...?; total.

ORAL AND MENTAL STARTER

ODDS AND EVENS: Ask children to count in twos up to 20 then beyond starting at 0. Ask individuals to give even numbers. Write these on the flip chart. Ask: *Which is the smallest even number? Which is the largest?* Order the numbers. Repeat with odd numbers.

WHOLE-CLASS TEACHING ACTIVITY

WHAT'S IN MY PURSE?: Play as in Lesson 1 of this unit, on page 160. Ask: *How many coins are there? How many of each coin? Which coin has the highest value?* Write the contents of the purse on the flip chart. Look at the price list from the Bakers' shop. *How much would it cost to buy a sandwich and a loaf of bread? Does a sausage roll cost more or less than a jam tart? Which costs more: a currant bun or a bread roll? Can you see anything that costs the same amount?* Choose an item from the price list: *What coins would I use to pay for this?*

GROUP ACTIVITIES

1. Give each child a copy of photocopiable page 164 (The Baker's). They have to place on the sheet the coins that they would use to pay for each item.
2. Place money cards face down on the table. Children turn over two cards and see whether the cards match.
3. Children choose a money card and then select coins to make the amount (up to 10p) for a money bag. They write the amount and label their money bag.
4. Children share out domino cards and take turns to match the cards (written amounts and coins).
5. In pairs, children sort money into labelled containers, eg 5 × 2p coins, 3 × 10p coins, 2 × 20p coins.
6. In groups, children place the correct value coins in purses labelled with amounts, eg 7p, 12p, 6p, 4p.
7. Children throw a dice (1p , 2p, 3p, 4p, 5p, 6p) and collect that amount of money from the 'banker' (an adult). First child to collect 10p wins. Extend to different amounts to win.
8. Children work in role-play shop. One child acts as a shop assistant. Customers are given selected amounts with which to buy items.

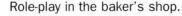 Role-play in the baker's shop.

DIFFERENTIATION

Less able: limit amounts of money to 5p, then extend to 10p and beyond.
More able: extend to 50p then £1.00.

PLENARY

Feedback from the **Group activities**. Select a money card. Ask individuals to read the amount and write it on the flip chart. Remind the children of the coins that can be used. Ask: *Which coins can we use to make that amount? Are there any other ways we can make it?* Repeat using a range of amounts.

LESSON 4

Before this lesson, place a selection of coins and coin cards on each table. Repeat Lesson 3, but in the **Oral and mental starter**, this time count in tens and in twos. For each count, ask: *What comes before...? What comes after...? What comes in between...?* In the **Whole-class teaching activity**, explain that you want the children to work out the problems you are going to say using the coins or money cards placed on the tables. Say: *Show me 7p. What is the total of 4p and 5p? If a currant bun costs 6p, which coins could I use to pay for it? How could I pay for a cake which costs 10p?* Ask individuals to show amounts. Ask: *Which is more, 20p or 13p? I have 10p and I spend 7p. How much change do I need?* Go on to choose from the **Group activities** in Lesson 3. For less able children, limit amounts of money to 10p initially, then extend to 20p and beyond, but extend to £1.00 for the more able.

RESOURCES	Flip chart; marker pen. **Group activities:** photocopiable page 164 (The baker's); pencils; sets of money cards; labelled containers; selection of different purses; dice; items for the baker's shop; Post-it notes.
LEARNING OUTCOMES	**ORAL AND MENTAL STARTER** ● **Begin to relate addition to combining two objects,** counting all the objects; extend to three groups of objects. **WHOLE-CLASS TEACHING ACTIVITY** ● **Use developing mathematical ideas and methods to solve practical problems** involving counting and comparing in a real or role play context. ● Begin to understand and use the vocabulary related to money. Sort coins, including the £1 and £2 coins, and use them in role play to pay and give change.
ORAL AND MENTAL STARTER	SHOW ME ADD: Ask: *What is 2 add 3? What is the total of 4 add 6? 3 add 3 add 1 is...?* Repeat, using numbers to 20 and beyond. Ask individuals to carry out addition sums.
WHOLE-CLASS TEACHING ACTIVITY	SORT THE COINS: Ask children in pairs to sort out 1p, 1p and 2p. Ask: *How much altogether? What is the total of 5p and 5p? How many ways can you make 5p?* Record these on the flip chart.
GROUP ACTIVITIES	Choose from the **Group activities** in Lesson 3, page 162.
DIFFERENTIATION	Less able: limit amounts of money to 10p, then extend to 20p and beyond. More able: encourage children to find and record different ways of making amounts.
PLENARY	Feedback from the **Group activities**.

The Baker's

sausage roll
4p

jam tart
3p

jam doughnut
6p

cheese and
tomato roll
12p

chocolate muffin
7p

currant bun
3p

UNIT 5

UNIT 6: Assess & review

Choose from the following activities over the course of the two lessons. During the group activities some of the children can work with you on practical tasks, while others complete assessment worksheets 3a and 3b which assess their skills with reading and writing numbers, and addition. The specific assessment criteria for the assessment sheets can be found at the bottom of each sheet.

RESOURCES

Numeral cards for each child (page 12); assessment photocopiables 3A and 3B; a selection of objects for counting; interlocking cubes, sets of 2-D and 3-D shapes, a feely bag; pieces of ribbon of different lengths and widths; a selection of items for measuring; 1p, 2p, 5p, 10p, 20p, 50p £1.00 and £2.00 coins; pencils and paper for recording.

ORAL AND MENTAL STARTER.

ASSESSMENT
● Can the children: **Say and use the number names in order in familiar contexts?**
KNOWING THEIR NUMBERS: Recite the rhyme '1, 2, 3, 4, 5, once I caught a fish alive' together.

GROUP ACTIVITIES
Assessment
● Can the children: **Recognise numerals 1 to 9? Use language such as more or less, greater or smaller to compare two quantities? Use language such as circle or bigger to describe the shape and size of solids and flat shapes? Use everyday words to describe position? Compare two lengths** by making direct comparison? **Compare mass** by making direct comparison of two objects? **Use developing mathematical ideas and methods to solve practical problems using adding and subtraction?**
RECOGNITION OF NUMERALS 1 TO 9: Ask children to place the numeral cards on the table face up. They take turns to find a numeral and read it out.
COMPARE TWO QUANTITIES: Ask children to count out a given quantity of cubes (between one and ten). Can they say how many objects they have? Repeat, using a different quantity (again between one and ten). Ask children if there are more or less/is a greater or smaller number of objects.
SHAPE SORT: Ask children to name 2-D and 3-D shapes. Can they find a shape according to different criteria, such as 2-D, a rectangle, straight edges, flat faces, four sides, four corners. Place a selection of shapes in a feely bag. Select a shape and describe it to the children. Ask them to guess the name of the shape. Ask individuals to feel a shape in the feely bag and describe it to others for them to guess what it is. Check that children are able to use the appropriate language correctly.
POSITIONAL LANGUAGE: Choose from the activities used for the whole-class teaching activity and group activities in Lessons 3 and 4 of Unit 3 of this term (page 147), or make up some similar ones.
COMPARING LENGTHS: Use 'Longer and shorter' (Unit 4, Lesson 3, page 152), using pieces of ribbon of different lengths and widths to make comparisons. Check that the children can understand and use the vocabulary of length.
COMPARING MASS: Use 'Heavier and lighter' (Unit 4, Lesson 5, page 153). Encourage children to choose their own objects to compare, estimate, then measure using hands and a balance. Check that the children can understand and use the vocabulary of mass.
PROBLEM-SOLVING: Either choose from the problems suggested in Unit 5, Lessons 2, 3, 4 and 5 (pages 161–163) or make up some similar ones. Provide counting resources such as cubes, everyday items and coins. Encourage children to show and describe how they worked out their answer for each problem.

Name

Assessment 3a

Count the items. Write the number of items. Count carefully.

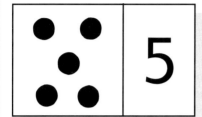  

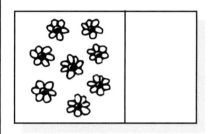  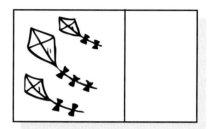

Draw the coins you need to buy these:

 currant bun
price 3p   =

 sausage roll
price7p   =

 bread roll
price 4p   =

● **Count reliably up to 10 everyday objects.**
● **Recognise numerals 1 to 9.**

Name

Assessment 3b

Circle the number that is more.

5   3   10   1

2   6   4   0

Circle the number that is smaller.

3   1   5   6   10   4

2   3   7   1   8   9

Complete the number track.

4	5		7		9	

● **Recognise numerals 1 to 9,** then 0 and 10.
● **Compare two numbers** and say which is more or less.

UNIT 7

ORGANISATION (5 LESSONS)

LEARNING OUTCOMES	ORAL AND MENTAL STARTER	WHOLE-CLASS TEACHING ACTIVITY	PLENARY
LESSON 1 ● **Recognise numerals 1 to 9,** then 0 and 10, then beyond 10. ● Begin to record numbers, initially by making marks, progressing to simple tallying and writing numerals. ●Count reliably in other contexts such as clapping sounds.	NUMBER LINE COUNT: Children count aloud from 0 to 20, then count along a number line.	HOW MANY BEATS?: Children count the number of beats played on an instrument.	Children count the different items on the photocopiable sheet.
LESSON 2 +3 ● Begin to understand and use ordinal numbers in different contexts.	SHOW ME: Children show a given number.	WHERE AM I?: Children carry out ordinal activities.	Reinforcement of ordinal recognition.
LESSON 4 ● Begin to record numbers, initially by making marks, progressing to simple tallying and writing numerals. ● **Use language such as more or less, greater or smaller, to compare two numbers** and say which is more or less, and say a number which lies between two given numbers.	SHOW ME: Children show a given number.	WRITING NUMBERS: Children write and compare numbers.	Feedback from activities. Recap numeral formation.
LESSON 5 ● **Use language such as more or less, greater or smaller, to compare two numbers** and say which is more or less, and say a number which lies between two given numbers. ● Order a given set of numbers: for example, the set of numbers 1 to 6 given in random order. ● Order a given set of selected numbers: for example, the set 2, 5 1, 8, 4	NUMBER LINE COUNT: Children count aloud from 0 to 20, then count along a number line.	ARRANGE THEM: Children order numeral cards.	Feedback from activities.

ORAL AND MENTAL SKILLS Recognise numerals 1 to 9, then 0 and 10, then beyond 10. **Say and use the number names in order in familiar contexts.**

Lessons 1 and 2 are given in full. Lessons 3–5 are extensions of what has already been taught. Lessons 4 and 5 are given in grid form.

RESOURCES

Number line 0–20; flip chart; marker pen; pointer; set of enlarged numeral cards (page 12); musical instruments, such as a drum, tambourine, triangle, Indian bells.
Group activities: paper plates; (1–5) spinner; paper bags; selection of counting objects; labels; pencils; paper; dice; copies of photocopiable page 173 (Under the sea) plus an enlarged copy.

LEARNING OUTCOMES
ORAL AND MENTAL STARTER
● **Recognise numerals 1 to 9,** then 0 and 10, then beyond 10.
● **Say and use the number names in order in familiar contexts**.
● Count reliably in other contexts such as clapping sounds.

WHOLE-CLASS TEACHING ACTIVITY
● **Recognise numerals 1 to 9,** then 0 and 10, then beyond 10.
● Begin to record numbers, initially by making marks, progressing to simple tallying and writing numerals.

VOCABULARY

Number; zero, one, two, three... to twenty; zero, ten, twenty...; none; how many...?; count; count (up) to; count on (from, to); how many times?

ORAL AND MENTAL STARTER

NUMBER LINE COUNT: The whole class counts aloud from 0 to 20. Point to the number line. Say: *Start at 3 count on 2. What number have you landed on?* Repeat using different numbers.

WHOLE-CLASS TEACHING ACTIVITY

HOW MANY BEATS?: Explain that the lesson is about counting and writing numbers. Arrange the large numeral cards so that the children can see them. Say that you are going to choose a number and you want the children to draw it in the air. Next, explain that you are going to play an instrument, for example the drum, and you want the children to count the number of beats. Ask: *How many beats did you count?* Write the number on the flip chart. Ask children to draw this number in the air, then on the floor. Repeat using different instruments. Start with numbers 0–5, then extend to 10. Ask individuals to record the numbers on the flip chart.

GROUP ACTIVITIES

1. Put out a set of paper plates. Children take turns to spin a (1–5) spinner. They count out the number of objects shown on the spinner and place them on the plate.
2. Give the children a selection of paper bags. In pairs, one child throws the dice (1–6) and counts out that number of objects. The other child writes the appropriate number on a label and attaches it to the bag. The game is finished when bags labelled 1–6 have all been filled.
3. Give each child a copy of photocopiable page 173 (Under the sea). Ask them to count the number of different objects and write the numerals in the bubbles.
Make number labels and booking tickets for seats in the role-play train, bus or aeroplane.

DIFFERENTIATION

Less able: ask a classroom assistant to work with them. Make sure children are counting correctly. Check number formation.
More able: extend with numbers to 10.

PLENARY

Display the enlarged copy of photocopiable page 173 (Under the sea). Ask children to count the different items. Say: *How many crabs?* Ask children to write the number in the air or on the floor. Ask individuals to write the numbers on the flip chart.

LESSON 2 + 3

RESOURCES

Individual sets of numeral cards (page 12); fruit, including an apple, banana, pear, orange, grapes; various different-coloured shapes; washing line; pegs; various objects such as a book, a teddy, a skipping rope, a beaker, a pencil case. **Group activities:** badges (1–6); pencils; thin card; coloured shapes; ordinal cards (1st–5th); a picture-sequencing activity; scissors; adhesive; paper; coloured beads; threading lace; stacking cubes or Russian dolls.

PREPARATION

Make a set of badges saying 1st, 2nd, 3rd, 4th, 5th and 6th. Make the required photocopies. Find a picture-sequencing activity – there are many examples of these in published resources. Find a simple one that the children will be familiar with, for instance a nursery rhyme such as 'Humpty Dumpty'.

LEARNING OUTCOMES

ORAL AND MENTAL STARTER
● **Recognise numerals 1 to 9,** then 0 and 10, then beyond 10.
● Say and use the number names in order in familiar contexts.

WHOLE-CLASS TEACHING ACTIVITY
● Begin to understand and use ordinal numbers in different contexts.

VOCABULARY

Number; zero, one, two, three... to twenty and beyond; how many...?; count; order; size; first, second, third... tenth; last; last but one; before; after; next; between.

ORAL AND MENTAL STARTER

SHOW ME: Hand out the set of numeral cards. *Show me five fingers. Show me number 7.* Children show you the relevant number of fingers or the appropriate numeral card.

WHOLE-CLASS TEACHING ACTIVITY

WHERE AM I?: Explain that in competitions, for example running or motor racing, there is a special order to show who has come where in the race – 1st, 2nd, 3rd, 4th, 5th, 6th. *If Hanif is the winner, he is first in the race.* Ask six children to come out to the front of the class. Ask: *Who is the first in the line? Who is last? Who is the last but one?* Say: *Peter is third in the line. How many people are in front of him? How many people are behind him?* Ask the children to count along the line. Point out that when you count, 3 is the third number, 6 is the sixth. Ask: *What is the fifth number? What is the second?* Now display the fruit in front of the class. Ask: *How many pieces of fruit are there?* Explain that you want the children to describe the fruit in order, eg 1st, 2nd, 3rd, 4th, 5th, 6th. Ask: *Which fruit is 3rd? The banana is in which place?* Invite the children to change the order of the fruit. *Put the grapes first, the apple second, the banana fourth, the pear fifth and the orange in last place. What is the third fruit? Is the pear third or fifth?*

GROUP ACTIVITIES

1. Organise a running and skipping race for a group of children. Ask the children to organise themselves in the order in which they came. Give out badges for 1st, 2nd, 3rd, 4th, 5th etc. Ask the children to organise themselves in a different order and rearrange the badges in the new order.
2. Children write their own names or are given their name card. Ask: *Which letter is first in your name? Which letter is last?*
3. Place a set of coloured shapes on the table. In pairs, children arrange these in any order. Give each pair a set of ordinal cards (1st–5th). They match the cards to the shapes.
4. Give each child a picture-sequencing activity. They cut out the pictures and sequence them in order. Ask: *What happened first? What happened second?*
5. Place an assortment of coloured beads on the table. In pairs, one child makes a necklace of five cubes using different colours. The child describes the necklace using ordinal numbers so that their partner can make an identical necklace.
6. Give the children a set of instructions, for example:
● First, go to the role-play area and collect a cup.
● Second, find page two in a book.
● Third, count how many children are in the sand.
● Fourth, write your first name.
● Fifth, make a necklace of beads.

Provide stacking cubes or Russian dolls for children to order.

DIFFERENTIATION

Less able: limit to 1st, 2nd, 3rd. Ask a classroom assistant to help extend vocabulary. Gradually extend up to 5th.
More able: read and record using first, second, third...

PLENARY

Write the school name on the flip chart. *Which is the first letter?* Count the letters. *Which is the tenth letter? Which is the last but one?* Ask children to come out and place the numeral cards on the washing line. Secretly remove a card. *Which one is missing?* Shuffle the cards. *Which numbers are in the wrong order?* Individuals place the cards correctly.

LESSON 3

Repeat Lesson 2, but in the **Whole-class teaching activity** use a set of different-coloured cut-out shapes, for example red triangle, blue circle, green square, yellow rectangle, red square, green circle etc. Give the cards to individuals. Ask children to peg the shape cards on the washing line in the order you give: *First the red square, second the green circle.* When all the cards are on the line, ask: *Which shape is third? How many shapes are before the fourth shape? Which colour shape is in between the fifth and the seventh?* Choose from the **Group activities** for Lesson 2. In the **Plenary** session, place five objects (for example, a book, a teddy, a skipping rope, a beaker and a pencil case) in front of the class. Ask: *Which is first? In which place is the skipping rope? What comes between the second and fourth object?* Explain that you want the children to remember the order of the objects. Ask them to cover their eyes. Remove an object and say: *I have taken away the fifth object? What has gone?* Repeat using different objects.

LESSON 4

RESOURCES	Classroom numeral frieze; enlarged set of numeral cards (page 12); flip chart; marker pen; enlarged ladybird template (page 15); dice. **Group activities:** individual ladybird templates (page 15); individual sets of numeral cards (page 12); assorted paper; pencils; crayons.
LEARNING OUTCOMES	**ORAL AND MENTAL STARTER** ● **Recognise numerals 1 to 9,** then 0 and 10, then beyond 10. ● **Say and use the number names in order in familiar contexts.** **WHOLE-CLASS TEACHING ACTIVITY** ● Begin to record numbers, initially by making marks, progressing to simple tallying and writing numerals. ● **Use language such as more or less, greater or smaller, to compare two numbers** and say which is more or less, and say a number which lies between two given numbers.
ORAL AND MENTAL STARTER	SHOW ME: As in Lesson 2, page 170.
WHOLE-CLASS TEACHING ACTIVITY	WRITING NUMBERS: Explain that the lesson is about writing and comparing numbers. Shuffle the numeral cards. Pick one and ask: *Who can tell me this number? Can you think of a number greater/smaller?* Write the number on the flip chart. Say the correct formation. Ask individuals to draw the number in the air or on the chart. Repeat using different numbers. Show children the enlarged ladybird template. Throw the dice and write that number of spots on one of the wings. Repeat for the other wing. *Which number is the greater/ smaller? Can you think of a number more/less/in between these ones?*
GROUP ACTIVITIES	**1.** Give each child a ladybird template. Children take turns to throw the dice and mark down the number of spots on each wing. **2.** Working with an adult, children use a range of mark-making resources (pencils, crayons, etc) to form numerals. **3.** Place the individual numeral cards face down on the table in front of each child. Each child turns over four cards and places them in order (smallest/ largest), then writes down the sequence they have made. ● Make numeral mobiles combining pictures and numbers.
DIFFERENTIATION	Less able: ask a classroom assistant to support them. More able: encourage children to compare two numbers and use language: more/less, greater/smaller.
PLENARY	Discuss the **Group activities**. Recap numeral formation.

LESSON 5

RESOURCES	Number line 0–20; pointer; enlarged numeral cards (page 12). **Group activities:** plastic numbers; individual sets of numeral cards (page 12); copies of photocopiable page 174 (Missing numbers); paper; pencils; crayons; number tracks (optional).
LEARNING OUTCOMES	**ORAL AND MENTAL STARTER** ● **Recognise numerals 1 to 9,** then 0 and 10, then beyond 10. ● **Say and use the number names in order in familiar contexts.** **WHOLE-CLASS TEACHING ACTIVITY** ● **Use language such as more or less, greater or smaller, to compare two numbers** and say which is more or less, and say a number which lies between two given numbers. ● Order a given set of numbers: for example, the set of numbers 1 to 6 given in random order. ● Order a given set of selected numbers: for example, the set 2, 5 1, 8, 4
ORAL AND MENTAL STARTER	NUMBER LINE COUNT: As in Lesson 1 on page 169.
WHOLE-CLASS TEACHING ACTIVITY	ARRANGE THEM: Shuffle the numeral cards (0–10) and arrange them in a row. *How can we order the cards? Which number comes first?* Ask a child to arrange the cards in order. As the child is placing the cards, ask the class: *What comes next?* Reshuffle the cards. Pick out six random cards and repeat the activity. *Is... greater than...? Which numbers come between... and...? Can we order the numbers in a different way?*
GROUP ACTIVITIES	**1.** Place sets of plastic numbers on the table. In pairs, children order the numbers from smallest to largest then vice versa. **2.** Give each child a set of shuffled numeral cards (0–10). Each child picks out five cards and arranges them in order. After checking by an adult, children write down their sequence. **3.** Give each child a copy of photocopiable page 174 (Missing numbers). Children fill in the numbers using a number track for support, if necessary. ● Children make their own board games.
DIFFERENTIATION	Less able: use numbers from 0 to 10. More able: provide more challenging numbers for ordering.
PLENARY	Discuss the **Group activities**. Ask for some of the sequences that pairs and individuals have made.

Name

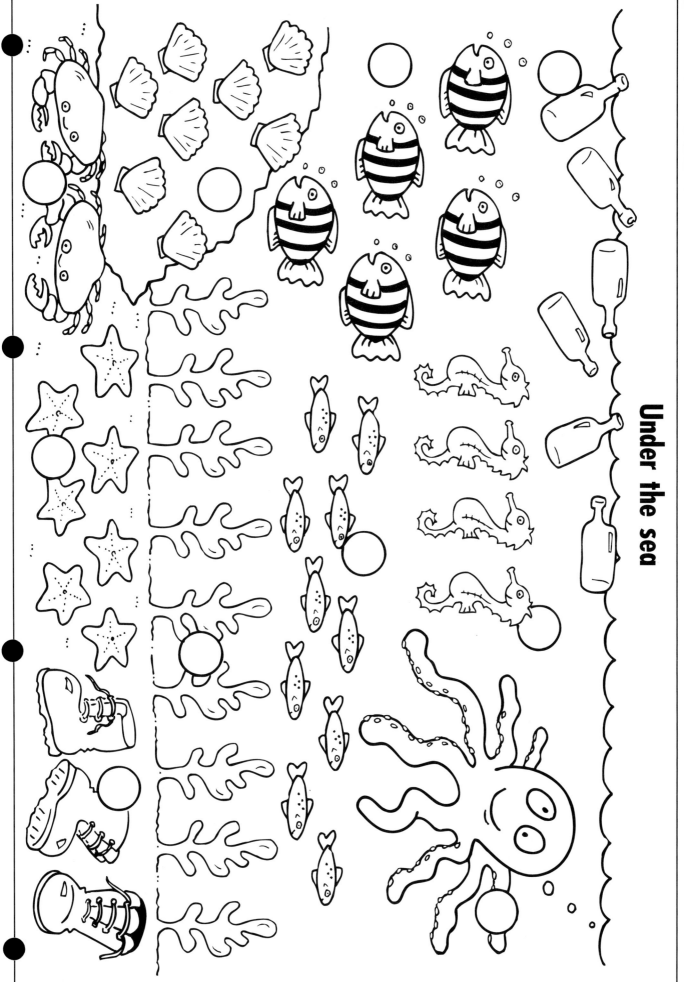

Under the sea

Missing numbers

| 1 | 2 | | 4 | |

7
9
10
12

0		2
	4	5
6	7	

6
0
1
3

9
7
5

UNIT 8

ORGANISATION (5 LESSONS)

	LEARNING OUTCOMES	ORAL AND MENTAL STARTER	WHOLE-CLASS TEACHING ACTIVITY	PLENARY
LESSON 1	● **Begin to relate addition to combining two groups of objects,** counting all the objects.	FINGER ADD: Children add different numbers to 10 using their fingers.	ADDING: Children combine sets with numbers to 10.	Feedback from activities. Counting objects in two sets.
LESSON 2	● Separate (partition) a given number of objects into two groups. ● Select two groups of objects to make a given total.	SHOW ME ADD: Children add two different numbers to 10.	FROGS: Children partition sets and make totals to 10.	Feedback from group activities. Repeat 'Show me add'.
LESSON 3	● **Begin to relate subtraction to 'taking away'** and counting how many are left.	FINGER SUBTRACT: Subtraction using numbers 0–10.	TAKE AWAY TOWERS: Subtraction using cubes.	Feedback from activities.
LESSON 4	● Remove a smaller number from a larger and find how many are left by counting back from the larger number.	SHOW ME SUBTRACT: Subtraction using numbers 0–10.	COUNT BACK: Children subtract by counting back.	Class completes photocopiable sheet.
LESSON 5	● **Begin to use the vocabulary involved in adding and subtracting.**	FINGER ADD AND SUBTRACT: Addition and subtraction using numbers 0–10	ADD OR TAKE AWAY?: Children solve addition and subtraction problems	Children repeat 'Finger add and subtract'.

ORAL AND MENTAL SKILLS Begin to relate addition to combining two groups of objects, counting all the objects. Begin to relate addition to counting on. Find a total by counting on when one group of objects is hidden. **Begin to relate subtraction to 'taking away'** and counting how many are left.

Lessons 1, 2 and 5 are given in full, while Lessons 3 and 4 are provided as grids.

LESSON 1

RESOURCES

Large class number track; individual sets of frogs and lily pads (page 14) plus a set for class use; flip chart; marker pen. **Group activities:** numeral cards (page 12); word cards; copies of photocopiable page 180 (Teatime); paper; pencils; sorting rings; counters.

PREPARATION

Display two lily pads on the flip chart. Attach Blu-Tack to the backs of five cut-out frogs and display them on the flip chart.

LEARNING OUTCOMES

ORAL AND MENTAL STARTER
● **Begin to relate addition to combining two groups of objects,** counting all the objects.

WHOLE-CLASS TEACHING ACTIVITY
● **Begin to relate addition to combining two groups of objects,** counting all the objects.

VOCABULARY

Add; more; and; make; total; altogether; score; one more; two more; how many more to make...?

ORAL AND MENTAL STARTER

FINGER ADD: Explain that you are going to say a number and you want the children to hold up that number of fingers on one hand. You will then say another number and they must hold up that number of fingers on their other hand. *How many fingers altogether?* Start with numbers to total 5, then extend up to 10.

WHOLE-CLASS TEACHING ACTIVITY

ADDING: Explain that the lesson is about adding. Point to the two lily pads and frogs. Ask the children to count the five frogs. Say that you are going to put some frogs on the lily pads. You want the children to count how many frogs altogether. Place one frog on a lily pad and four on the other. Point to the first lily pad and ask: *How many frogs are there?* Repeat with the second lily pad. *How many frogs altogether?* Say: *One frog add four frogs together makes five.* Write the number sentence on the flip chart. Repeat using different numbers.

GROUP ACTIVITIES

1. Give children their own lily pads and frogs and ask them to make their own number sentences using numbers to 6. Children use numeral and word cards to record their work.
2. Give each child a copy of photocopiable page 180 (Teatime). Children count the number of cakes on each plate and write the number in the square.
3. In pairs, children use sorting rings and counters to make number sentences (0–10). They choose a number of counters to place in each sorting ring, then find the total. They record using word and numeral cards or by writing a number sentence.

 In PE ask children to form sets using different numbers. Then combine the sets.

DIFFERENTIATION

Less able: ask a classroom assistant to work with them. Use numbers to total 5, then extend.
More able: encourage children to write their number sentences down themselves.

PLENARY

Invite individuals to read out their number sentences. Draw two sets on the flip chart with a number of objects in each set (0–6). Children count how many in each set then combine the number in each set to find how many altogether. Write the number sentence on the flip chart.

RESOURCES

Large class number track; individual sets of numeral cards (page 12); frogs and lily pads (page 14); flip chart; marker pen. **Group activities:** pencils; paper; counters; copies of photocopiable page 181 (Number friends); sets of dominoes; labels; pennies.

PREPARATION

Display two lily pads and ten frogs on the flip chart. Write ten labels from 'What makes 1?' to 'What makes 10?, plus 'add' and 'make'.

LEARNING OUTCOMES

ORAL AND MENTAL STARTER
● **Begin to relate addition to combining two groups of objects**, counting all the objects.
● Begin to relate addition to counting on.
● Find a total by counting on when one group of objects is hidden.

WHOLE-CLASS TEACHING ACTIVITY
● Separate (partition) a given number of objects into two groups.
● Select two groups of objects to make a given total.

VOCABULARY

Add; more;
and; make;
sum; total;
altogether;
how many
more to
make...?

ORAL AND MENTAL STARTER

SHOW ME ADD: Hand out the numeral cards. Explain that you are going to say a number and you want the children to hold this first number in their heads. Give another number. Say: *I want you to add that number to the first. Show your answer by holding up the numeral card.* Use numbers 0–10.

WHOLE-CLASS TEACHING ACTIVITY

FROGS: Explain that the lesson is about adding. Ask children to count out the frogs displayed on the flip chart. Explain that you want to separate the frogs onto the two lily pads. Say: *How many frogs shall we put on the first lily pad?* Invite one child to place the given number of frogs on the lily pad. Ask the class to count the number of frogs on the lily pad. Invite another child to place the remaining frogs on the other lily pad. Ask children to count the number of frogs on each lily pad. *How many frogs did we have to start? How many on here?* Write the number of frogs under each lily pad. Say: *10: 2 add 8 makes 10.* Repeat using different numbers.

GROUP ACTIVITIES:

1. In pairs, children have a given number of frogs, two lily pads and a label 'What makes 5?'. They place the frogs onto the lily pads and record their answers using numeral cards or pencils and paper.
2. Give each child a copy of photocopiable page 181 (Number friends). Children place counters on each person to make a given total, then record their number sentence.
3. Each pair of children has a set of dominoes and a 'What makes...?' label. They find all the dominoes that make their given number.

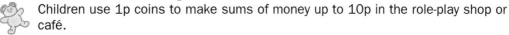 Children use 1p coins to make sums of money up to 10p in the role-play shop or café.

DIFFERENTIATION

Less able: limit numbers to 5, then extend up to 10.
More able: extend to 10. Encourage children to record number sentences in their own way.

PLENARY

Invite children to read out some of the number friends they have found. Repeat 'Show me add'.

UNIT 8

LESSON 3

RESOURCES	Large class number track; cubes; flip chart; marker pen. **Group activities:** counters; dice; frogs and lily pads (page 14); sets of numeral cards (page 12); paper; pencils.
LEARNING OUTCOMES	**ORAL AND MENTAL STARTER** ● **Begin to relate subtraction to 'taking away'** and counting how many are left. **WHOLE-CLASS TEACHING ACTIVITY** ● **Begin to relate subtraction to 'taking away'** and counting how many are left.
ORAL AND MENTAL STARTER	FINGER SUBTRACT: Explain that when you say a number, you want the children to hold up that number of fingers on one hand. Give another number for them to take away from the number of fingers held up. Ask: *How many fingers left?* Start with numbers to 5, then extend totals to 10.
WHOLE-CLASS TEACHING ACTIVITY	TAKE AWAY TOWERS: Explain that the lesson is about taking away – subtraction. Each child makes a tower of six cubes. Say: *Take away one cube. How many are left?* Write the number sentence on the flip chart. *6 take away 1 is 5. 6 subtract 1 is 5.* Repeat with five cubes. Invite individuals to say the number sentence. *5 take away 1 is 4.* Record this on the flip chart. Point out the number pattern – 6, 5, 4, 3, 2, 1, 0. *The number of cubes that are left is going down in ones.*
GROUP ACTIVITIES	**1.** Give each child six counters. Children take turns to throw the dice and remove the appropriate number of counters. The winner is the first player who removes all the counters by throwing the correct number, eg if one counter remains a 1 must be thrown on the dice to finish. **2.** Working in pairs, children have a lily pad and ten frogs. They place ten frogs on the lily pad, then take away 1 each time and record the number sentences. **3.** Place a set of numeral cards (1–10) face down on the table. In pairs, children take turns to turn over two cards. The smallest number is taken away from the largest. Children write down their number sentences. ● Sing number songs such as 'Ten green bottles'.
DIFFERENTIATION	Less able: limit numbers to 6. More able: extend numbers to 10.
PLENARY	Feedback from the **Group activities**. Sing 'Five little men in a flying saucer'.

LESSON 4

RESOURCES	Individual numeral cards (page 12); ten flowers; vase. **Group activities:** sets of frogs and lily pads (page 14); dice (0–5); paper; pencils; copies of photocopiable page 182 (Ten in a bed) plus an enlarged copy; (0–10) number tracks (page 13); purse; pennies; tray; various objects for counting.
LEARNING OUTCOMES	**ORAL AND MENTAL STARTER** ● **Begin to relate subtraction to 'taking away'** and counting how many are left. **WHOLE-CLASS TEACHING ACTIVITY** ● Remove a smaller number from a larger and find how many are left by counting back from the larger number.
ORAL AND MENTAL STARTER	SHOW ME SUBTRACT: Hand out the numeral cards. Explain that you are going to say a number and you want the children to hold this number in their heads. Give another number. The children take away/subtract that number from the first number and hold up the numeral card to show the answer.
WHOLE-CLASS TEACHING ACTIVITY	COUNT BACK: Ask the class to count out the number of flowers as you place them in the vase. Remove two flowers. *I have six flowers in the vase. Take away two flowers. How many are left?* Tell the children you can find how many are left by counting back. *Count back 2 from 6: 6 – 5, 4. 6 take away 2 is four. There are four flowers left.* Repeat using different numbers, then extend to 10.
GROUP ACTIVITIES	**1.** In pairs, children have six frogs and a lily pad. They take turns to throw the dice (0–5) and remove the appropriate number of frogs. Children write down their number sentences. They then replace the frogs and throw again. **2.** Give each child a copy of photocopiable page 182 (Ten in a bed). Children choose the number of children to take away. They use the number track to find how many are left, then record their answers on the sheet. **3.** In pairs, children have 8p in a purse. They take turns to remove a number of coins. The other child counts how many coins are left. ● Children guess how many are missing from a tray of objects.
DIFFERENTIATION	Less able: The children count out loud, touching each item as they subtract, and find the number left. Ask a classroom assistant to give support where necessary. More able: encourage children to make up their own questions for others.
PLENARY	Use the enlarged copy of 'Ten in the bed'. Say: *Ten in the bed, eight fall out. How many are left?* Find out by counting back together. *Count back 8 from 10. 10 – 9, 8, 7, 6, 5, 4, 3, 2. 10 take away 8 is 2.* Repeat using different numbers.

RESOURCES
Class number track; flip chart; marker pen; cubes; coins. **Group activities:** individual number tracks (page 13); sets of individual numeral cards (page 12).

PREPARATION
Place sets of cubes, coins, individual numeral cards and number tracks on tables.

LEARNING OUTCOMES

ORAL AND MENTAL STARTER
● **Begin to relate addition to combining two groups of objects,** counting all the objects.
● Begin to relate addition to counting on.
● Find the total by counting on when one group of objects is hidden.
● **Begin to relate subtraction to 'taking away'** and counting how many are left.

WHOLE-CLASS TEACHING ACTIVITY
● **Begin to use the vocabulary involved in adding and subtracting.**

VOCABULARY
Add; more; and; make; sum; total; altogether; one more, two more; how many more to make...?; how many more is 0... than...?; take (away); leave; how many are left/left over?; how many have gone?; one less, two less.

ORAL AND MENTAL STARTER
FINGER ADD AND SUBTRACT: Ask the children to hold up their fingers to show you the answers to various adding and subtracting questions, using numbers 0–10. For example: *8 take away 6; 5 add 0; 4 add 4; 10 subtract 5.*

WHOLE-CLASS TEACHING ACTIVITY
ADD OR TAKE AWAY?: Remind the children that they have been learning about adding and subtracting. Tell them that you are going to give them some addition and subtraction problems and you want them to work out the answers. Explain that they must listen carefully to see whether they need to use addition or subtraction. Use the following examples:
• There are four red pencils and five blue pencils in my box. How many altogether?
• I make nine cakes and we eat three. How many are left?
• There are ten in the bed and five fall out. How many are left?
• I have 5p in my purse. Then I put in 1p more. How many pence are in my purse?
After each question, ask the children whether they need to add or subtract (take away). Go through each question and write the number sentences on the flip chart.

GROUP ACTIVITIES
Choose from the selection given in Lessons 1, 2, 3 and 4.
Set up a tape with addition and subtraction activities for children working in pairs to listen to and carry out.

DIFFERENTIATION
Less and more able: target the questions appropriately.

PLENARY
Repeat 'Finger add and subtract'.

Name

Teatime

Count the cakes on each plate.

Name

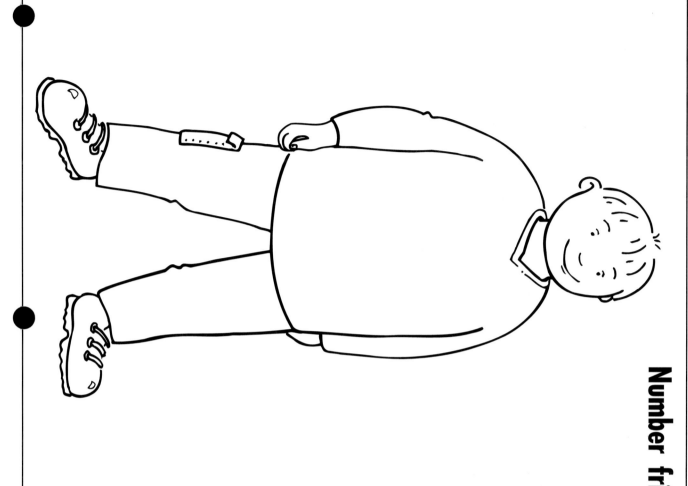

Number friends

Name

Ten in a bed

UNIT 9

ORGANISATION (5 LESSONS)

LEARNING OUTCOMES	ORAL AND MENTAL STARTER	WHOLE-CLASS TEACHING ACTIVITY	PLENARY
LESSON 1 ● **Use everyday words to describe position.** ● Put sets of objects in order of size.	ORDERING: Children order numbers.	GETTING BIGGER: Activities involving reasoning, sorting and ordering.	Feedback from activities.
LESSON 2 ● **Use everyday words to describe position,** direction and movement.	ORDERING: Children order numbers.	OBSTACLE COURSE NUMBERS: Positional and directional activities	Feedback from activities.
LESSON 3 ● **Use everyday words to describe position,** direction and movement.	PUT US IN ORDER: Ordinal recognition.	INTO THE WOODS:. Positional and directional activities.	Feedback from activities.
LESSON 4 ● Talk about, recognise and recreate patterns: for example, simple repeating or symmetrical patterns in the environment.	TEN FAT SAUSAGES: Children recite the rhyme, then count in twos.	ROUND AND ROUND: Children spot and continue patterns.	Children spot the mistake in patterns.
LESSON 5 ● Talk about, recognise and recreate patterns: for example, simple repeating or symmetrical patterns in the environment.	SHOW ME: Children show numbers less than a given number.	SYMMETRY: Introducing symmetry.	Feedback from activities. Children look for symmetrical patterns in the classroom.

ORAL AND MENTAL SKILLS **Use language such as more or less, greater or smaller, to compare two numbers** and say which is more or less, and say a number which lies between two given numbers. **Say and use the number names in order in familiar contexts.** Count in twos. Order a given set of numbers given in random order. Order a given set of selected numbers. Begin to understand and use ordinal numbers in different contexts.

Lessons 1 and 5 are given in grid form, with Lessons 2–4 provided as full plans.

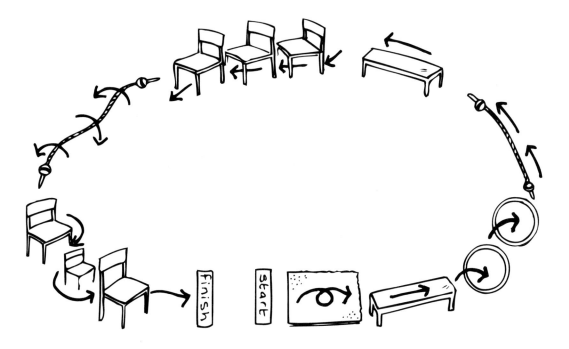

LESSON 1

RESOURCES	Large set of numeral cards to 20; *You'll soon grow into them, Titch* by Pat Hutchins (Red Fox); collection of clothes of different sizes such as socks, T-shirts, shoes; washing line; pegs. **Group activities:** range of items for sorting: socks, ribbons, Russian dolls, teddy bears, paintbrushes, empty containers; Play-Doh; Plasticine; clay; a selection of items such as socks, shoes, toy animals (you will need three different sizes of each item); pencils.
LEARNING OUTCOMES	**ORAL AND MENTAL STARTER** ● **Use language such as more or less, greater or smaller, to compare two numbers** and say which is more or less, and say a number which lies between two given numbers. ● Order a given set of selected numbers. **WHOLE-CLASS TEACHING ACTIVITY** ● **Use everyday words to describe position.** ● Put sets of objects in order of size.
ORAL AND MENTAL STARTER	ORDERING: Display a set of numeral cards, eg 0, 6, 10, 12, 19 in random order. Say: *Tell me the greatest number. What is the smallest number?* Ask individuals to come out and order the numbers from smallest to largest. *Which numbers come in between 10 and 19? Which numbers are smaller than 12?* Repeat, ordering the cards from largest to smallest.
WHOLE-CLASS TEACHING ACTIVITY	GETTING BIGGER: Read *You'll soon grow into them, Titch.* Ask: *Why did Titch need different clothes? What happens to your clothes when you get bigger?* Show children the selection of clothes. Invite a group of children to sort the clothes into order of size and peg them on the washing line. Ask: *How have they sorted the clothes? Is there another way they can be sorted?* Peg another set of clothes on the line using a different focus, eg type of clothes, material, etc. Ask: *What could we try next?* Explain that we use sorting and ordering every day. Give examples: lining up, packing items away, doing the shopping.
GROUP ACTIVITIES	**1.** In pairs, children sort and order a wide range of items: socks, ribbons, Russian dolls, teddy bears, paintbrushes, empty containers. They then describe how they have sorted the items. **2.** Children use Play-Doh, Plasticine, clay, etc to make families of creatures, for example snakes or snails, then describe how they can order them. **3.** Give children the selection of items and ask them to match the families of objects. ● The children can carry out painting activities using self-defined families, animals or imaginative characters.
DIFFERENTIATION	Less able: use three items for sorting and ordering and extend when confident. Suggest other ways to order. More able: extend to five items. Encourage children to find and describe other ways of ordering.
PLENARY	Feedback from the **Group activities**.

LESSON 2

RESOURCES

Flip chart; marker pen; large space, large and small apparatus such as mats, benches, hoops, skipping ropes, large and small chairs. **Group activities:** small building blocks; play-people; programmable toy; Play-Doh; thread; wire; art straws; card; adhesive; spreaders; copies of photocopiable page 189 (Treasure hunt); counters; (1–6) dice; pencils; large play toys; cubes; large squared paper; crayons; paint.

PREPARATION

Set up an obstacle course in the hall or a large space. Turn over some benches, arrange the skipping ropes to make straight and curved tracks, place the hoops next to each other in a zigzag, and arrange the chairs in twos and threes. See the example plan on page 183.

LEARNING OUTCOMES

ORAL AND MENTAL STARTER
● Order a given set of numbers given in random order.
● **Use language such as more or less, greater or smaller, to compare two numbers** and say which is more or less, and say a number which lies between two given numbers.

WHOLE-CLASS TEACHING ACTIVITY
● **Use everyday words to describe position,** direction and movement.

ORAL AND MENTAL STARTER

ORDERING: Write a set of six numbers from 0–20 in random order on the flip chart, eg 5, 1, 9, 12, 3, 15. Ask children to read the numbers. *Which is the greatest number? Which is the smallest?* Tell the children that you want them to put the numbers in order, starting with the greatest number. Write the numbers on the flip chart as the children tell you them. Ask: *Is that the right order? What comes next?* When the numbers are in descending order, ask children to read them out: *What numbers are missing?*

WHOLE-CLASS TEACHING ACTIVITY

OBSTACLE COURSE NUMBERS: Gather the children in the hall or a large space. Explain that you are going to give instructions that the children must follow. Give instructions for individuals, pairs and the whole class. Use these examples to begin with, then add to and amend them accordingly:

Stand in a row across the room. Walk forwards five steps. Turn to the left. Take four jumps forwards. Walk backwards eight steps. Choose a partner. Face your partner. Walk backwards ten steps. Turn right. Skip forwards five. Whole class make a circle and join hands. Move to the left ten steps. Stand and clap five times. Move to the left ten times. Stand and clap five times.

Explain the obstacle course, telling children what you want them to do at each piece of apparatus, for example jump into the hoops, walk along the overturned benches, go under the chairs, walk through the skipping rope tracks. Assemble the children at the start and stagger the route through the course.

Repeat several times and revise the route as appropriate. Ask children to describe what they were doing, and emphasise the directional and positional language. Take children back into the classroom and explain the **Group activities** available.

GROUP ACTIVITIES

1. In pairs, children make mazes using small building blocks for the play-people.
2. Ask an adult to take a small group around the school to make a simple map showing classrooms and other important features. When the map has been made, children pick out the things they have included and describe where they are.
3. Children give directions to a programmable toy to move it forwards, backwards, left, right.
4. Children use a range of materials, for example, string, Play-Doh, thread, wire, art straws, to make straight, curved and zigzag lines. Mount on card. When finished, ask children to 'feel' and describe the lines.
5. Give each child a copy of photocopiable page 189 (Treasure hunt). Children can play in pairs. Their task is to reach the treasure. They take it in turns to throw a dice, counting on and moving a counter along the footprints.
6. Draw with chalk or paint a route for children to navigate with outdoor/large play toys. Include straight and curved paths, roundabouts and left and right turns. Encourage the children to describe their route.
7. Children work individually to investigate the number of different shapes they can make using cubes. They record the shapes they have made on large squared paper.
8. Children draw or paint a route for Goldilocks to visit the Three Bears Cottage, the Wolf to find the Three Little Pigs houses, or the way to Grandma's house for Red Riding Hood.

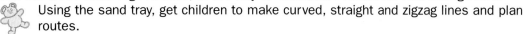 Using the sand tray, get children to make curved, straight and zigzag lines and plan routes.

DIFFERENTIATION

Less able: encourage the children to describe their actions and reinforce vocabulary.
More able: encourage children to describe and record their routes.

PLENARY

Feedback from the **Group activities**. Sing the song 'The Grand Old Duke of York' with children doing the actions.

RESOURCES

Flip chart; marker pen; large piece of card; green, white and blue paper or fabric; cut-outs of cottage, trees, flowers, wolf, Red Riding Hood, mother. **Group activities:** small building blocks; play people; programmable toy; Play Doh; thread; wire; art straws; card; adhesive; spreaders; copies of photocopiable page 189 (Treasure hunt); pencils; large play toys; cubes; large squared paper; crayons; paint.

PREPARATION

Cover the large piece of card to make a background. Cut out hills, sky and some clouds and stick onto the background. Attach Blu-Tack onto the back of the cut-outs and place nearby. Make the required photocopies.

LEARNING OUTCOMES

ORAL AND MENTAL STARTER
● Begin to understand and use ordinal numbers in different contexts.

WHOLE-CLASS TEACHING ACTIVITY
● **Use everyday words to describe position,** direction and movement.

ORAL AND MENTAL STARTER

PUT US IN ORDER: Ask six children to come to the front of the class and make a line. *Who is first, second, last, fourth, sixth?* Say: *The last but one person can sit down. The first person change places with the fourth person. Anna is third in the line. How many children are in front? How many behind?* Write a word on the flip chart. *What is the second letter? Which letter is third? How many letters altogether?*

WHOLE-CLASS TEACHING ACTIVITY

INTO THE WOODS: Remind the children of the story of 'Little Red Riding Hood'. Explain that Red Riding Hood went through the forest to visit her grandma. Show the children the background scene and suggest that they build it up to show the items in the story and the route Red Riding Hood took to visit her Grandma's cottage. Ask: *What do we need to position first? Did Grandma live near Red Riding Hood?* Invite individuals to come out and place the cut-outs on the scene. Ask: *Where is the Wolf? What's between the tree and the cottage? What happened next?*

GROUP ACTIVITIES

Choose from the **Group activities** in Lesson 2, given on page 185.

PLENARY

Feedback from group activities.

RESOURCES

Pattern blocks; cubes; large squared paper; flip chart; marker pen. **Group activities:** numeral pattern cards; beads; learning links; paper; crayons.

PREPARATION

Make a range of pattern cards with alternating shape patterns (triangle, square, triangle), numeral patterns (2, 1, 2, 1, 2, 1) and link patterns using two, three and four colours. Collect a selection of buttons of different sizes with varying numbers of holes.

VOCABULARY

Position; over; under; above; below; top; bottom; side; on; in; outside; inside; around; in front; behind; front; back; before; after; beside; next to; opposite; apart; between; middle; edge; corner; direction; left; right; up; down; forwards; backwards; sideways; across; next to; close; far; along; through; to; from; towards; away from; movement; slide; roll; turn; stretch; bend.

LEARNING OUTCOMES
ORAL AND MENTAL STARTER
● **Say and use the number names in order in familiar contexts.**
● Count in twos.

WHOLE-CLASS TEACHING ACTIVITY
● Talk about, recognise and recreate patterns: for example, simple repeating or symmetrical patterns in the environment.

ORAL AND MENTAL STARTER

TEN FAT SAUSAGES: Children hold up fingers to show number of sausages each time. Play 'Carry on counting' in twos to 20 and beyond around the class.

WHOLE-CLASS TEACHING ACTIVITY

ROUND AND ROUND: Sing 'Row row row your boat'. Explain that the song is a round because it can be repeated over and over, just like a pattern. Organise the children into two groups and sing the song again as a round. Next, make towers of blocks or cubes using two colours and two different amounts of cubes (two green, four red, two green). *What comes next?* Get individuals to continue the pattern. Describe the pattern: *Two red, four green, two red, four green.* Repeat, using different colours and amounts of cubes or blocks. Show the children how to record the pattern on squared paper. Point out that it shows the pattern of the cubes. Choose a numeral pattern (2, 1, 2, 1) card and ask the children to read out the number pattern. Demonstrate how to make the pattern using cubes. Repeat the activity, asking individual children to make the pattern. Show the children the shape pattern cards. *What is the pattern? What would come next?*

GROUP ACTIVITIES

1. Children make their own repeating patterns using cubes. They copy the pattern onto squared paper. Repeat using different colours and numbers of cubes.
2. Children use numeral pattern cards to make their patterns using beads and learning links.
3. Children make alternating patterns using 2-D then 3-D shapes. Then record their patterns by drawing round the shapes.

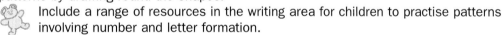 Include a range of resources in the writing area for children to practise patterns involving number and letter formation.

DIFFERENTIATION

Less able: encourage children to describe their patterns. Involve children in a range of practical activities before they record their patterns.
More able: use different colours, shapes, number and size of objects for pattern making. Get children to work in pairs to continue each other's patterns and describe the pattern.

PLENARY

Organise the class into two then three groups to sing 'Row, row, row your boat' as a round. Make a pattern using the cubes, incorporating a mistake. Ask the children to describe your pattern. *Is it correct?* Encourage children to 'spot the mistake' and correct the pattern. Repeat several times and make a correct pattern to see if the children recognise it as so. Repeat the activity by drawing patterns on the flip chart.

UNIT 9

LESSON 5

RESOURCES	Paper; marker pen. **Group activities:** peg boards; pegs; pattern blocks; pictures of ladybirds and butterflies; copies of photocopiable page 190 (Match it); pencils; paints.
LEARNING OUTCOMES	**ORAL AND MENTAL STARTER** ● **Use language such as more or less, greater or smaller, to compare two numbers** and say which is more or less, and say a number which lies between two given numbers. **WHOLE-CLASS TEACHING ACTIVITY** ● Talk about, recognise and recreate patterns: for example, simple repeating or symmetrical patterns in the environment.
ORAL AND MENTAL STARTER	SHOW ME: Ask children to show a number more than/less than a given number. *Draw a number greater than 10 in the air. Tell me a number between 9 and 13. Draw a number less than 7.*
WHOLE-CLASS TEACHING ACTIVITY	SYMMETRY: Remind the children of the repeating patterns work in Lesson 4, page 187. Hold up a paper square. *What shape is this?* Fold the square in half. *What shape is it now?* Draw a line down the middle and show the children that both sides are the same. Introduce the word 'symmetrical': *One side matches the other.* Show children how to fold other shapes to see if the sides match. Look at other objects that are symmetrical, for example people, letters, buildings.
GROUP ACTIVITIES	**1.** Children make simple symmetrical patterns using a peg board and pegs. **2.** Children use pattern blocks to make symmetrical patterns. **3.** Look at pictures of butterflies and ladybirds and see if they have symmetrical patterns. Give each child a copy of photocopiable page 190 (Match it) for them to make symmetrical patterns. ● Set up an activity area for 'blob' painting.
DIFFERENTIATION	Less able: give the children opportunities to fold shapes and complete the other half of a symmetrical pattern. More able: investigate reflective symmetry using mirrors.
PLENARY	Take feedback from the **Group activities**. Look for symmetrical objects in the classroom. Set up a display.

Name

Treasure hunt

Throw the dice and see where you land. Throw the dice again and count along until you reach the treasure.

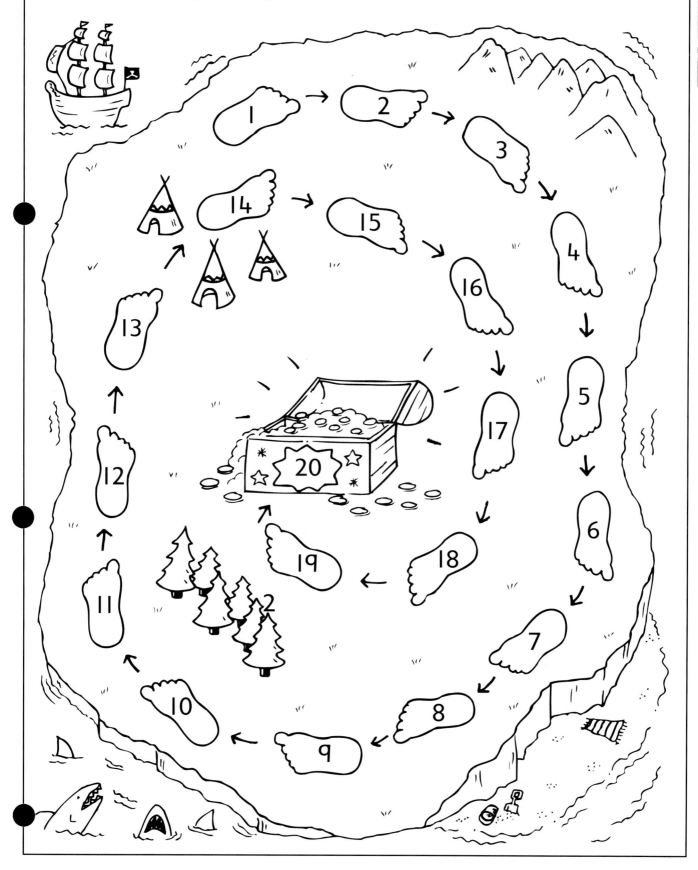

Name

Match it

Make the other sides of these pictures match:

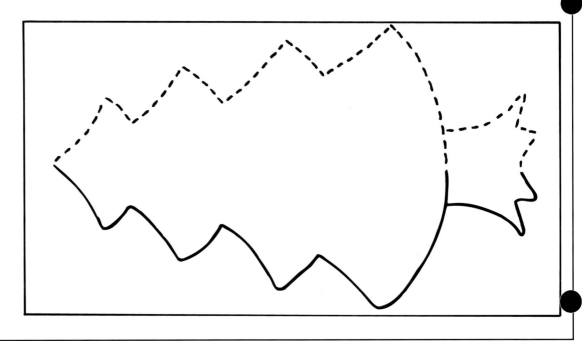

UNIT 10

ORGANISATION (8 LESSONS)

	LEARNING OUTCOMES	ORAL AND MENTAL STARTER	WHOLE-CLASS TEACHING ACTIVITY	PLENARY
LESSON 1	● Begin to understand and use the vocabulary of time. Sequence familiar events.	COUNT OUT: Children count a given number of objects.	TIME: Understanding the concept of time.	Children discuss things they do at different times of the day.
LESSON 2	● Begin to understand and use the vocabulary of time. Sequence familiar events.	GUESS MY NUMBER: Children work out a number by listening to clues.	TAKE YOUR TIME: Children time how long it takes to do certain tasks.	Feedback from activities.
LESSON 3	● Begin to read o'clock time.	CARRY ON COUNTING: Children count around the class.	TELL THE TIME: Learning to tell the time.	Children listen to 'What's the time, Mr Wolf?'
LESSON 4	● Begin to read o'clock time.	COUNT DOWN: Children count down in ones.	WHAT TIME IS IT?: Time activities.	Feedback from activities.
LESSON 5	● **Use language such as longer or shorter to compare two quantities,** then more than two, by making direct comparisons of lengths.	COUNTING IN TWOS: Children count in twos.	MEASURES: Children compare the length of various items.	Feedback from activities. Children tell the time on the clock.
LESSON 6	● **Use language such as heavier or lighter to compare two quantities,** then more than two, by making direct comparisons of masses.	COUNTING IN TWOS: Children count on and back in twos.	COMPARING MASS: Children compare the mass of various items.	Feedback from activities.
LESSON 7	● **Use language such as more or less to compare two quantities,** then more than two, by filling and emptying containers.	ODDS AND EVENS: Children count in ones. Recognition of odd numbers.	POUR IT IN: Children compare the capacity of different containers.	Feedback from activities.
LESSON 8	● **Use language such as more or less, longer or shorter, heavier or lighter... to compare two quantities,** then more than two, by making direct comparisons of lengths or masses, and by filling and emptying containers.	COUNTING IN TWOS. Children count in twos.	MEASURE IT: Reinforcement of measuring activities.	Feedback from activities.

ORAL AND MENTAL SKILLS **Say and use the number names in order in familiar contexts.** Recite the number names in order, continuing the count forwards or backwards from a given number. **Count reliably up to 10 everyday objects.** Count in twos.

Lessons 1–3 and 5 are given in full, while Lessons 4 and 6–8 extend what has already been taught and are provided as grids.

UNIT 10

LESSON 1

RESOURCES

Flip chart; marker pen; paper. **Group activities:** pencils; crayons; felt-tipped pens; set rings; picture-sequencing activity; spinner; selection of objects and pictures, for example, toothbrush, breakfast cereal, pencil, pencil case, story book, television, bed, bath; scissors; paste; assorted paper.

PREPARATION

Make labels saying 'today', 'tomorrow' and 'yesterday'. On the card, draw large circles, one for each child and divide them into three sections. Write 'morning', 'afternoon' and 'evening' at the top of the sections. Stick labels on the spinner saying 'morning', 'afternoon' and 'evening'. Stick the pictures onto thick card. Find a picture-sequencing activity showing activities that happen in the morning, for example a child asleep in bed, getting dressed, eating breakfast etc. There are many examples of these in published resources.

LEARNING OUTCOMES

ORAL AND MENTAL STARTER
● **Say and use the number names in order in familiar contexts.**
● **Count reliably up to 10 everyday objects.**

WHOLE-CLASS TEACHING ACTIVITY
● Begin to understand and use the vocabulary of time.
● Sequence familiar events.

VOCABULARY

Time; morning; afternoon; evening; night; bedtime; dinnertime; playtime; today; tomorrow.

ORAL AND MENTAL STARTER

COUNT OUT: Ask the children to count out a given number of objects. Say: *Count out eight beads. Count out 12 cubes. How many beads? How many cubes?*

WHOLE-CLASS TEACHING ACTIVITY

TIME: Explain that the lesson is about time. Hold up the cards saying 'yesterday', 'today' and 'tomorrow'. Read 'yesterday' Say: *Yesterday we had PE.* Ask individuals to tell you some activities they did yesterday. Repeat with 'today'. Say: *Today we are going to watch television. What else are we going to do today?* Point out 'tomorrow'. *Tomorrow we have class assembly.* Explain that you are going to make a time wheel. Show the children one of the circles and point out the words 'morning', 'afternoon' and 'evening'. Explain that in each section you are going to draw an activity that you do at these times. *In the morning I have my breakfast – I could draw my breakfast. What do you do in the morning?* Write a list of ideas on the flip chart. Repeat with afternoon and evening.

GROUP ACTIVITIES

1. Give each child a time wheel and ask them to draw their own activities for 'morning', 'afternoon' and 'evening'.
2. Place three set rings and the selection of objects and pictures on the table. Place the labels 'morning', 'afternoon' and 'evening' in each set ring. Children take turns to spin the spinner. They choose an object or picture appropriate to the time displayed on the spinner and place it in the appropriate ring.
3. Give each child a picture-sequencing activity. Ask them to cut out the pictures and sequence them in the correct order.

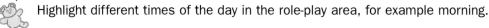 Highlight different times of the day in the role-play area, for example morning.

DIFFERENTIATION

Less able: ask a classroom assistant to support them to reinforce vocabulary.
More able: encourage children to think of their own ideas of what they do at different times of the day.

PLENARY

Ask children to tell you some of the activities they do at different times of the day. Point out that we may do the same activity at different times, for example we could shower or bath in the morning or evening.

LESSON 2

RESOURCES

Individual number tracks (page 13); Aesop's fable 'The hare and the tortoise'; egg timers (1 minute or less); beads; lace; cubes; washing line; pegs; large set of numeral cards (0–10) (page 12); **Group activities:** pencils; paper, kitchen timers.

LEARNING OUTCOMES

ORAL AND MENTAL STARTER
● **Say and use the number names in order in familiar contexts.**
● Recite the number names in order, continuing the count forwards or backwards from a given number.

WHOLE-CLASS TEACHING ACTIVITY
● Begin to understand and use the vocabulary of time.
● Sequence familiar events.

VOCABULARY

Next; last; now; soon; early; late; quick; quicker; quickest; quickly; slow; slower; slowest; slowly; old; older; oldest; new; newer; newest; takes longer; takes less time.

ORAL AND MENTAL STARTER

GUESS MY NUMBER: Ask children to look at their individual number tracks. Explain that you are thinking of a number. You want them to guess the number by listening to the clues you give. Say: *My number comes after 4 and before 6. What is it? My number is missing in this sequence. 10, 9, 8, 6, 5, 4, 3, 2, 1, 0. What is it?* Repeat using different numbers. Ask individuals and the whole class for answers.

WHOLE-CLASS TEACHING ACTIVITY

TAKE YOUR TIME: Read the story of 'The hare and the tortoise'. *Who won the race? Does a hare move quickly or slowly? Does a tortoise move quicker or slower than a hare? Why did the hare take longer?* Explain that time is used to measure how long it takes to do things. Say: *Count quickly to 10. Now count slowly back from 10 to 0.* Explain that you are going to see how many numbers you can write from 0 to 20 before the children have counted to 20. Write the numbers on the flip chart. Show the children the egg timer and explain how it works. Invite three individuals to come out and explain that you are going to give each of them a task to complete. You are going to time them with the egg timer. Ask the first child to thread beads onto a lace, the second child to build a tower using cubes, and the third to order a set of numbers on the washing line. Point out that some things can be carried out more quickly than others. Repeat using different children and different activities.

GROUP ACTIVITIES

1. Children thread as many beads as they can before an adult counts to 50. Repeat with different numbers. A classroom assistant records the number of beads threaded by each child.
2. Place an egg timer on the table. Children write or copy as many numbers 0–10 as possible before the timer finishes.
3. In pairs, children carry out a number of activities, for example 20 skips, sequence a set of numeral cards (0–10), sing a nursery rhyme, before the kitchen timer goes off.

In PE ask children to move in different ways, for example, walk quickly, hop slowly, make a circle before you count 10.

DIFFERENTIATION

Less able: limit the time allowed for each activity.
More able: encourage them to record their own times.

PLENARY

Take feedback from the **Group activities**. Ask: *Does it take longer to thread the beads or write the numbers?* Ask children how many skips they did before the timer went off.

RESOURCES

Flip chart; marker pen; large analogue clock face with movable hands; the story 'What's the time Mr Wolf'?'. **Group activities:** small analogue clock faces with movable hands; copies of photocopiable page 198 (What time is it?); pencils; sets of time cards; collection of clocks and watches.

LEARNING OUTCOMES

ORAL AND MENTAL STARTER
● **Say and use the number names in order in familiar contexts.**
● Recite the number names in order, continuing the count forwards or backwards from a given number.

WHOLE-CLASS TEACHING ACTIVITY
● Begin to read o'clock time.

VOCABULARY

Time; takes longer; takes less time; hour; o'clock; clock; watch; hands.

ORAL AND MENTAL STARTER

CARRY ON COUNTING: Tell the children you want them to carry on counting around the class. Start counting from 0 to 10, then repeat with different starting and finishing numbers. Repeat until all the children have taken part.

WHOLE-CLASS TEACHING ACTIVITY

TELL THE TIME: Explain to the children that it is important to be able to tell the time. Ask: *Why do we need to know what time it is?* Show the children the clock face and point out the big and small hands. Say: *The small hand tells the hour.* Explain that when the large hand points to the 12 it says 'o'clock'. Move the large hand to the 12. Then move the hour hand to 7. *What time does it say?* Individuals come out and set the hands to show different o'clock times in order, eg, 8 o'clock, 9 o'clock. Write each time on the flip chart. *What time does it say?*

GROUP ACTIVITIES

1. Place a set of clock faces on the table. Ask children to make their clocks show different times.
2. Give each child a copy of photocopiable page 198 (What time is it?) and a set of time cards. The children have to draw a line linking the time on the clock face to the written time.
3. Place a set of time cards and a clock face for each pair of children on the table. One child takes a card and reads the time. The other child sets the hands to show that time.
Display a collection of clocks and watches. Let the children play with these and set different times.

DIFFERENTIATION

Less able: ask a classroom assistant to support them.
More able: encourage children to write the times shown on the clock face.

PLENARY

Read children the story 'What's the time, Mr Wolf?'.

LESSON 4

RESOURCES	A set of large clock face cards showing different o'clock times from 1 o'clock to 12 o'clock; large analogue clock face with movable hands; washing line; pegs. **Group activities:** small analogue clock faces with movable hands; copies of photocopiable page 198 (What time is it?); pencils; sets of time cards.
LEARNING OUTCOMES	**ORAL AND MENTAL STARTER** ● **Say and use the number names in order in familiar contexts.** ● Recite the number names in order, continuing the count forwards or backwards from a given number. **WHOLE-CLASS TEACHING ACTIVITY** ● Begin to read o'clock time.
ORAL AND MENTAL STARTER	COUNT DOWN: Ask the children to count down in ones with you. Start from 10 to 0 then extend from 20 to 0.
WHOLE-CLASS TEACHING ACTIVITY	WHAT TIME IS IT? Choose some of the large clock cards. Ask: *What time is it?* Remind the children that the small hand tells the hour. *Where does the large hand point for o'clock?* Ask children to read the numerals on the clock. Explain that both hands go around the clock twice each day. Give out the clock cards. Children peg them on the washing line in order from 1 o'clock to 12 o'clock.
GROUP ACTIVITIES	Use the **Group activities** in Lesson 3, page 194. ● Play 'What's the time Mr Wolf?' in PE and outdoor play.
DIFFERENTIATION	Less able: use a classroom assistant to support them. More able: encourage children to write the times shown on the clock faces.
PLENARY	Feedback from the **Group activities**. Ask class and individuals to tell the times shown on the clock. Repeat, with children making the clocks show a given time.

LESSON 5

RESOURCES

Story of 'Jack and the Beanstalk'; assorted lengths of string, ribbon, scarf; tie; sock.
Group activities: threading laces; beads; cubes; copies of photocopiable page 157 (Compare me); pencils; paper; scissors.

PREPARATION

Write labels saying 'longer than', 'shorter than', 'the same as'.

LEARNING OUTCOMES

ORAL AND MENTAL STARTER
● Count in twos.

WHOLE-CLASS TEACHING ACTIVITY
● **Use language such as longer or shorter to compare two quantities,** then more than two, by making direct comparisons of length.

VOCABULARY
Measure; size; compare; enough; not enough; too much; too little; nearly; close to; about the same as; length; width; height; long; short; tall; high; longer; shorter; taller; higher; longest; shortest; tallest; highest.

ORAL AND MENTAL STARTER

COUNTING IN TWOS: Children count in twos starting from 0 to 10. Repeat using different starting numbers and extend to 20.

WHOLE-CLASS TEACHING ACTIVITY

MEASURES: Explain that the next few lessons are about measures. Remind the children of the story of 'Jack and the Beanstalk'. *Was Jack shorter or taller than the giant? How high did the beanstalk grow? Who is the tallest in the class? Is the door higher than the board? Which is wider, the chair or the table?*

Show the children the scarf, tie and sock separately and ask them which they think is the longest item. Ask: *How can we compare them to find out?* Say: *The tie is longer than the sock but shorter than the scarf.* Place the labels when the items have been compared to show that the scarf is 'longer than' the tie etc. Repeat the activity using three other objects.

GROUP ACTIVITIES

1. Provide different lengths of string, ribbon, rods, etc. Each child chooses one item. The children make a necklace, or a tower of cubes etc, and cut three strips of paper longer, shorter, the same length as their chosen item.

2. Children choose a length of threading lace and make a necklace. Working in threes, they compare the necklaces to find which is the shortest/longest and place them in order.

3. Give each child a copy of photocopiable page 157 (Compare me). Each child chooses an object. They compare different objects to find something shorter, longer and the same length as their chosen object. Children record their findings on the sheet.

Set up the role-play area as the Giant's castle.

DIFFERENTIATION

Less able: ask a classroom assistant to reinforce the vocabulary.
More able: extend comparisons to four, then five items.

PLENARY

Feedback from the **Group activities**.

RESOURCES	Story of 'Jack and the Beanstalk'; toy brick; small teddy; pencil; sets of balances; labels saying 'heavier than', 'lighter than', 'the same as'. **Group activities:** selection of items: cubes, beads, shells, conkers; copies of photocopiable page 199 (Compare: mass); small containers.
LEARNING OUTCOMES	**ORAL AND MENTAL STARTER** ● Count in twos. **WHOLE-CLASS TEACHING ACTIVITY** ● **Use language such as heavier or lighter to compare two quantities,** then more than two, by making direct comparisons of masses.
ORAL AND MENTAL STARTER	COUNTING IN TWOS: Count on in twos starting from 0 to 10, then 20. Repeat using different starting numbers. Count back in twos starting from 10, then 20.
WHOLE-CLASS TEACHING ACTIVITY	COMPARING MASS: Remind children of the story of 'Jack and the Beanstalk'. *Was Jack heavier or lighter than the giant? Name things heavier than Jack. Name things lighter than the giant.* Ask children to compare the mass of the brick, teddy and pencil. *Which is the heaviest? Which is the lightest? How can we measure them?* Use the balance to compare the mass of each item. Read and place the labels. *The brick is heavier than the teddy, the teddy is lighter than the pencil.* Find a couple of items that are the same weight and place this label.
GROUP ACTIVITIES	**1.** Place sets of balances and a selection of items on the table. Each child chooses one object, then selects an object heavier and lighter than it. Children first compare by holding the items then check using the balance. They use photocopiable page 199 (Compare: mass) to record their findings. **2.** In pairs, children select three items and compare their mass to order them from heaviest to lightest then lightest to heaviest. They weigh by hand then check using the balance. **3.** Provide three containers and a range of small objects for each pair. Different items are placed in the containers. Children compare the mass of each container and order them from heaviest to lightest. They weigh by hand then check using the balance. ● During PE activities, children use small apparatus to balance on different body parts.
DIFFERENTIATION	Less able: make sure children can compare two objects then extend to three. More able: extend to compare with four, then five objects.
PLENARY	Feedback from the **Group activities**.

LESSON 7

RESOURCES	Selection of different-sized containers, a jug, water, food colouring. **Group activities:** plastic beakers or cups; range of items: pasta, conkers, lentils, beads; labels saying 'holds more than', 'holds less than'; stacking containers; cubes.
LEARNING OUTCOMES	**ORAL AND MENTAL STARTER** ● Recite the number names in order, continuing the count forwards or backwards from a given number. ● Count in twos. **WHOLE-CLASS TEACHING ACTIVITY** ● **Use language such as more or less to compare two quantities,** then more than two, by filling and emptying containers.
ORAL AND MENTAL STARTER	ODDS AND EVENS: Explain that you want the children to count in ones from 1 to 10, then to 20. Tell children to say the starting number in a loud voice then whisper the next number. Say: **1**, 2, **3**, 4, **5**, 6, **7**, 8, **9**, 10. Repeat by shouting the even numbers.
WHOLE-CLASS TEACHING ACTIVITY	POUR IT IN: Select three containers. Ask children to guess which holds the most and least and place the containers in the order given by the class. Pour different amounts of water into the containers. *Do they hold the same amount? Which one holds the most/least?* Rearrange the containers in order of capacity. Repeat the activity by filling the containers with the same amount of water. *Do they all hold the same amounts? Which is full/nearly empty?*
GROUP ACTIVITIES	**1.** Give children three beakers and a jug of water. In pairs, ask them to fill the beakers so that they hold different amounts. Repeat with children filling beakers with the same amount. **2.** Place a range of items (pasta, conkers, lentils, beads) on the table. Give each child three small containers and labels saying 'holds more than', 'holds less than'. Children choose one item with which to fill the containers and then order them using the labels. **3.** In pairs, children have a set of three stacking containers. They fill each container with cubes to find which holds the most/least. ● Set up the water and sand play with a range of different sized and shaped containers.
DIFFERENTIATION	Less able: ask a classroom assistant to support them More able: extend to compare with four then five containers.
PLENARY	Feedback from the **Group activities**.

LESSON 8

RESOURCES	See Lessons 5, 6 and 7, pages 195–197.
LEARNING OUTCOMES	**ORAL AND MENTAL STARTER** ● Count in twos. **WHOLE-CLASS TEACHING ACTIVITY** ● **Use language such as more or less, longer or shorter, heavier or lighter ... to compare two quantities,** then more than two, by making direct comparisons of lengths or masses, and by filling and emptying containers.
ORAL AND MENTAL STARTER	Repeat 'Counting in twos' from Lesson 5, page 195.
WHOLE-CLASS TEACHING ACTIVITY	MEASURE IT: Explain that there are many ways of measuring. Remind the children of when they measured time, length, mass and capacity. Reinforce vocabulary. Choose examples from Lessons 5, 6 and 7. Ask individuals to name items longer/ shorter, heavier/lighter/, that hold more/less than given items.
GROUP ACTIVITIES	Choose from the **Group activities** given in Lessons 5, 6 and 7. Encourage the children to compare three quantities each time. ● Play activity: Set up a weaving activity using different widths and lengths of materials.
DIFFERENTIATION	Less able: ask a classroom assistant to support them. More able: extend to compare with four, then five, containers.
PLENARY	Feedback from the **Group activities**.

What time is it?

5 o'clock

3 o'clock

10 o'clock

8 o'clock

12 o'clock

Name

Compare: mass

I chose this object:

This item is heavier:	This item is lighter:

UNIT 11

ORGANISATION (5 LESSONS)

	LEARNING OUTCOMES	ORAL AND MENTAL STARTER	WHOLE-CLASS TEACHING ACTIVITY	PLENARY
LESSON 1	● **Use developing mathematical ideas and methods to solve practical problems** involving counting and comparing in a real or role play context.	MORE/LESS: Children show a number that is one more or less than a given number.	COMING AND GOING: Problem-solving activities.	Feedback from activities.
LESSON 2	● **Use developing mathematical ideas and methods to solve practical problems** involving counting and comparing in a real or role play context.	SHOW ME ADD: Children add two numbers.	FALLING OUT: Addition and subtraction problems.	SHOW ME SUBTRACT: Children subtract two numbers.
LESSON 3	● **Use developing mathematical ideas and methods to solve practical problems** involving counting and comparing in a real or role play context.	SHOW ME ADD AND SUBTRACT: Children add and subtract two numbers.	POP AND BANG: Children work out subtraction problems	Feedback from activities.
LESSON 4	● Begin to understand and use the vocabulary related to money. Sort coins, including the £1 and £2 coins, and use them in role play to pay and give change	DUOS: Pairs find two numbers that add to a given total.	COUNT OUT: Children use coins in role-play shopping activities.	Children solve addition problems.
LESSON 5	● Begin to understand and use the vocabulary related to money. Sort coins, including the £1 and £2 coins, and use them in role play to pay and give change	DOUBLES: Children double the throw of a dice.	HOW MUCH?: Addition and subtraction problems involving money.	Repeat 'How much?'.

ORAL AND MENTAL SKILLS Find one more or one less than a number from 1 to 10. Recognise numerals **1 to 9,** then 0 and 10, then beyond 10. **Begin to use the vocabulary involved in adding and subtracting. Begin to relate addition to combining two objects,** counting all the objects. Begin to relate the addition of doubles to counting on. Begin to relate addition to counting on.

Lessons 2, 3 and 5 are extensions of what has been taught previously and are presented as grids. Lessons I and 4 are given in full.

RESOURCES

Individual sets of numeral cards (page 12); flip chart; marker pen; a large blank domino drawn on the flip chart. **Group activities:** toy bus; play people; pencils; paper; sets of dominoes; selection of toy farm animals; different socks; crayons; assorted buttons.

LEARNING OUTCOMES

ORAL AND MENTAL STARTER
● **Find one more or one less than a number from 1 to 10.**

WHOLE-CLASS TEACHING ACTIVITY
● **Use developing mathematical ideas and methods to solve practical problems** involving counting and comparing in a real or role play context.

ORAL AND MENTAL STARTER

MORE/LESS: Hand out the numeral cards. Say a number and ask children to say or show the number that is one more. They can use fingers or numeral cards. Use numbers from 0 to 10. Repeat with different numbers, this time asking the children to tell you what is one less. Extend with numbers to 20 and beyond.

VOCABULARY

Add; more; and; make; sum; total; one more; take (away); leave; how many are left/left over?; how many have gone?; one less; compare; count out.

WHOLE-CLASS TEACHING ACTIVITY

COMING AND GOING: Say: *There are five people on the bus. If one more gets on, how many people are there on the bus?* Say: *There are five people on the bus, three get off. How many are left?* Repeat using different numbers. Show children the enlarged blank domino template. Explain that you want to draw spots on the domino to make a total of 6. *How shall we do it?* Ask individuals to give suggestions. Draw a set of spots totalling 6 on the domino. Ask: *Are there any other ways of making six?* Record the other ways on the flip chart. *There are different ways of making 6. Have we found them all? How can we check?*

GROUP ACTIVITIES

1. Give the children a toy bus. They have to add and take away play people to the bus.
2. Place a set of dominoes on the table. In pairs, ask children to find dominoes with totals of 7. They record their answers by drawing spots or writing numerals.
3. Place a selection of farm animals, buttons, socks and crayons on the table. Give each pair a group of various items and ask them to find how many ways they can be sorted. A classroom assistant can give support.

Ask children to find out favourite foods/colours/pets etc. by carrying out their own surveys.

DIFFERENTIATION

Less able: ask a classroom assistant to support them.
More able: set more challenging activities.

PLENARY

Feedback from the **Group activities**.

LESSON 2

RESOURCES	Individual sets of numeral cards (page 12); flip chart; marker pen. **Group activities:** Frogs and lily pads (page 14); copies of photocopiable page 204 (Sizzling sausages); counters; cubes; dice.
LEARNING OUTCOMES	**ORAL AND MENTAL STARTER** ● **Begin to use the vocabulary involved in adding and subtracting.** ● **Find one more or one less than a number from 1 to 10.** **WHOLE-CLASS TEACHING ACTIVITY** ● **Use developing mathematical ideas and methods to solve practical problems** involving counting and comparing in a real or role play context.
ORAL AND MENTAL STARTER	SHOW ME ADD: Hand out the numeral cards. Explain that you are going to say a number. The children must hold the first number in their heads. You will say another number and the children add that number to the first. They show you the answer by holding up the relevant numeral card.
WHOLE-CLASS TEACHING ACTIVITY	FALLING OUT: Sing 'Ten in the bed'. Invite ten children to take part in a role-play activity. Pick out a numeral card to show how many fall out each time. The children 'in the bed' see the card but the rest of the class do not. Say: *How many were in the bed? How many are left? How many fell out?* Repeat several times. Record the number sentences on the flip chart. Say and write them: *10 take away 4 makes 6. How can we check that? What is the total of 6 add 4?*
GROUP ACTIVITIES	**1.** Give each child a copy of Frogs and lily pads (page 14). Ask children how many ways they can find to put eight frogs on the lily pads. **2.** Give each child a copy of photocopiable page 204 (Sizzling sausages) and a set of counters. Children cover each sausage with a counter. They then take two sausages away, using the counters, and record how many are left. Repeat until all the sausages have gone. **3.** Place cubes, dice and paper on the table. In pairs, children start with ten cubes each. Each child takes turns to throw the dice and removes the appropriate number of cubes. The first child with no cubes left is the winner. They record on paper. ● Role-play other counting songs and rhymes.
DIFFERENTIATION	Less able: use numbers 0–10. More able: encourage them to record in their own way.
PLENARY	SHOW ME SUBTRACT: Repeat as for 'Show me add' but use subtraction.

RESOURCES	Copies of photocopiable page 204 (Sizzling sausages); flip chart; marker pen. **Group activities:** apropriate resources listed for Lessons 1 and 2.
LEARNING OUTCOMES	**ORAL AND MENTAL STARTER** ● **Begin to use the vocabulary involved in adding and subtracting.** **WHOLE-CLASS TEACHING ACTIVITY** ● **Use developing mathematical ideas and methods to solve practical problems** involving counting and comparing in a real or role play context.
ORAL AND MENTAL STARTER	SHOW ME ADD AND SUBTRACT: Repeat from Lesson 2, using addition and subtraction.
WHOLE-CLASS TEACHING ACTIVITY	Recite the rhyme 'Ten fat sausages'. Display photocopiable page 204 (Sizzling sausages)'. Children count out the sausages as you point to them in the pan. *What happens if two sausages go pop and two go bang each time? How many sausages shall we take away? How many are left? What happens next?* Record the number sentences on the flip chart.
GROUP ACTIVITIES	Choose from the **Group activities** in Lessons 1 and 2. ● Provide opportunities for children to give out equipment, drinks etc. to groups and class.
DIFFERENTIATION	Less able: use numbers 0–10, then extend. More able: encourage them to record in their own way.
PLENARY	Take feedback from the **Group activities**.

RESOURCES

Assorted coins; cut-outs of take-away food items: pizza, burger, chips, chicken nuggets, hot dog, ice-cream cornet, soft drink; labels. **Group activities:** collection of small toys; paper; pencils; copies of photocopiable page 205 (The Take-away); dice; containers; money dice (1p, 2p, 5p, 10p, 20p, 50p).

PREPARATION

Price the 'take away' food cut-outs. Make the food prices on the worksheet match the ones on the cut-outs. Enlarge photocopiable page 205 (The Take-away). Place a selection of assorted coins on each table. Write prices on the labels and attach to the toys.

LEARNING OUTCOMES

ORAL AND MENTAL STARTER
● **Begin to relate addition to combining two groups of objects,** counting all the objects.
● Begin to relate addition to counting on.

WHOLE-CLASS TEACHING ACTIVITY
● Begin to understand and use the vocabulary related to money. Sort coins, including the £1 and £2 coins, and use them in role play to pay and give change.

VOCABULARY

Count out; share out; left; left over; money; coin; penny; pence; pound; price; cost; buy; sell; spend; spent; pay; change; costs more; cost less; costs the same as; how much...?; how many...?; total.

ORAL AND MENTAL STARTER

DUOS: This is a variation of the activity in Unit 2, Lesson 2, of this term, on page 141. Explain that you will give the children a number. In pairs, you want them to find two numbers that add together to give that total.

WHOLE-CLASS TEACHING ACTIVITY

COUNT OUT: Ask children to count out a number of coins. *Count out five 1p coins. Count out two 10p coins. Count out one 50p, two 10p and three 1p coins.* Repeat using different amounts. Show the children the take-away food and ask them to read out the prices. Explain that you want the children to work in pairs and to buy food from the 'Take-away'. Say: *How much is a slice of pizza? Show me the coins you need to buy it.* Ask children to tell the class which coins they have used. Repeat using different food items.

GROUP ACTIVITIES

1. Place the labelled toys, assorted coins, pencils and paper on the table. Ask children to 'buy' a toy and work out which coins they would use to pay for it. Get them to record these on the paper by drawing round the coins or writing the figures.

2. Give each child photocopiable page 205 (The Take-away) and selection of coins. Ask children to choose three items of food and show the coins they would use to pay for these.

3. Place a container, coins and money dice on the table. Each child takes a turn to throw the dice. Children collect the amount shown on the dice from the container and place it in front of them. The first child to collect 20p is the winner.

 Set up the role-play area as a 'Take-away'.

DIFFERENTIATION

Less able; limit the total value of coins to 20p, then extend to 50p.
More able: encourage children to make up their own price lists for food items.

PLENARY

Sing 'Five currant buns in the baker's shop'. *How much would three buns cost if they were 2p each?* Repeat using different amounts.

RESOURCES	See Lesson 4 (on page 202), plus large foam dice (0–5).
LEARNING OUTCOMES	**ORAL AND MENTAL STARTER** ● Begin to relate the addition of doubles to counting on. **WHOLE-CLASS TEACHING ACTIVITY** ● Begin to understand and use the vocabulary related to money. Sort coins, including the £1 and £2 coins, and use them in role play to pay and give change.
ORAL AND MENTAL STARTER	DOUBLES: Explain that you are going to throw the dice. When you give the number, the children have to double it and hold up their hands to answer. Check they know how to count on to do this.
WHOLE-CLASS TEACHING ACTIVITY	HOW MUCH?: Ask children to give the answers to these money problems. *5p and 3p make? What is the total of 6p and 1p? If I have 10p and I spend 3p, how much is left? A teddy costs 50p and a car costs 30p. Which costs the most?* Repeat using adding and subtracting. Ask children to show which coins they would use to make 9p. *What else could you use?* Repeat using different amounts.
GROUP ACTIVITIES	Choose from the **Group activities** in Lesson 4, above. ● Make pretend food and menus for the role-play 'Take-away'.
DIFFERENTIATION	Less able: ask a classroom assistant to support them. More able: extend value of coins to £1.00
PLENARY	Repeat 'How much?'.

LESSON 5

UNIT 11

Sizzling sausages

Name

The take away

Choose three food items. Show the coins you would use to pay for them.

60p

25p

12p

30p

8p

42p

UNIT 12: Assess & review

Choose from the following activities over the two lessons. During the group activities some of the children can work with you on practical tasks, while others complete assessment worksheets 4a and 4b which assess their skills with reading and writing numbers, subtraction and addition. The specific assessment criteria for the assessment sheets can be found at the bottom of each sheet.

RESOURCES

Assessment photocopiables 4A and 4B; class number track (0–20); pointer; individual sets of numeral cards; a selection of counting objects; interlocking cubes; sets of 3-D and 2-D shapes; articles which can be used for making direct comparisons of mass; different-sized parcels; everyday objects; different-size, shape and capacity containers; lentils, conkers, beads and water; 1p, 2p, 5p, 10p, 20p, 50p £1 and £2 coins; pencils; paper.

ORAL AND MENTAL STARTER

ASSESSMENT

● Can the children: **Find one more or one less than a number from 1 to 10? Begin to relate addition to combining two groups of objects, and subtraction to 'taking away'?**
COUNTING IN TWOS: Repeat counting in twos to 10 then 20.
COUNTING IN TENS: Children count on in tens to 50 then beyond. Count back in tens from 50, then 100. Note children who count confidently and those who need more practice.
ONE MORE/ONE LESS: Point to some numbers on the number track. Children call out the number that is one more/one less. Give a number and ask individuals to say/find the number that is one more/less.
SHOW ME ADD: Say two numbers. Children hold up a numeral card to show the total of the numbers when they are added together. Note who is confident, and who requires practice.

GROUP ACTIVITIES

ASSESSMENT

● Can the children: **Count reliably up to 10 everyday objects? Recognise numerals 1 to 9? Talk about, recognise and recreate simple patterns? Use everyday words to describe position? Compare length, mass and capacity by direct comparison of two objects? Use developing mathematical ideas and methods to solve practical problems** using adding and subtraction?
COUNTING OBJECTS: children count a given quantity of cubes. *How many are there?* They rearrange them in different ways. *Are there more or less? How many are there?* Children count by touching the objects, then repeat without touching. Check the children count accurately and can tell you how many objects they have.
RECOGNISE AND ORDER NUMERALS: Ask children to lay out their numeral cards in front of them. Say: *Show me 5, 9, 2.* Ask them to put the cards in order starting from 1 to 10. Ask: *Which number comes before 5, after 9, in front of 3, next to 8.*
PATTERNS: Repeat the activities in Lesson 4 of Unit 9, on page 187, or make some similar ones. Check children can recognise and recreate simple patterns. Ask children to spot the patterns you make and make their own.
COMPARING MASS: Use 'Compare: mass' (Lesson 6 of Unit 10, on page 196). Encourage children to choose their own objects to compare, estimate, then measure using hands and a balance. Check children can understand and use the vocabulary of mass.
COMPARING CAPACITY: Choose from the activities in Lesson 7, Unit 10, page 197, choosing different items for filling. Each child works with 'wet' and 'dry' materials. Children choose their own objects to compare, estimate, then measure by filling and emptying containers. Check children can understand and use the vocabulary of capacity.
SOLVING PROBLEMS: Repeat the activities in Lessons 1 and 5 of Unit 11, pages 201 and 203, or make up similar ones. Check they recognise when they need to add or subtract.

Assessment 4a

Join the numbers in order starting with 0.

18

1

10

19

3

7

8

4

6

15

17

5

16

12

2

0

11

13

20

9

14

How many altogether?

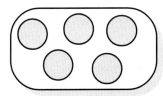 add  is altogether

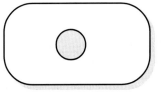 add 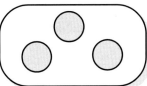 is 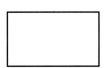 altogether

 add  is  altogether

● **Recognise numerals 1 to 9,** then 0 and 10, then beyond 10.
● **Begin to relate addition to combining two groups of objects.**

UNIT 12

Assessment 4b

Use your number track to help you find the answers.

I less than 8 is   I less than 2 is

I less than 5 is    I less than 9 is

I less than 4 is    I less than 6 is

Now try these:

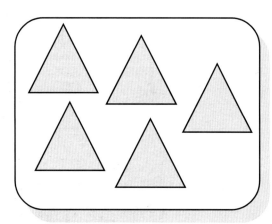   take away 2 makes

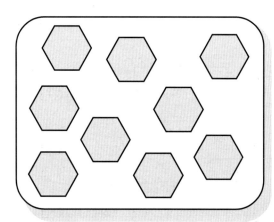   take away 4 makes

● **Find one more or one less than a number from 1 to 10.**
● **Begin to relate subtraction to 'taking away'.**